MW00598446

PREPARE!

An Ecumenical
Music and Worship Planner

2018–2019, CEB Edition

David L. Bone
and
Mary Scifres

Abingdon Press
Nashville

PREPARE! AN ECUMENICAL MUSIC AND WORSHIP PLANNER 2018–2019

Copyright © 2018 by Abingdon Press

This book is printed on acid-free, recycled paper.

ISBN 978-1-5018-5651-8

18 19 20 21 22 23 24 25 26 27—10 9 8 7 6 5 4 3 2 1

MANUFACTURED IN CHINA

Do you have the book you need?

We want you to have the best planner, designed to meet your specific needs. How do you know if you have the right resource? Simply complete this one-question quiz:

Do you lead worship in a United Methodist congregation?

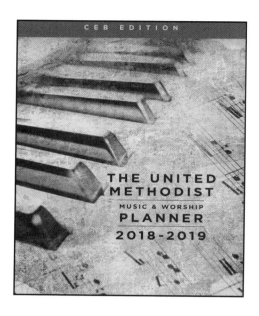

Yes.

Use *The United Methodist Music and Worship Planner, 2018–2019*
(CEB Edition—ISBN: 9781501856471)
(NRSV Edition—ISBN: 9781501856495)

No.

Use *Prepare! An Ecumenical Music and Worship Planner, 2018–2019*
(CEB Edition—ISBN: 9781501856518)
(NRSV Edition—ISBN: 9781501856532)

To order these resources, call Cokesbury toll free at 1-877-877-8674, or shop online at www.cokesbury.com. Do you find yourself rushing at the last minute to order your new planner? Subscribe today and receive your new *The United Methodist Music and Worship Planner* or *Prepare!* automatically next year and every year. Call toll free 1-800-672-1789 to request a subscription.

USING *PREPARE!*

How We Organize the Resource Lists

Prepare! is designed to give you as many ideas as possible about a given worship service. Use it along with a worship plan notebook that you create, a copy of your church's hymnal, and other supplements you use such as *The Faith We Sing, Sing the Faith, Songs for Praise and Worship,* or *Worship & Song.* Features of *Prepare!* include:

- The lectionary verses found on left-hand pages of *Prepare!* come from the Common English Bible. Where available, we have added psalter numbers from standard hymnals, including New Century, Presbyterian, United Methodist, and the new Presbyterian Hymnal, *Glory to God. Prepare!* is also available with lectionary texts from the New Revised Standard Version of the Bible (ISBN: 9781501856532).

- Each week **Primary Hymns and Songs for the Day** are suggested first. These suggestions include various helps for singing the hymns. These hymns and songs have the closest relationship to the scriptures and are widely known. The lengthier lists of **Additional Hymn Suggestions** and **Additional Contemporary Suggestions** will add variety to your musical selections.

- The musical suggestions are chosen to suggest a wide variety of styles.

- Each item is referenced to scripture and/or occasion.

- **Opening (O)** and **Closing (C)** hymns are suggested for each worship service.

- At least one **Communion (Comm.)** hymn is recommended for the first Sunday of each month and liturgical season. When appropriate, Communion hymns related to the scriptures are noted on other days as well.

- **Additional Contemporary Suggestions** include not only praise choruses but also global and ethnic music, folk music, and meditative music from traditions such as Taizé. Information about resources referenced in this section can be found on page 7. Please note that contemporary songs may also be listed under **Additional Hymn Suggestions**, **Vocal Solos**, or **Other Suggestions**.

- **Vocal Solos** and **Anthems** provide ideas for vocal music "performance" offerings, and may also inspire ideas for additional congregational selections.

- The recommended **Vocal Solos** are taken from a group of eleven collections that range from contemporary settings of hymn texts and praise choruses to spirituals to well-known classics (see p. 7). Augment these suggestions from your own library.

- The **Anthem** suggestions include new works as well as generally known works that are already in many church choral libraries. Your study of the scripture and hymn texts will lead you to anthems in your church library that are appropriate. Many anthem suggestions are taken from the three volumes of the *Augsburg Easy Choirbook* (AEC) series.

- **One word of advice:** Be sure to consult all the music suggestions regardless of the type of service you are planning. In the changing world of worship, no one style defines a song or a worship service. Many items appropriate for contemporary and emergent styles are listed under the **Additional Hymn Suggestions** and many resources for traditional and blended services can be found in the **Additional Contemporary Suggestions** list. **Vocal Solos**, **Anthems**, and **Other Suggestions** may be appropriate for congregational use as well. Don't let the "category" here deter you from using any item that will enhance your worship service. Planners should consult all lists when choosing congregational music.

- Suggestions for "**Visuals**" are offered for each service. See the article "Visuals in Worship" (p. 4) for discussion on these suggestions. Visual ideas are found in **Other Suggestions**. They have been compiled by Ashley M. Calhoun and supplemented by our authors. Ashley is known for his inventive use of "found" items in creating visual worship settings. Worship committees, visual artists, dancers, and altar guilds can use these ideas to create their own unique worship centers, altar pieces, banners, and dance images. Screen visual artists can use these themes to select appropriate background and theme screens for worship.

- **Other Suggestions** also include words for worship, suggestions for choral introits and sung benedictions, and ideas for musical responses related to the spoken liturgy.

- A two-year, at-a-glance **2018–2019 Lectionary Calendar** follows the **Worship Planning Sheets** (see p. 142). It includes a note on the lectionary years covered in this edition of *Prepare!*

- *Prepare!* uses the *Revised Common Lectionary.* From the Second Sunday after Pentecost to Christ the King Sunday, the lectionary includes two patterns of readings. One pattern includes semi-continuous readings from the Hebrew Scriptures, Epistles, and Gospels. These readings are not necessarily related but allow for a sequential experience of the biblical narrative. **This is the pattern used to determine the** scripture texts included in *Prepare!* It is the pattern followed by most users of the hymnals referenced. In the second pattern, the Hebrew scripture is chosen to relate to the Gospel passage. This pattern is used primarily in traditions where Communion is celebrated at every service of worship. These **Alternate Lections** may be found in *The Revised Common Lectionary* (Abingdon Press, 1992) or online at http://lectionary.library.vanderbilt.edu/. Worship planners may certainly choose to follow the pattern that best serves the needs and traditions of your church. Neither pattern is necessarily better than the other; they are simply different ways of offering scripture in the worship setting over a three-year cycle in the church.

Planning Worship with These Resources

When planning any worship service, it is always best to start with the Scripture and let it guide your thoughts and plans. If your church is not using the *Revised Common Lectionary*, but you do know what the scripture text will be for a service, look up that text in the **Scripture Index**, beginning on p. 134.

As you read and study the Scripture passages, read all of the suggested hymn texts. The hymns may remind you of anthems, solos, or keyboard selections. It is wise to mark your hymnal with the dates individual hymns are sung to avoid singing some too frequently. The **Hymn Resources** (see p. 7) can enhance congregational singing, but should be used sparingly.

Use a three-ring binder to organize your plans. For each service of worship, include a copy of one of the **Worship Planning Sheets** found on pages 138–140 (or design your own!) along with blank paper for listing further ideas. Do not simply "fill in the blanks" for each service, but use the Planning Sheet to guide your work.

Use the suggestions in *Prepare!* along with your own page of ideas to begin making decisions about worship. Will the choir sing a "Call to Worship"? Can a hymn verse serve as a prayer response? Can a particular anthem or vocal solo give direction to the sermon? What prayers will be used? Once your decisions are made, complete the **Worship Planning Sheet**. Make a separate list of tasks related to that service. Planning worship is an awesome responsibility that can be accomplished with an organized effort along with spiritual guidance.

VISUALS IN WORSHIP
Ashley M. Calhoun

The suggestions for visuals in this planner are meant to help worship leaders use objects and images to increase the impact of the gospel on a people who are increasingly visually oriented. These suggestions can be incorporated into many visual elements: hanging and processional banners, worship settings (whether on the altar or in the chancel or narthex), worship folder covers, and bulletin boards. The ideas can also be used to suggest ways to use classical and contemporary works of art, sculpture, needlework, and photography in worship services

With more churches incorporating screens and video walls into their worship spaces, there is tremendous potential for the use of still or moving imagery. Also, interpretive movement and drama can be very strong in visual impact.

The visual suggestions in this *Planner* have several characteristics:

- The suggestions are not meant to give detailed plans, but to spark your imagination and creativity.

- Some are drawn literally from the lessons; others are thematic.

- The suggestions are organized by reference to the lectionary passages:

O Old Testament or Easter season, Acts reading
P Psalm reading or Canticle
E Epistle or New Testament reading
G Gospel reading

- Chapter and verse numbers are sometimes given to indicate actual phrases in the scripture passage that can serve as visual elements.

- Themes such as "forgiveness," "love," or "rejoicing" are offered to encourage creative use of video and photographic images of people engaged in demonstrating those themes.

So much about worship is visual and intended to strengthen the proclamation of the gospel. The worship space is filled with visual elements that send a message. The church year is a treasure trove of color, texture, symbolism, and visual imagery. Special Sundays and special days in the cultural and denominational calendars also offer opportunities for visual expression. Evaluate the visual aspects of your worship services and find ways to enhance the worship experience with thoughtful, intentional use of visual elements and images.

PLANNING WORSHIP IN ALTERNATIVE STYLES

Mary Scifres

Various forms of nontraditional worship have become increasingly popular in the last thirty years, mass labeled as "contemporary." These alternative styles of worship may be foreign to the experience of traditional worship planners. Nevertheless, the popularity of modern music and public events, the increasing diversity of today's culture, the growing comfort with informal approaches to worship, and the high energy of young people may encourage you to use contemporary resources and alternative styles in one or more of your worship services.

Planning alternative worship provides an exciting opportunity for church staff members and volunteers to work together as a team. Such planning can also provide a vehicle in which worship committees find new opportunity for ministry.

If alternative or contemporary worship is new to you, spend time in prayer and planning long before your first service. Know your own gifts and those of your congregation, and observe what other churches and worship leaders are doing around your community and around the country. If you're beginning an added worship service, build the necessary groundwork to support this new mission of the church by recruiting leadership from within your congregation, advertising the event before it happens, and setting a goal for this mission. If you are integrating new elements into an existing worship service, include your current leadership alongside young adults and new leadership in planning for the changes. As you embark on this new venture, be careful not to abandon your current worshiping congregation or set up a competition between existing worship services and new ones. As you explore the possibility of new worship styles, be open not only to contemporary praise music and alternative Christian music, but also to global praise music or quieter forms of contemporary worship using folk music or Taizé music. Secular resources and music may also be of help in developing new styles of worship. With these things in mind, you are ready to begin the planning process.

As you design your alternative worship service, several decisions need to be made:

- Whom do you want to reach (traditions, faith backgrounds, ages, theology)?

- What type of worship experience shall you start or improve? (You may want to consider blending styles.)

- How much are you willing to spend?

With those decisions in mind, you are ready to build your planning team. "Team?" you may ask. "Our pastor does all the worship planning!" If that is the case, this is the perfect opportunity to explore a new model of planning worship. Contemporary expressions of worship are foreign to many pastors and musicians. Increasing the number of planners will expand the diversity and creativity of ideas—important elements of alternative worship! With this resource, we hope that many pastors, musicians, and worship leaders find encouragement and assistance planning worship in advance and in cooperation with one another.

Planning team members may include musicians, artists, organizers, writers, and pastors. All members of the worship planning team meet regularly, at least biannually. Some worship teams find weekly, monthly, or seasonal planning meetings helpful, but even two meetings a year can improve communication and coordination efforts immensely. Planning meetings are necessary, common, and often frequent in alternative worship planning.

However often one plans, pastors need to know the time requirements for planning music and other artistic elements of worship. Each pianist or song leader can communicate to the pastor the average length of time needed to pick new songs, order the music or songbooks, obtain copyright permissions, and rehearse the songs prior to Sunday morning. Each drama coordinator can decide the length of time needed to write or find a vignette to illustrate the Scripture or sermon topic. Visual coordinators can let worship planners know the time needed to locate photographs, develop altar displays, or prepare electronic slide shows for worship. Finally, musicians and artists can communicate with the pastor their visions for music and art ministry in the context of worship.

Pastors, likewise, need to inform musicians of special needs for musical and visual support. Some pastors establish cues to alert the musician that light background music is needed during an unexpected situation in worship. A pastor can tell artists of expectations regarding worship leadership roles (e.g., listen attentively to the sermon, smile during the opening songs, stand or kneel during the prayer). Additionally, pastors can communicate their visions for the music and worship arts ministry of the church. These initial communications are essential when worship planners begin to work together and when there are personnel changes in the worship planning team.

Many models for the actual planning might be used, but we offer one model to help a team in starting integrated planning. In order to use this model, the team needs several copies of *Prepare!* (particularly for Scripture readings and song lists), a Bible (if lectionary is not being used or for team members who do not have access to a copy of *Prepare!*), hymnals and/or songbooks. You may also wish to have a copy of *The Abingdon Worship Annual.* Musicians may find it helpful to have copies of each of the music collections suggested in this guide as well as a single copy file of the song collection of your church. Copies of the planning sheet from page 140 can be distributed to each team member for each Sunday being discussed.

- Before the meeting, the pastor(s) prepares Scripture and sermon outlines; musicians prepare repertoire lists as well as repertoire wish lists.

- Team meets for a designated time. (A retreat setting is appropriate, especially if this is to be only a bi-annual event.)

- Open meeting with prayer and discussion of worship.

- Read Scriptures (perhaps in advance to meeting), and select specific Scriptures for each Sunday being planned.

- The pastor(s) introduces and outlines sermon topics or emphases.

- Discuss and outline seasonal needs.

- Choose songs and/or hymns, keeping in mind: thematic and scriptural emphases, musical abilities, sermon topics, congregational music preferences, and desire for introduction of new songs in a helpful way.

- Visual artists begin outlining plans for visual emphases or focal points.

- Introduce and discuss special ideas or plans for specific worship services (e.g., Easter, new member celebration, children's Sunday, stewardship Sunday).

- Write or choose spoken prayers, responses, and other worship words (full team or subgroup, depending on number of people participating). *The Abingdon Worship Annual, Worship and Song Worship Resources Edition* are particularly helpful resources here.

- Choose vocal and instrumental music (full team or subgroup, depending on number of people participating).

- Review services for integration and unity as well as diversity.

- Discuss concerns regarding specific services and plans for improvement.

- Close meeting with song and prayer.

In planning alternative worship, you want to offer a quality experience; planning with a team can help. At any step, members of the planning team may have valuable input. A pastor may have an idea for a dramatic sketch to enhance a sermon idea; a musician may have insight into a sermon topic as it relates to the congregation. Members of the team will find helpful suggestions in this *Planner* at any of these steps. The text of each Scripture reading is provided, season and color are noted, music and visual suggestions are offered, liturgical suggestions are provided, and other ideas are mentioned that may spark interest in innovations for your worship service.

When planning alternative worship, try to:

- Offer a high-quality experience of worship

- Employ your heritage creatively

- Offer as many opportunities for participation as possible

- Use language and theology that affirms

- Use creative, diverse, understandable language and music

- Be honest, open, and genuine in word and action

- Offer a welcoming experience for visitors

- Use a variety of media (video, drama, live music, visual arts)

- Avoid dependence on handouts (such as bulletins)

- Obtain a copyright license if you plan to duplicate for overhead projection or bulletins (Christian Copyright License at ccli.com or One License at Onelicense.net).

- Have fun!

Alternative worship planning need not be a point of departure for a worship staff. Rather, it can be an opportunity for unity and team building. The team that works together models corporate worship for the congregation. If we want people who enter the church on Sunday mornings from their many walks of life to have a community experience, we need to offer worship that incorporates many ideas from different voices to connect with our congregation's diverse journeys of faith. In so doing, we will find that the Holy Spirit has found a new freedom in which to work.

For weekly worship inspiration, themes, and liturgies, subscribe to www.maryscifresministries.com.
Free Communion resource book available at www.maryscifresministries.com/free1.

RESOURCE KEY

AH   *The Africana Hymnal*. Nashville: Abingdon Press, 2015. ISBN #9781426776441.

B   Forbis, Wesley, ed. *The Baptist Hymnal*. Nashville: Convention Press, 1991.

C   Merrick, Daniel and Polk, David, ed. *Chalice Hymnal*. St. Louis: Chalice Press, 1996.

E   *The Hymnal 1982*. New York: The Church Hymnal Corporation, 1985.

EL   *Evangelical Lutheran Worship*. Minneapolis: Augsburg Fortress, 2006.

F   Bock, Fred, ed. *Hymns for the Family of God*. Nashville: Paragon Associates, Inc., 1976.

G   *Glory to God: The Presbyterian Hymnal*. Louisville: Presbyterian Publishing Corporation, 2013.

L   *Lutheran Book of Worship*. Minneapolis: Augsburg Publishing House, 1978.

N   Clyde, Arthur G., ed. *The New Century Hymnal*. Cleveland, OH: The Pilgrim Press, 1995.

P   McKim, LindaJo, ed. *The Presbyterian Hymnal*. Louisville: Westminster/John Knox Press, 1990.

S   Hickman, Hoyt L., ed. *The Faith We Sing*. Nashville: Abingdon Press, 2000. Cokesbury Ord. #090547 (Pew Edition).

SF   Hickman, Hoyt L., ed. *Sing the Faith*. Louisville: Westminster/John Knox Press, 2003.

UM   Young, Carlton R., ed. *The United Methodist Hymnal*. Nashville: The United Methodist Publishing House, 1989. ISBN: 9780687431328.

VU   Ambrose, John E., ed. *Voice United*. Etobicoke, Ontario, Canada: The United Church Publishing House, 1996.

W   Batastini, Robert J., ed. *Worship*. Chicago: GIA Publications, Inc., 1986.

WS   Smith, Gary Alan, ed. *Worship & Song*. Nashville: Abingdon Press, 2011. Accompaniment, singer, guitar, and planning editions available. Cokesbury Ord. #090547.

WSL   Smith, Gary Alan, ed. *Worship & Song Leader's Edition*. Nashville: Abingdon Press, 2011. ISBN: 9781426709944 (Leader's edition). *These resources, WSL1–WSL222, refer to the written words for worship (prayers, litanies, benedictions) available in worship resource editions of* Worship & Song.

HYMN RESOURCES

S-1   Smith, Gary Alan, ed. *The United Methodist Hymnal: Music Supplement*. Nashville: Abingdon Press, 1991. Cokesbury Ord. #431476.

S-2   Bennett, Robert C., ed. *The United Methodist Hymnal: Music Supplement II*. Nashville: Abingdon Press, 1993. Cokesbury Ord. #430135.

H-3   Hopson, Hal H. *The Creative Church Musician Series*. Carol Stream, IL: Hope Publishing Co.
     Hbl Vol. 1. *The Creative Use of Handbells in Worship*. 1997. Cokesbury Ord. #921992.
     Chr Vol. 2. *The Creative Use of Choirs in Worship*. 1999. Cokesbury Ord. #732807.
     Desc *The Creative Use of Descants in Worship*. 1999. Cokesbury Ord. #732864.
     Org *The Creative Use of the Organ in Worship*. 1997. Cokesbury Ord. #323904.

CONTEMPORARY RESOURCES

SP   Various. *Songs for Praise and Worship Singalong Edition*. Waco, TX: Word Music, 1992. ISBN: 9783010203494.

M1-M55   Barker, Ken, ed. *More Songs for Praise and Worship Choir/ Worship Team Edition*. Waco, TX: Word Music, 2000. Cokesbury Ord. #509802 (*Keyboard Edition*: Cokesbury Ord. #509776. *Piano/Guitar/Vocal Edition*: Cokesbury Ord. #509764).

M56-M115   Barker, Ken, ed. *More Songs for Praise and Worship 2 Choir/ Worship Team Edition*. Waco, TX: Word Music, 2002. Cokesbury Ord. #512053 (*Keyboard Edition*: Cokesbury Ord. #512075. *Piano/Guitar/Vocal Edition*: Cokesbury Ord. #080689314186).

M116-M168   Barker, Ken, ed. *More Songs for Praise and Worship 3 Choir/ Worship Team Edition*. Waco, TX: Word Music, 2005. Cokesbury Ord. #523357 (*Keyboard Edition*: Cokesbury Ord. # 523418. *Piano/Guitar/Vocal Edition*: Cokesbury Ord. #523369).

M169-M219   Barker, Ken, ed. *More Songs for Praise and Worship 4 Choir/ Worship Team Edition*. Waco, TX: Word Music, 2006. Cokesbury Ord. # 529198 (*Keyboard Edition*: Cokesbury Ord. # 529244. *Piano/Guitar/Vocal Edition*: ISBN: 9785557996822).

M220-M279   McClure, Mark and Sarah G. Huffman, eds. *More Songs for Praise and Worship 5*. Waco, TX: Word Music, 2011. (*Piano/Guitar/Vocal Edition*. ISBN: 9781458418807. *Choir/Worship Team Edition*. ISBN: 9781458418814; *Keyboard/SATB Edition*. Catalog #080689-50087-9).

See also Vocal Solo suggestions from V-3 and V-5.

VOCAL SUGGESTION RESOURCES

V-1   Kimbrough, Steven, ed. *Sweet Singer: Hymns of Charles Wesley*. Chapel Hill, NC: Hinshaw Music, 1987. Catalogue #CV-1 Cokesbury Ord. #811712

V-2   Handel, George Frederick. *Messiah*. Various editions available.

V-3   Hayes, Mark. *The Mark Hayes Vocal Solo Collection*
     V-3 (1) *Ten Spirituals for Solo Voice*. Van Nuys, CA: Alfred Music Publishing, 2007. ISBN: 9780882848808
     V-3 (2) *Seven Praise and Worship Songs for Solo Voice*. Van Nuys, CA: Alfred Music Publishing, 2010. ISBN: 9780739037249
     V-3 (3) *Ten Hymns and Gospel Songs for Solo Voice*. ISBN: 9780739006979

V-4   Scott, K. Lee. *Sing a Song of Joy*. Minneapolis, MN: Augsburg Fortress, 1989. ISBN: 9780800647889 (Medium High Voice) ISBN: 9780800647889 (Medium Low Voice) ISBN: 9780800652821.

V-5   Various Editors. *With All My Heart: Contemporary Vocal Solos*. Minneapolis, MN: Augsburg Fortress, 2004.
     V-5 (1) Volume 1: Autumn and Winter. ISBN: 9780800676841
     V-5 (2) Volume 2: Spring and Summer. ISBN: 9780800676858
     V-5 (3) Volume 3: Baptisms, Weddings, Funerals. ISBN: 9780800679460

V-6   Walters, Richard, arr. *Hymn Classics: Concert Arrangements of Traditional Hymns for Voice and Piano*. Milwaukee, WI: Hal Leonard Publishing, 1993. ISBN: 9780793560080. High Voice: Cokesbury Ord. #811290. Low Voice: Cokesbury Ord. #811233.

V-7   Johnson, Hall, arr. *Thirty (30) Spirituals*. New York: G. Schirmer, Inc., 1949. ISBN: 9780793548033.

V-8   Wilson, John F., Don Doig, and Jack Schrader, eds. *Everything for the Church Soloist*. Carol Stream, IL: Hope Publishing Company, 1980. Cokesbury Ord. #810103.

V-9   Scott, K. Lee. *Rejoice Now My Spirit: Vocal Solos for the Church Year*. Minneapolis, MN: Augsburg Fortress, 1992. ISBN: 9780800651084

V-10   Hayes, Mark, et al. *From the Manger to the Cross—Seasonal Solos for Medium Voice*. Dayton, OH: The Lorenz Corporation, 2006. Cokesbury Ord. #526369.

V-11   Pote, Allen. *A Song of Joy*. Carol Stream, IL: Hope Publishing, 2003. Cokesbury Ord. #505068.

ANTHEM RESOURCES

AEC   *Augsburg Easy Choirbook Volumes 1-3: Music for the Church Year*. Minneapolis, MN: Augsburg Fortress.
     AEC-1 Volume 1: 2003. ISBN: 9780800676025
     AEC-2 Volume 2: 2005. ISBN: 9780800677510
     AEC-3 Volume 3: 2016. ISBN: 9781506414041

Song of Solomon 2:8-13

[8]Listen! It's my lover: here he comes now,
    leaping upon the mountains,
    bounding over the hills.
[9]My lover is like a gazelle
    or a young stag.
Here he stands now,
    outside our wall,
    peering through the windows,
    peeking through the lattices.
[10]My lover spoke and said to me,
"Rise up, my dearest,
    my fairest, and go.
[11]Here, the winter is past;
    the rains have come and gone.
[12]Blossoms have appeared in the land;
    the season of singing has arrived,
    and the sound of the turtledove is heard in our land.
[13]The green fruit is on the fig tree,
    and the grapevines in bloom are fragrant.
Rise up, my dearest,
    my fairest, and go.

Psalm 45:1-2, 6-9 (G333/398, N650, UM795)

A marvelous word has stirred my heart
    as I mention my works to the king.
        My tongue is the pen of a skillful scribe.
[2]You are the most handsome of men;
    grace has been poured out on your lips.
        No wonder God has blessed you forever!
. . . .
[6]Your divine throne is eternal and everlasting.
    Your royal scepter is a scepter of justice.
[7]You love righteousness and hate wickedness.
    No wonder God, your God, has anointed you
    with the oil of joy more than all your companions!
[8]All your clothes have the pleasing scent of myrrh, aloes, and
        cinnamon.
    The music of stringed instruments coming from ivory pal-
        aces entertains you.
[9]The royal princess is standing in your precious jewels;
    the queen stands at your right, dressed in the gold of Ophir.

James 1:17-27

[17]Every good gift, every perfect gift, comes from above. These gifts come down from the Father, the creator of the heavenly lights, in whose character there is no change at all. [18]He chose to give us birth by his true word, and here is the result: we are like the first crop from the harvest of everything he created.

[19]Know this, my dear brothers and sisters: everyone should be quick to listen, slow to speak, and slow to grow angry. [20]This is because an angry person doesn't produce God's righteousness. [21]Therefore, with humility, set aside all moral filth and the growth of wickedness, and welcome the word planted deep inside you—the very word that is able to save you.

[22]You must be doers of the word and not only hearers who mislead themselves. [23]Those who hear but don't do the word are like those who look at their faces in a mirror. [24]They look at themselves, walk away, and immediately forget what they were like. [25]But there are those who study the perfect law, the law of freedom, and continue to do it. They don't listen and then forget, but they put it into practice in their lives. They will be blessed in whatever they do.

[26]If those who claim devotion to God don't control what they say, they mislead themselves. Their devotion is worthless. [27]True devotion, the kind that is pure and faultless before God the Father, is this: to care for orphans and widows in their difficulties and to keep the world from contaminating us.

Mark 7:1-8, 14-15, 21-23

The Pharisees and some legal experts from Jerusalem gathered around Jesus. [2]They saw some of his disciples eating food with unclean hands. (They were eating without first ritually purifying their hands through washing. [3]The Pharisees and all the Jews don't eat without first washing their hands carefully. This is a way of observing the rules handed 1 by the elders. [4]Upon returning from the marketplace, they don't eat without first immersing themselves. They observe many other rules that have been handed down, such as the washing of cups, jugs, pans, and sleeping mats.) [5]So the Pharisees and legal experts asked Jesus, "Why are your disciples not living according to the rules handed down by the elders but instead eat food with ritually unclean hands?"

[6]He replied, "Isaiah really knew what he was talking about when he prophesied about you hypocrites. He wrote,
    This people honors me with their lips,
    but their hearts are far away from me.
    [7]*Their worship of me is empty*
    since they teach instructions that are human words.
[8] You ignore God's commandment while holding on to rules created by humans and handed down to you." . . .

[14]Then Jesus called the crowd again and said, "Listen to me, all of you, and understand. [15] Nothing outside of a person can enter and contaminate a person in God's sight; rather, the things that come out of a person contaminate the person." . . .

[21]"It's from the inside, from the human heart, that evil thoughts come: sexual sins, thefts, murders, [22] adultery, greed, evil actions, deceit, unrestrained immorality, envy, insults, arrogance, and foolishness. [23]All these evil things come from the inside and contaminate a person in God's sight."

Primary Hymns and Songs for the Day

"For the Beauty of the Earth" (Song, Jas) (O)
  B44, C56, E416, EL879, F1, G14, L561, P473, N28, UM92
  (PD), VU226, W557
       H-3   Chr-33, 65; Desc-30; Org-29
       S-1   #93-96. Various treatments

"Fairest Lord Jesus" (Song, Pss, Mark)
  B176, C97, E383, EL838, F240, G630, L518, N44, P306,
  UM189 (PD), VU341

"The Gift of Love" (Song, Pss)
  B423, C526, G693, P335, UM408, VU372
       H-3   Chr-200; Org-45

"Take My Life, and Let It Be" (Jas, Mark) (C)
  B277/283, C609, E707, EL583/685, G697, L406, P391, N448,
  UM399 (PD), VU506

"Lord, I Want to Be a Christian" (Jas, Mark) (C)
  B489, C589, F421, G729, N454, P372 (PD), UM402
       H-3   Chr-130

Additional Hymn Suggestions

"When Love Is Found" (Song, Pss)
  (Same tune as "The Gift of Love" above)
  C499, N362, UM643, VU489, W745

"Jesus, Joy of Our Desiring" (Song, Pss)
  UM644 (PD), VU328

"O Perfect Love" (Song, Pss, Wedding)
  B512, F530, L287, P533, UM645, VU491

"I Love the Lord" (Song, Pss)
  G799, P362, N511, VU617, WS3142

"Immortal, Invisible, God Only Wise" (Jas)
  B6, C66, E423, EL834, F319, G12, L526, N1, P263, UM103
  (PD), VU264, W512

"Great Is Thy Faithfulness" (Jas)
  B54, C86, EL733, F98, G39, N423, P276, UM140, VU288

"I Sing the Almighty Power of God" (Jas)
  B42, C64, E398, G32, N12, P288 (PD), UM152 (PD), VU231,
  W502

"We Give Thee But Thine Own" (Jas)
  B609, C382, EL686, F515, G708, L410, N785, P428, VU543

"This Is My Song" (Jas)
  C722, EL887, G340, N591, UM437

"Where Charity and Love Prevail" (Jas)
  E581, EL359, G316, L126, N396, UM549

"Blest Be the Tie That Binds" (Jas) (C)
  B387, C433, EL656, F560, G309, L370, N393, P438, UM557
  (PD), VU602

"Father, We Thank You" (Jas)
  E302, EL478, UM563/565, W558

"Praise Our God Above" ("Harvest Song") (Jas)
  N424, P480, S2061

"Together We Serve" (Jas)
  G767, S2175, SF2175

"Here Am I" (Jas)
  C654, S2178, SF2178

"Just as I Am, Without One Plea" (Matt)
  B303/307, C339, E693, EL592, F417, G442, L296, N207,
  P370, UM357 (PD), VU508

"All Who Love and Serve Your City" (Mark)
  C670, E571, G351, P413, UM433

"As a Chalice Cast of Gold" (Mark)
  C287, G429, P336, VU505

"Lord of the Dance" (Mark)
  G157, P302, UM261, VU352, W636

Contemporary Suggestions

"Jesus, Name Above All Names" (Song)
  S2071, SF2071, SP76

"I Love You, Lord" (Pss)
  B212, G627, S2068, SF2068, SP72

"In the Lord I'll Be Ever Thankful" (Jas)
  G654, S2195, SF2195

"Lord, Be Glorified" (Jas)
  B457, EL744, G468, S2150, SF2150, SP196

"Make Me a Servant" (Jas)
  S2176, SF2176, SP193

"Forevermore" (Jas)
  M229

"One Way" (Jas, Mark)
  M248

"I Will Enter His Gates" (Jas, Mark)
  S2270, SF2270, SP168

"Change My Heart, O God" (Jas, Mark)
  EL801, G695, SP195, S2152, SF2152

"Give Thanks" (Jas, Mark)
  C528, G647, S2036, SF2036, SP170

"Open Our Eyes, Lord" (Mark)
  B499, S2086, SF2086, SP199

"Open the Eyes of My Heart" (Mark)
  G452, M57, W3008

Vocal Solos

"Cord of Three Strands" (Song, Wedding)
  V-5(3)   p. 10

"The Call" (Song)
  V-4   p. 31

"Thank You for These Gifts" (Song, Jas)
  V-8   p. 129

"Take My Life" (Jas, Mark)
  V-3 (3)   p. 17
  V-8   p. 262

Anthems

"Arise, My Love, My Fair One" (Song)
Richard DeLong; EC Schirmer 4666
SATB divisi (bit.ly/ECS4666)

"Take My Life, That I May Be" (Jas, Mark)
Arr. Mark Sedio; AEC-2 p. 76
SATB and piano, flute, perc., opt. guitar (bit.ly/AEC-2-76)

Other Suggestions

Today would be a good day for reaffirmation of marital vows (Song, Pss)
Visuals:
     O   gazelle, stag, heart, flowers, birds, fruit, fig tree, lovers
     P   scepter, robe, oil, instruments
     E   images of giving, listening, ministry to children,
            widows, elderly
     G   hands/dishwashing (pots, pans, cups), heart
Opening Prayer: WSL60 (Jas)
Canticle: UM646. "Canticle of Love" (Song) See S-1, p. 387
Prayer: UM69 and UM409 (Jas, Mark)
Offertory Prayer: WSL114 (Jas)
Alternate Lessons: Deut. 4;1-2, 6-9, Ps 15 (See p. 4)

Proverbs 22:1-2, 8-9, 22-23

A good reputation is better than much wealth;
    high esteem is better than silver and gold.
² The rich and the poor have this in common:
    the LORD made them both.

. . . .

⁸ Those who sow injustice will harvest evil;
    the rod of their fury will come to an end.
⁹ Happy are generous people,
    because they give some of their food to the poor.

. . . .

²² Don't steal from the poor, because they are poor.
    Don't oppress the needy in the gate.
²³ The LORD will take up their case
    and press the life out of those who oppress them.

Psalm 125 (G848, N707)

The people who trust in the LORD
    are like Mount Zion:
    never shaken, lasting forever.
² Mountains surround Jerusalem.
    That's how the LORD surrounds his people
    from now until forever from now!
³ The wicked rod won't remain
    in the land given to the righteous
    so that they don't use their hands to do anything wrong.
⁴ LORD, do good to people who are good,
    to people whose hearts are right.
⁵ But as for those people who turn to their own twisted ways—
    may the LORD march them off with other evildoers!

Peace be on Israel!

James 2:1-10 (11-13), 14-17

My brothers and sisters, when you show favoritism you deny the faithfulness of our Lord Jesus Christ, who has been resurrected in glory. ² Imagine two people coming into your meeting. One has a gold ring and fine clothes, while the other is poor, dressed in filthy rags. ³ Then suppose that you were to take special notice of the one wearing fine clothes, saying, "Here's an excellent place. Sit here." But to the poor person you say, "Stand over there"; or, "Here, sit at my feet." ⁴ Wouldn't you have shown favoritism among yourselves and become evil-minded judges?

⁵ My dear brothers and sisters, listen! Hasn't God chosen those who are poor by worldly standards to be rich in terms of faith? Hasn't God chosen the poor as heirs of the kingdom he has promised to those who love him? ⁶ But you have dishonored the poor. Don't the wealthy make life difficult for you? Aren't they the ones who drag you into court? ⁷ Aren't they the ones who insult the good name spoken over you at your baptism?

⁸ You do well when you really fulfill the royal law found in scripture, *Love your neighbor as yourself.* ⁹ But when you show favoritism, you are committing a sin, and by that same law you are exposed as a lawbreaker. ¹⁰ Anyone who tries to keep all of the Law but fails at one point is guilty of failing to keep all of it. ¹¹ The one who said, *Don't commit adultery,* also said, *Don't commit murder.* So if you don't commit adultery but do commit murder, you are a lawbreaker. ¹² In every way, then, speak and act as people who will be judged by the law of freedom. ¹³ There will be no mercy in judgment for anyone who hasn't shown mercy. Mercy overrules judgment.

¹⁴ My brothers and sisters, what good is it if people say they have faith but do nothing to show it? Claiming to have faith can't save anyone, can it? ¹⁵ Imagine a brother or sister who is naked and never has enough food to eat. ¹⁶ What if one of you said, "Go in peace! Stay warm! Have a nice meal!"? What good is it if you don't actually give them what their body needs? ¹⁷ In the same way, faith is dead when it doesn't result in faithful activity.

Mark 7:24-37

²⁴ Jesus left that place and went into the region of Tyre. He didn't want anyone to know that he had entered a house, but he couldn't hide. ²⁵ In fact, a woman whose young daughter was possessed by an unclean spirit heard about him right away. She came and fell at his feet. ²⁶ The woman was Greek, Syrophoenician by birth. She begged Jesus to throw the demon out of her daughter. ²⁷ He responded, "The children have to be fed first. It isn't right to take the children's bread and toss it to the dogs."

²⁸ But she answered, "Lord, even the dogs under the table eat the children's crumbs."

²⁹ "Good answer!" he said. "Go on home. The demon has already left your daughter." ³⁰ When she returned to her house, she found the child lying on the bed and the demon gone.

³¹ After leaving the region of Tyre, Jesus went through Sidon toward the Galilee Sea through the region of the Ten Cities. ³² Some people brought to him a man who was deaf and could hardly speak, and they begged him to place his hand on the man for healing. ³³ Jesus took him away from the crowd by himself and put his fingers in the man's ears. Then he spit and touched the man's tongue. ³⁴ Looking into heaven, Jesus sighed deeply and said, *"Ephphatha,"* which means, "Open up." ³⁵ At once, his ears opened, his twisted tongue was released, and he began to speak clearly.

³⁶ Jesus gave the people strict orders not to tell anyone. But the more he tried to silence them, the more eagerly they shared the news. ³⁷ People were overcome with wonder, saying, "He does everything well! He even makes the deaf to hear and gives speech to those who can't speak."

Primary Hymns and Songs for the Day

"In Christ There Is No East or West" (Jas, Mark) (O)
    B385, C687, E529, EL650 (PD), F685, G317/318, L359,
    N394/395, P439/440, UM548, VU606, W659

"*Cuando El Pobre*" ("When the Poor Ones") (Prov, Jas, Mark)
    C662, EL725, G762, P407, UM434, VU702

"Open My Eyes, That I May See" (Jas, Mark)
    B502, C586, F486, G451, P324, UM454, VU371
        H-3   Chr-157; Org-108

"Open Our Eyes, Lord" (Mark)
    B499, S2086, SF2086, SP199

"Thee We Adore, O Hidden Savior, Thee" (Mark)
    EL476 (PD), G495, L199, P519

"Where Cross the Crowded Ways of Life" (Jas) (C)
    C665, E609, EL719, F665, G343, L429, N543, P408, UM427
    (PD), VU681
        H-3   Chr-178, 180; Org-44
        S-1   #141-3 Various treatments

Additional Hymn Suggestions

"All Things Bright and Beautiful" (Prov)
    C61, E405, G20, N31, P267, UM147 (PD), VU291, W505

"When the Church of Jesus" (Prov, Jas) (O)
    B396, C470, UM592

"Lord, Whose Love Through Humble Service" (Prov, Jas, Mark)
    C461, E610, EL712, L423, P427, UM581, W630

"Forth in Thy Name, O Lord" (Jas) (C)
    L505, UM438 (PD), VU416

"Now Let Us from This Table Rise" (Jas, Comm.)
    UM634, W625, VU483

"Sent Forth by God's Blessing" (Jas) (C)
    EL547, L221, N76, UM664, VU481

"Living for Jesus" (Jas)
    B282, C610, F462, S2149, SF2149

"Together We Serve" (Jas, Mark)
    G767, S2175, SF2175

"Healer of Our Every Ill" (Jas, Mark)
    C506, EL612, G795, S2213, SF2213, VU619

"A Place at the Table" (Jas, Mark, Comm.)
    G769, WS3149

"O For a Thousand Tongues to Sing" (Mark)
    B216, C5, E493, EL886, F349, G610, L559, N42, P466, UM57
    (PD), VU326

"Heal Me, Hands of Jesus" (Mark)
    C504, UM262, VU621

"O Christ, the Healer" (Mark)
    C503. EL610, G793, L360, N175, P380, UM265, W747

"Jesus' Hands Were Kind Hands" (Mark)
    B477, UM273, VU570

"He Touched Me" (Mark)
    C564, F628, UM367

"Lord, Listen to Your Children Praying" (Mark)
    C305, G469, S2193, SF2193, VU400

"O For a Thousand Tongues to Sing" (Mark)
    WS3001

"We Cannot Measure How You Heal" (Mark)
    G797, WS3139, VU613

Additional Contemporary Suggestions

"Song of Hope" (Prov, Jas, Mark)
    G765, P432, S2186, VU424

"Change My Heart, O God" (Prov, Pss, Jas)
    EL801, G695, SP195, S2152, SF2152

"Live in Charity" ("*Ubi Caritas*") (Jas)
    C523, EL642, G205, S2179, SF2179, W604

"These Hands" (Jas, Stewardship)
    M101

"*Jesu, Jesu*" (Jas, Mark)
    B501, C600, E602, EL708, G203, N498, P367, UM432,
    VU593, W431, S-1 #63. Vocal part

"Awesome God" (Mark)
    G616, S2040, SF2040, SP11

"Open Our Eyes, Lord" (Mark)
    B499, S2086, SF2086, SP199

"I Know the Lord's Laid His Hands on Me" (Mark)
    S2139, SF2139

"Open the Eyes of My Heart" (Mark)
    G452, M57, WS3008

"Amazing Grace" ("My Chains Are Gone") (Mark)
    M205, WS3104

"The Power of Your Love" (Mark)
    M26

"Hear Us from Heaven" (Mark)
    M267

Vocal Solos

"Bright and Beautiful" (Prov)
    V-3 (3)   p. 10

"Jesus Revealed in Me" (Jas)
    V-8   p. 347

"O For a Thousand Tongues to Sing" (Mark)
    V-1   p. 32
    V-6   p. 28

Anthems

"God Is the Lord of All" (Pss)
Handel/arr. Hopson; AEC-2 p. 55
2-part mixed and keyboard, opt. trumpet (bit.ly/AEC-2-55)

"Healing Grace" (Mark)
Arr. Jane Holstein; Hope C 5265
SATB and piano (bit.ly/C-5265)

Other Suggestions

Visuals:
    O   bread, generosity, ministering hands
    P   Mountain(s), scepter, ministry, river, bird, snare
    E   rich/poor, hands, ministry w/poor, clothes, food,
              blanket
    G   sick child/well child, healing hands, hearing impaired
Mark's reading could lead to a worship emphasis on healing
Call to Prayer: C456. Prayer from the Heart (Jas)
Sung Prayer of Confession: S2138, SF2138, VU107. "Sunday's
    Palms Are Wednesday's Ashes," stanza 3 (Jas)
Words of Assurance: G445, S2169, SF2169. "God, How Can We
    Forgive," stanza 2 (Jas)
Prayer of Confession: WSL90 (Prov, Jas)
Prayer: C653, UM639. Bread and Justice (Prov, Jas, Comm.)
Prayer: C505. Prayer for Healing
Responsive Prayer: F74. A Pledge of Trust (Pss)
Prayer: UM456. For Courage to Do Justice (Prov, Jas, Mark)
Healing Prayer: WSL204 or WSL209 (Mark)
Offertory Prayer: WSL114 (Jas)
Litany of Thanksgiving and Sending Forth: WSL175 (Mark)
Sung Benediction: E347, UM670, VU418. "Go Forth for God"
    (Pss)
Alternate Lessons: Isa 35:4-7a; Ps 146 (see p. 4)

Proverbs 1:20-33

²⁰Wisdom shouts in the street;
  in the public square she raises her voice.
²¹Above the noisy crowd, she calls out.
  At the entrances of the city gates, she has her say:
²²"How long will you clueless people love your naïveté,
  mockers hold their mocking dear,
  and fools hate knowledge?
²³You should respond when I correct you.
  Look, I'll pour out my spirit on you.
  I'll reveal my words to you.
²⁴I invited you, but you rejected me;
  I stretched out my hand to you,
  but you paid no attention.
²⁵You ignored all my advice,
  and you didn't want me to correct you.
²⁶So I'll laugh at your disaster;
  I'll make fun of you when dread comes over you,
    ²⁷when terror hits you like a hurricane,
  and your disaster comes in like a tornado,
  when distress and oppression overcome you.
²⁸Then they will call me, but I won't answer;
  they will seek me, but won't find me
    ²⁹because they hated knowledge
  and didn't choose the fear of the Lᴏʀᴅ.
³⁰They didn't want my advice;
  they rejected all my corrections.
³¹They will eat from the fruit of their way,
  and they'll be full of their own schemes.
³²The immature will die because they turn away;
  smugness will destroy fools.
³³Those who obey me will dwell securely,
  untroubled by the dread of harm."

Psalm 19 (G61/690, N630, P166/167, UM750)

Heaven is declaring God's glory;
  the sky is proclaiming his handiwork.
²One day gushes the news to the next,
  and one night informs another what needs to be known.
³Of course, there's no speech, no words—
    their voices can't be heard—
    ⁴but their sound extends throughout the world;
    their words reach the ends of the earth.
God has made a tent in heaven for the sun.
⁵The sun is like a groom
  coming out of his honeymoon suite;
  like a warrior, it thrills at running its course.
⁶It rises in one end of the sky;
  its circuit is complete at the other.
    Nothing escapes its heat.
⁷The Lᴏʀᴅ's Instruction is perfect,
  reviving one's very being.
The Lᴏʀᴅ's laws are faithful,
  making naive people wise.
⁸The Lᴏʀᴅ's regulations are right,
  gladdening the heart.
The Lᴏʀᴅ's commands are pure,
  giving light to the eyes.
⁹Honoring the Lᴏʀᴅ is correct,
  lasting forever.
The Lᴏʀᴅ's judgments are true.
  All of these are righteous!
¹⁰They are more desirable than gold—
    than tons of pure gold!
  They are sweeter than honey—
    even dripping off the honeycomb!
¹¹No doubt about it:
  your servant is enlightened by them;
  there is great reward in keeping them.
¹²But can anyone know
  what they've accidentally done wrong?
  Clear me of any unknown sin
    ¹³and save your servant from willful sins.
    Don't let them rule me.
Then I'll be completely blameless;
  I'll be innocent of great wrongdoing.
¹⁴Let the words of my mouth
  and the meditations of my heart
  be pleasing to you,
  Lᴏʀᴅ, my rock and my redeemer.

James 3:1-12

My brothers and sisters, not many of you should become teachers, because we know that we teachers will be judged more strictly. ²We all make mistakes often, but those who don't make mistakes with their words have reached full maturity. Like a bridled horse, they can control themselves entirely. ³When we bridle horses and put bits in their mouths to lead them wherever we want, we can control their whole bodies.

⁴Consider ships: They are so large that strong winds are needed to drive them. But pilots direct their ships wherever they want with a little rudder. ⁵In the same way, even though the tongue is a small part of the body, it boasts wildly.

Think about this: A small flame can set a whole forest on fire.⁶The tongue is a small flame of fire, a world of evil at work in us. It contaminates our entire lives. Because of it, the circle of life is set on fire. The tongue itself is set on fire by the flames of hell.

⁷People can tame and already have tamed every kind of animal, bird, reptile, and fish. ⁸No one can tame the tongue, though. It is a restless evil, full of deadly poison. ⁹With it we both bless the Lord and Father and curse human beings made in God's likeness. ¹⁰Blessing and cursing come from the same mouth. My brothers and sisters, it just shouldn't be this way! ¹¹Both fresh water and salt water don't come from the same spring, do they? ¹²My brothers and sisters, can a fig tree produce olives? Can a grapevine produce figs? Of course not, and fresh water doesn't flow from a saltwater spring either.

Mark 8:27-38

²⁷Jesus and his disciples went into the villages near Caesarea Philippi. On the way he asked his disciples, "Who do people say that I am?"

²⁸They told him, "Some say John the Baptist, others Elijah, and still others one of the prophets."

²⁹He asked them, "And what about you? Who do you say that I am?"

Peter answered, "You are the Christ." ³⁰Jesus ordered them not to tell anyone about him.

³¹Then Jesus began to teach his disciples: "The Human One must suffer many things and be rejected by the elders, chief priests, and the legal experts, and be killed, and then, after three days, rise from the dead." ³²He said this plainly. But Peter took hold of Jesus and, scolding him, began to correct him. ³³Jesus turned and looked at his disciples, then sternly corrected Peter: "Get behind me, Satan. You are not thinking God's thoughts but human thoughts."

³⁴After calling the crowd together with his disciples, Jesus said to them, "All who want to come after me must say no to themselves, take up their cross, and follow me. ³⁵ All who want to save their lives will lose them. But all who lose their lives because of me and because of the good news will save them. ³⁶ Why would people gain the whole world but lose their lives? ³⁷ What will people give in exchange for their lives? ³⁸Whoever is ashamed of me and my words in this unfaithful and sinful generation, the Human One will be ashamed of that person when he comes in the Father's glory with the holy angels."

Primary Hymns and Songs for the Day

"I Sing the Almighty Power of God" (Prov, Pss) (O)
   C64, G32, N12, P288 (PD)
   H-3 Hbl-16, 22, 68; Chr-101; Desc-37
   S-1 #115. Harm.
   B42, E398, UM152 (PD)
   H-3 Hbl-44; Chr-21; Desc-40; Org-40
   S-1 #131-132. Intro. and descant
   VU231 (PD), W502 (PD)

"Be Thou My Vision" (Prov, Pss)
   B60, C595, E488, EL793, F468, G450, N451, P339, UM451,
   VU642
   H-3 Hbl-15, 48; Chr-36; Org-153
   S-1 #319. Arr. for organ and voices in canon

"How Great Thou Art" (Pss)
   B10, C33, EL856, G625, N35, P467, UM77, VU238
   H-3 Chr-103; Org-105
   S-1 #163. Harm.

"God of Wonders" (Pss)
   M80, WS3034

"I Have Decided to Follow Jesus" (Mark)
   B305, C344, S2129, SF2129

"Take Up Thy Cross" (Mark) (C)
   B494, E675, EL667, G718, L398, N204, P393, UM415, VU561,
   W634
   H-3 Chr-178, 180; Org-44
   S-1 #141-3 Various treatments

Additional Hymn Suggestions

"O Word of God Incarnate" (Prov)
   C322, E632, EL514, G459, L231, N315, P327, UM598 (PD),
   VU499

"Open Your Ears" (Prov)
   E536, EL519, G453, VU272

"Morning Has Broken" (Prov, Pss)
   B48, C53, E8, EL556, F5, G664, P469, UM145, VU409

"For the Beauty of the Earth" (Pss)
   B44, C56, E416, EL879, F1, G14, L561, P473, N28, UM92
   (PD), VU226, W557

"Jesus Shall Reign" (Jas)
   B587, C95, E544, EL434, F238, G265, L530, N157, P423,
   UM157 (PD), VU330, W492

"The Gift of Love" (Jas)
   B423, C526, G693, P335, UM408, VU372

"Lord, Speak to Me" (Jas)
   B568, EL676, F625, G722, L403, N531, P426, UM463 (PD),
   VU589

"Where Charity and Love Prevail" (Jas)
   E581, EL359, G316, L126, N396, UM549

"Woke Up This Morning" (Jas)
   C623, N85, S2082, SF2082

"Lord Jesus, You Shall Be My Song" (Jas)
   EL808, G737, VU641 (Fr.)

"Lift High the Cross" (Mark) (O)
   B594, C108, E473, EL660, G826, L377, N198, P371, UM159,
   VU151, W704

"Lord of the Dance" (Mark)
   G157, P302, UM261, VU352, W636

"O Master, Let Me Walk with Thee" (Mark)
   B279, C602, E E659/660, EL818, F442, G738, L492, N503,
   P357, UM430 (PD), VU560

"Nearer, My God, to Thee" (Mark)
   B458, C577, N606, UM528 (PD), VU497 (Fr.)

"Swiftly Pass the Clouds of Glory" (Mark)
   G190, P73, S2102

"Living for Jesus" (Mark)
   B282, C610, F462, S2149, SF2149

Additional Contemporary Suggestions

"I Will Call upon the Lord" (Pss, Jas)
   G621, S2002, SF2002, SP224

"More Precious than Silver" (Pss)
   S2065, SF2065, SP99

"Praise the Name of Jesus" (Pss)
   S2066, SF2066, SP87

"All Heaven Declares" (Pss)
   M58

"The Heavens Shall Declare" (Pss)
   M111

"Cry of My Heart" (Mark)
   M39, S2165, SF2165

"Let It Be Said of Us" (Mark)
   M53

"Every Move I Make" (Mark)
   M122

"Everyday" (Mark)
   M150

"Surrender" (Mark)
   M157

"One Way" (Mark)
   M248

Vocal Solos

"Be Thou My Vision" (Prov)
   V-6   p. 13

"The Heavens Declare His Glory" (Pss)
   V-8   p. 248

"Courage, My Heart" (Mark)
   V-9   p. 20

Anthems

"As a Tree" (Prov)
Mark Sirett; Augsburg 978-1-5064-1381-5
SATB a cappella (bit.ly/1381-5)

"A Covenant Prayer" (Mark)
Dan Forrest; Hinshaw HMC2289 (a cappella HMC2290)
SATB with keyboard (bit.ly/HMC2289)

Other Suggestions

Visuals:
  O Crowded street corner, gates, storm, tornado, listening
  P Light/darkness, rising/setting sun, gold, honeycomb, honey
  E Teaching, bridle, ship rudder, fire
  G Christ, teaching, rugged cross, descending Christ/ angels
Emphasize children's education, using Proverbs and James.
Greeting: N824 (Pss)
Canticle: N740 or UM112 (Prov)
Prayer: C1, C256, or N851 (Prov)
Prayers: WSL47 (Prov) and WSL71 (Pss) and WSL62 (Pss)
Prayer of Confession: N837 (Jas)
Words of Assurance: N840 (Pss)
Alternate Lessons: Isa 50:4-9a; Ps 116:1-9 (see p. 4)

Proverbs 31:10-31

[10]A competent wife, how does one find her?
　　Her value is far above pearls.
[11]Her husband entrusts his heart to her,
　　and with her he will have all he needs.
[12]She brings him good and not trouble
　　all the days of her life.
[13]She seeks out wool and flax;
　　she works joyfully with her hands.
[14]She is like a fleet of merchant ships,
　　bringing food from a distance.
[15]She gets up while it is still night,
　　providing food for her household,
　　even some for her female servants.
[16]She surveys a field and acquires it;
　　from her own resources, she plants a vineyard.
[17]She works energetically;
　　her arms are powerful.
[18]She realizes that her trading is successful;
　　she doesn't put out her lamp at night.
[19]She puts her hands to the spindle;
　　her palms grasp the whorl.
[20]She reaches out to the needy;
　　she stretches out her hands to the poor.
[21]She doesn't fear for her household when it snows,
　　because they are all dressed in warm clothes.
[22]She makes bedspreads for herself;
　　fine linen and purple are her clothing.
[23]Her husband is known in the city gates
　　when he sits with the elders of the land.
[24]She makes garments and sells them;
　　she supplies sashes to traders.
[25]Strength and honor are her clothing;
　　she is confident about the future.
[26]Her mouth is full of wisdom;
　　kindly teaching is on her tongue.
[27]She is vigilant over the activities of her household;
　　she doesn't eat the food of laziness.
[28]Her children bless her;
　　her husband praises her:
[29]"Many women act competently,
　　but you surpass them all!"
[30]Charm is deceptive and beauty fleeting,
　　but a woman who fears the LORD is to be praised.
[31]Let her share in the results of her work;
　　let her deeds praise her in the city gates.

Psalm 1 (G457, N621, P158, UM738)

The truly happy person
　　doesn't follow wicked advice,
　　doesn't stand on the road of sinners,
　　and doesn't sit with the disrespectful.
[2]Instead of doing those things,
　　these persons love the LORD's Instruction,
　　and they recite God's Instruction day and night!
[3]They are like a tree replanted by streams of water,
　　which bears fruit at just the right time
　　and whose leaves don't fade.
　　　Whatever they do succeeds.

[4]That's not true for the wicked!
　　They are like dust that the wind blows away.
[5]And that's why the wicked will have no standing in the court of justice—
　　neither will sinners
　　in the assembly of the righteous.
[6]The LORD is intimately acquainted
　　with the way of the righteous,
　　but the way of the wicked is destroyed.

James 3:13–4:3, 7-8a

[13]Are any of you wise and understanding? Show that your actions are good with a humble lifestyle that comes from wisdom. [14]However, if you have bitter jealousy and selfish ambition in your heart, then stop bragging and living in ways that deny the truth. [15]This is not the wisdom that comes down from above. Instead, it is from the earth, natural and demonic. [16]Wherever there is jealousy and selfish ambition, there is disorder and everything that is evil. [17]What of the wisdom from above? First, it is pure, and then peaceful, gentle, obedient, filled with mercy and good actions, fair, and genuine. [18]Those who make peace sow the seeds of justice by their peaceful acts.

4What is the source of conflict among you? What is the source of your disputes? Don't they come from your cravings that are at war in your own lives? [2]You long for something you don't have, so you commit murder. You are jealous for something you can't get, so you struggle and fight. You don't have because you don't ask. [3]You ask and don't have because you ask with evil intentions, to waste it on your own cravings. . . .

[7]Therefore, submit to God. Resist the devil, and he will run away from you. [8]Come near to God, and he will come near to you.

Mark 9:30-37

[30]From there Jesus and his followers went through Galilee, but he didn't want anyone to know it. [31]This was because he was teaching his disciples, "The Human One will be delivered into human hands. They will kill him. Three days after he is killed he will rise up." [32]But they didn't understand this kind of talk, and they were afraid to ask him.

[33]They entered Capernaum. When they had come into a house, he asked them, "What were you arguing about during the journey?" [34]They didn't respond, since on the way they had been debating with each other about who was the greatest. [35]He sat down, called the Twelve, and said to them, "Whoever wants to be first must be least of all and the servant of all." [36]Jesus reached for a little child, placed him among the Twelve, and embraced him. Then he said, [37]"Whoever welcomes one of these children in my name welcomes me; and whoever welcomes me isn't actually welcoming me but rather the one who sent me."

Primary Hymns and Songs for the Day
"Praise the Source of Faith and Learning" (Prov, Pss, Jas) (O)
　N411, S2004, SF2004
　　　　H-3　　Hbl-46; Chr-26, 134; Desc-53; Org-56
　　　　S-1　　#168-171. Various treatments
"O Word of God Incarnate" (Prov, Pss)
　C322, E632, EL514, G459, L231, N315, P327, UM598 (PD),
　VU499
　　　　H-3　　Hbl-86; Chr-153; Org-95
　　　　S-1　　#243. Harm.
"Lord, I Want to Be a Christian" (Jas, Mark)
　B489, C589, F421, G729, N454, P372 (PD), UM402
　　　　H-3　　Chr-130
"*Jesu, Jesu*" (Mark)
　B501, C600, E602, EL708, G203, N498, P367, UM432,
　VU593, W431, S-1 #63. Vocal part
　　　　H-3　　Chr-114; Org-19
　　　　S-1　　#63. Vocal part
"Make Me a Servant" (Mark)
　S2176, SF2176, SP193
"Make Me a Captive, Lord" (Mark) (C)
　B278, P378, UM421
　　　　H-3　　Hbl-55; Chr-60; Desc-30; Org-27
　　　　S-1　　#86-88. Various treatments

Additional Hymn Suggestions
"Morning Glory, Starlit Sky" (Prov)
　E585, UM194, W587
"All Who Love and Serve Your City" (Prov, Mark)
　C670, E571, G351, P413, UM433
"Lord, Speak to Me" (Prov, Mark)
　B568, EL676, F625, G722, N531, P426, UM463, VU589
"I Sing a Song of the Saints of God" (Prov, Mark)
　E293, G730, N295, P364, UM712 (PD)
"Blessed Assurance" (Jas)
　B334, C543, EL638, G839, N473, P341, UM369, VU337
"Just a Closer Walk with Thee" (Jas)
　B448, C557, EL697, F591, G835, S2158, SF2158
"Christ Beside Me" (Jas)
　G702, S2166, SF2166
"We Walk by Faith" (Jas)
　E209, EL635, G817, N256, P399, S2196, SF2196, W572
"Spirit of Jesus, If I Love My Neighbor" (Jas)
　N590
"God of the Fertile Fields" (Jas)
　C695, G714
"Together We Serve" (Jas, Mark)
　G767, S2175, SF2175
"Jesus Loves Me" (Mark)
　B344 (PD), C113, EL595 (PD), F226, G188, N327, P304,
　UM191, VU365
"O Master, Let Me Walk with Thee" (Mark)
　B279, C602, E659/660, EL818, F442, G738, L492, N503,
　P357, UM430 (PD), VU560
"All Who Love and Serve Your City" (Mark)
　C670, E571, G351, P413, UM433
"The Church of Christ, in Every Age" (Mark)
　B402, C475, EL729, G320, L433, N306, P421, UM589,
　VU601, W626
"O Word of God Incarnate" (Mark)
　C322, E632, EL514, G459, N315, P327, UM598, VU499
"I Sing a Song of the Saints of God" (Mark)
　E293, G730, N295, P364, UM712 (PD)
"Like a Child" (Mark)
　C133, S2092, SF2092, VU366

"As We Gather at Your Table" (Mark, Comm.)
　EL522, N332, S2268, SF2268, VU457
"Lord, Whose Love Through Humble Service" (Mark) (C)
　C461, E610, EL712, L423, P427, UM581, W630

Additional Contemporary Suggestions
"As the Deer" (Prov)
　G626, S2025, SF2025, SP200, VU766
"I Will Enter His Gates" (Pss)
　S2270, SF2270, SP168
"Thy Word Is a Lamp" (Pss)
　C326, G458, SP183, UM601
"Humble Thyself in the Sight of the Lord" (Jas)
　S2131, SF2131, SP223
"Jesus, Draw Me Close" (Jas)
　M48, S2159, SF2159
"Song of Hope" (Jas)
　G765, P432, S2186, VU424
"They'll Know We Are Christians" (Jas)
　C494, G300, S2223, SF2223
"Make Me a Channel of Your Peace" (Jas)
　G753, S2171, SF2171, VU684
"The Servant Song" (Mark)
　C490, EL659, G727, N539, S2222, SF2222, VU595

Vocal Solos
"A Worthy Woman" (Prov)
　V-8　　　　p. 364
"Just a Closer Walk with Thee" (Jas)
　V-5(2)　　p. 31
　V-8　　　　p. 323

Anthems
"*Kyrie*" (Jas)
Arr. Ruth Elaine Schram; Alfred 44237
SAB, C-Instrument, piano (bit.ly/44237-Kyrie)

"As We Gather at Your Table" (Mark, Comm.)
K. Lee Scott; AEC-2 p. 12
SAB and organ (bit.ly/AEC-2-12)

Other Suggestions
Visuals:
　　O　　Jewels, women at work, speaking, laughing, praise
　　P　　Open Bible, chaff/wind, scales of justice
　　E　　Gentle touch, fruit/harvest, conflict/treaty, Jas 3:8
　　G　　Crucifixion/Resurrection, arguing, child, Mark 9:37
Introit: EL522, N332, S2268, SF2268, VU457. "As We Gather at
　Your Table" (Mark, Comm.)
Opening Prayer: WSL54 (Jas, Mark)
Response: C299, EL152, S2275/2277, SF2275/2277, WS3133.
　"*Kyrie*" ("Lord, Have Mercy") (Jas)
Sung Confession: WS3138. "Confession" (Jas)
Prayer for Illumination: WSL72 (Prov, Pss, James)
Prayers: C31, N851, and UM401 (Jas)
Offertory Prayer: WSL144 (Mark)
Sung Benediction: G765, P432, S2186, VU424. "Song of Hope"
　(Jas)
See last week's suggestions for add'l wisdom-themed ideas.
Alternate Lessons: Wis 1:16 - 2:1, 12-22 (or Jer 11:18-20); Ps 54 (see
　p. 4)

Esther 7:1-6, 9-10; 9:20-22

When the king and Haman came in for the banquet with Queen Esther, [2]the king said to her, "This is the second day we've met for wine. What is your wish, Queen Esther? I'll give it to you. And what do you want? I'll do anything—even give you half the kingdom."

[3]Queen Esther answered, "If I please the king, and if the king wishes, give me my life—that's my wish—and the lives of my people too. That's my desire. [4]We have been sold—I and my people—to be wiped out, killed, and destroyed. If we simply had been sold as male and female slaves, I would have said nothing. But no enemy can compensate the king for this kind of damage."

[5]King Ahasuerus said to Queen Esther, "Who is this person, and where is he? Who would dare do such a thing?"

[6]Esther replied, "A man who hates, an enemy—this wicked Haman!" Haman was overcome with terror in the presence of the king and queen. . . .

[9]Harbona, one of the eunuchs serving the king, said, "Sir, look! There's the stake that Haman made for Mordecai, the man who spoke up and did something good for the king. It's standing at Haman's house—seventy-five feet high."

"Impale him on it!" the king ordered. [10]So they impaled Haman on the very pole that he had set up for Mordecai, and the king's anger went away. . . .

9[20]Mordecai wrote these things down and sent letters to all the Jews in all the provinces, both near and far, of King Ahasuerus.[21]He made it a rule that Jews keep the fourteenth and fifteenth days of the month of Adar as special days each and every year.[22]They are the days on which the Jews finally put to rest the troubles with their enemies. The month is the one when everything turned around for them from sadness to joy, and from sad, loud crying to a holiday. They are to make them days of feasts and joyous events, days to send food gifts to each other and money gifts to the poor.

Psalm 124 (G330, N706, P236, UM846)

If the LORD hadn't been for us—
    let Israel now repeat!—
    [2]if the LORD hadn't been for us,
        when those people attacked us
[3]then they would have swallowed us up whole
    with their rage burning against us!
[4]Then the waters would have drowned us;
    the torrent would have come over our necks;
    [5]then the raging waters would have come over our necks!
[6]Bless the LORD
    because he didn't hand us over
    like food for our enemies' teeth!
[7]We escaped like a bird from the hunters' trap;
    the trap was broken so we escaped!
[8]Our help is in the name of the LORD,
    the maker of heaven and earth.

James 5:13-20

[13]If any of you are suffering, they should pray. If any of you are happy, they should sing. [14]If any of you are sick, they should call for the elders of the church, and the elders should pray over them, anointing them with oil in the name of the Lord. [15]Prayer that comes from faith will heal the sick, for the Lord will restore them to health. And if they have sinned, they will be forgiven.[16]For this reason, confess your sins to each other and pray for each other so that you may be healed. The prayer of the righteous person is powerful in what it can achieve. [17]Elijah was a person just like us. When he earnestly prayed that it wouldn't rain, no rain fell for three and a half years. [18]He prayed again, God sent rain, and the earth produced its fruit.

[19]My brothers and sisters, if any of you wander from the truth and someone turns back the wanderer, [20]recognize that whoever brings a sinner back from the wrong path will save them from death and will bring about the forgiveness of many sins.

Mark 9:38-50

[38]John said to Jesus, "Teacher, we saw someone throwing demons out in your name, and we tried to stop him because he wasn't following us."

[39]Jesus replied, "Don't stop him. No one who does powerful acts in my name can quickly turn around and curse me.[40]Whoever isn't against us is for us. [41]I assure you that whoever gives you a cup of water to drink because you belong to Christ will certainly be rewarded.

[42]"As for whoever causes these little ones who believe in me to trip and fall into sin, it would be better for them to have a huge stone hung around their necks and to be thrown into the lake. [43]If your hand causes you to fall into sin, chop it off. It's better for you to enter life crippled than to go away with two hands into the fire of hell, which can't be put out.[45]If your foot causes you to fall into sin, chop it off. It's better for you to enter life lame than to be thrown into hell with two feet. [47]If your eye causes you to fall into sin, tear it out. It's better for you to enter God's kingdom with one eye than to be thrown into hell with two. [48]That's a place *where worms don't die and the fire never goes out.* [49]Everyone will be salted with fire. [50]Salt is good; but if salt loses its saltiness, how will it become salty again? Maintain salt among yourselves and keep peace with each other."

Primary Hymns and Songs for the Day

"Sing Praise to God Who Reigns Above" (Esth, Jas) (O)
   B20, C6, E408, EL871, F343, G645, N6, P483, UM126 (PD),
   VU216, W528
         H-3   Hbl-92; Chr-173; Desc-76; Org-91
         S-1   #237. Descant
"O Christ, the Healer" (Jas, Mark)
   C503. EL610, G793, L360, N175, P380, UM265, W747
"Sois la Semilla" ("You Are the Seed") (Mark)
   C478, N528, UM583
"They'll Know We Are Christians" (Jas) (C)
   C494, G300, S2223, SF2223

Additional Hymn Suggestions

"What Gift Can We Bring" (Esth)
   N370, UM87
"A Mighty Fortress Is Our God" (Esth)
   B8, C65, E687/688, EL503/504/505, F118, G275, L228/229,
   N439/440, P259/260, UM110 (PD), VU261/262/263,
   W575/576
"For the Healing of the Nations" (Esth)
   C668, G346, N576, UM428, VU678, W643
"Give to the Winds Thy Fears" (Esth, Pss)
   G815, N404, P286, UM129 (PD), VU636
"We Gather Together" (Esth, Pss)
   B636, C276, E433, F387, G336, N421, P559, UM131
"Praise to the Lord, the Almighty" (Esth, Pss)
   B14, C25, E390, EL858 (PD) and 859, F337, G35, L543, N22,
   P482, UM139, VU220 (Fr.) and VU221, W547
"If Thou But Suffer God to Guide Thee" (Esth, Pss)
   B57, C565, E635, EL769, G816, L453, N410, P282, UM142
   (PD), VU285 (Fr.) and VU286
"Lift Every Voice and Sing" (Esth, Pss)
   B627, C631, E599, EL841, G339, L562, N593, P563, UM519
"His Eye Is on the Sparrow" (Esth, Pss)
   C82, G661, N475, S2146, SF2146
"We Sing to You, O God" (Esth, Jas)
   EL791, N9, S2001, SF2001
"God, How Can We Forgive" (Esth, Jas)
   G445, S2169, SF2169
"When in Our Music God Is Glorified" (Jas)
   B435, C7, E420, EL850 and 851, G641, N561, P264, UM68,
   VU533, W549
"Let All the World in Every Corner Sing" (Jas)
   B28, E402/403, G636, P468, UM93, W536
"Rejoice, Ye Pure in Heart" (Phil)
   B39, C15, E556/557, EL873/874, F394, G804, N55/71,
   P145/146, UM160/161
"When Morning Gilds the Skies" (Jas)
   B221, C100, E427, EL853 (PD), F322, G667, L546, N86,
   P487, UM185, VU339 (Fr.), W675
"Come Back Quickly to the Lord" (Jas)
   G416, P381, UM343
"What a Friend We Have in Jesus" (Jas)
   B182, C585, EL742, F466, G465, L439, N506, P403, UM526
   (PD), VU661
"Cuando El Pobre" ("When the Poor Ones") (Jas, Mark)
   C662, EL725, G762, P407, UM434, VU702
"Lord, Speak to Me" (Jas, Mark)
   B568, EL676, F625, G722, N531, P426, UM463, VU589
"These I Lay Down" (Mark)
   C391, G428, VU462
"How Clear Is Our Vocation, Lord" (Mark)
   EL580, G432, P419, VU504 2 Tim 3:16-17

"O Jesus, I Have Promised" (Mark)
   B276, C612, E655, EL810, F402, G724/725, L503, N493,
   P388/389, UM396 (PD), VU120
"God of Grace and God of Glory" (Mark)
   B395, C464, E594/595, EL705, F528, G307, L415, N436,
   P420, UM577, VU686
"Blessed Jesus, at Thy Word" (Mark)
   E440, EL520, G395, N74, P454, UM596 (PD), VU500
"Deep in the Shadows of the Past" (Mark)
   G50, N320, P330, S2246

Additional Contemporary Suggestions

"Trading My Sorrows" (Esth)
   M75, WS3108
"Lord, Listen to Your Children Praying" (Jas)
   C305, G469, S2193, SF2193, VU400
"O Lord, Hear My Prayer" (Jas)
   EL751, G471, S2200, SF2200
"Lord, Listen to Your Children" (Jas)
   EL752, S2207, SF2207
"Jesus, We Are Here" ("Yesu Tawa Pano") (Jas)
   EL529, G392, S2273, SF2273
"Make Me a Servant" (Jas, Mark)
   S2176, SF2176, SP193
"The Lord's Prayer" (Jas, Mark)
   B462, C307-C310, F440, G464, P589, S2278, SF2278. UM271,
   WS3068-WS3071
"Make Me a Channel of Your Peace" (Mark)
   G753, S2171, SF2171, VU684
"Song of Hope" (Mark)
   G765, P432, S2186, VU424

Vocal Solos

"God Will Make a Way" (with "He Leadeth Me") (Esth)
   V-3 (2)   p. 9
"In Jesus' Name" (Mark)
   V-8   p. 188

Anthems

"He Leadeth Me" (Esth, Pss)
Benjamin Wenger; MorningStar MSM-50-4310
SATB and piano (bit.ly/50-4310)

"Put Peace Into Each Other's Hands" (Mark)
Arr. Jane Holstein; Hope C 5192
SATB and keyboard (bit.ly/C-5192)

Other Suggestions

Visuals:
   O   Hand, crown, festival, joy, food, gifts
   P   Flood, bird, snare
   E   Praying hands, oil, James 5:15a, parched earth/rain/
          harvest, return
   G   Cup of water, stumbling block, millstone/sea, hand/
          foot, eye, fire salt
Prayer: WSL59 (Mark)
Response: C663, E648, G52, N572, P334, UM448, W508, stanza
   11, without refrain. "Go Down, Moses" (Esth)
Blessing: WSL176 (Esth, Jas, Mark)
Sung Benediction: G753, S2171, SF2171, VU684. "Make Me a
   Channel of Your Peace" (Mark)
Alternate Lessons: Num 11:4-6, 10-16, 24-29; Ps 19 (see p. 4)

Job 1:1; 2:1-10

A man in the land of Uz was named Job. That man was honest, a person of absolute integrity; he feared God and avoided evil. . . .

2 One day the divine beings came to present themselves before the LORD. The Adversary also came among them to present himself before the LORD. [2]The LORD said to the Adversary, "Where have you come from?"

The Adversary answered the LORD, "From wandering throughout the earth."

[3]The LORD said to the Adversary, "Have you thought about my servant Job, for there is no one like him on earth, a man who is honest, who is of absolute integrity, who reveres God and avoids evil? He still holds on to his integrity, even though you incited me to ruin him for no reason."

[4]The Adversary responded to the LORD, "Skin for skin—people will give up everything they have in exchange for their lives.[5]But stretch out your hand and strike his bones and flesh. Then he will definitely curse you to your face."

[6]The LORD answered the Adversary, "There he is—within your power; only preserve his life."

[7]The Adversary departed from the LORD's presence and struck Job with severe sores from the sole of his foot to the top of his head. [8]Job took a piece of broken pottery to scratch himself and sat down on a mound of ashes. [9]Job's wife said to him, "Are you still clinging to your integrity? Curse God, and die."

[10]Job said to her, "You're talking like a foolish woman. Will we receive good from God but not also receive bad?" In all this, Job didn't sin with his lips.

Psalm 26 (G723, N636)

Establish justice for me, LORD,
    because I have walked with integrity.
    I've trusted the LORD without wavering.
[2]Examine me, LORD; put me to the test!
    Purify my mind and my heart.
[3]Because your faithful love is right in front of me—
    I walk in your truth!
[4]I don't spend time with people up to no good;
    I don't keep company with liars.
[5]I detest the company of evildoers,
    and I don't sit with wicked people.
[6]I wash my hands—they are innocent!
    I walk all around your altar, LORD,
      [7]proclaiming out loud my thanks,
    declaring all your wonderful deeds!
[8]I love the beauty of your house, LORD;
    I love the place where your glory resides.
[9]Don't gather me up with the sinners,
    taking my life along with violent people
    [10] in whose hands are evil schemes,
    whose strong hands are full of bribes.
[11]But me? I walk with integrity.
    Save me! Have mercy on me!
[12]My feet now stand on level ground.
    I will bless the LORD in the great congregation.

Hebrews 1:1-4; 2:5-12

In the past, God spoke through the prophets to our ancestors in many times and many ways. [2]In these final days, though, he spoke to us through a Son. God made his Son the heir of everything and created the world through him. [3]The Son is the light of God's glory and the imprint of God's being. He maintains everything with his powerful message. After he carried out the cleansing of people from their sins, he sat down at the right side of the highest majesty. [4]And the Son became so much greater than the other messengers, such as angels, that he received a more important title than theirs. . . .

2 [5]God didn't put the world that is coming (the world we are talking about) under the angels' control. [6]Instead, someone declared somewhere,

What is humanity that you think about them?
    Or what are the human beings that you care about them?
    [7]*For a while you made them lower than angels.*
    You crowned the human beings with glory and honor.
    [8]*You put everything under their control.*

When he puts everything under their control, he doesn't leave anything out of control. But right now, we don't see everything under their control yet. [9]However, we do see the one who was made lower in order than the angels for a little while—it's Jesus! He's the one who is now crowned with glory and honor because of the suffering of his death. He suffered death so that he could taste death for everyone through God's grace.

[10]It was appropriate for God, for whom and through whom everything exists, to use experiences of suffering to make perfect the pioneer of salvation. This salvation belongs to many sons and daughters whom he's leading to glory. [11]This is because the one who makes people holy and the people who are being made holy all come from one source. That is why Jesus isn't ashamed to call them brothers and sisters when he says,

    [12]*I will publicly announce your name to my brothers and sisters.*
    I will praise you in the middle of the assembly.

Mark 10:2-16

[2]Some Pharisees came and, trying to test him, they asked, "Does the Law allow a man to divorce his wife?"

[3]Jesus answered, "What did Moses command you?"

[4]They said, "Moses allowed a man to write a divorce certificate and to divorce his wife."

[5]Jesus said to them, "He wrote this commandment for you because of your unyielding hearts. [6] At the beginning of creation, *God made them male and female.* [7]*Because of this, a man should leave his father and mother and be joined together with his wife,* [8]*and the two will be one flesh.* So they are no longer two but one flesh. [9] Therefore, humans must not pull apart what God has put together."

[10]Inside the house, the disciples asked him again about this.[11]He said to them, "Whoever divorces his wife and marries another commits adultery against her; [12] and if a wife divorces her husband and marries another, she commits adultery."

[13]People were bringing children to Jesus so that he would bless them. But the disciples scolded them. [14]When Jesus saw this, he grew angry and said to them, "Allow the children to come to me. Don't forbid them, because God's kingdom belongs to people like these children. [15] I assure you that whoever doesn't welcome God's kingdom like a child will never enter it."[16]Then he hugged the children and blessed them.

Primary Hymns and Songs for the Day

"Tell Me the Stories of Jesus" (Mark) (O)
  B129, C190, F212, UM277 (PD), VU357
"Rejoice in God's Saints" (Job)
  C476, EL418, G732, UM708
      H-3   Hbl-90, 105; Chr-221; Desc-49; Org-51
      S-2   #71-74. Intro. and Harm.
"Fairest Lord Jesus" (Heb, Mark)
  B176, C97, E383, EL838, F240, G630, L518, N44, P306,
  UM189 (PD), VU341
      H-3   Hbl-57; Chr-63; Desc-25, 94; Org-22
      S-1   #301. Descant
      S-2   #158. Choral Harm.
"One Bread, One Body" (World Comm.)
  C393, EL496, G530, UM620, VU467
      H-3   Chr-156
"How Firm a Foundation" (Job, Pss) (C)
  B338, C618, E636/637, EL796, F32, G463, L507, N407, P361,
  UM529 (PD), VU660, W585
      H-3   Hbl-27, 69; Chr-102; Desc-41; Org-41
      S-1   #133. Harm.
            #134. Performance note

Additional Hymn Suggestions

"Lift Every Voice and Sing" (Job)
  B627, C631, E599, EL841, G339, N593, P563, UM519
"My Life Flows On" ("How Can I Keep from Singing") (Job)
  C619, EL763, G821, N476, S2212, SF2212, VU716
"When the Morning Stars Together" (Job)
  G689, N453, P486
"If Thou But Suffer God to Guide Thee" (Job, Pss)
  B57, C565, E635, EL769, G816, L453, N410, P282, UM142
  (PD), VU285 (Fr.) and VU286
"My Hope Is Built" (Job, Pss)
  B406, C537, E636/597, F92, G353, L293/ 294, N368, P379,
  UM368 (PD)
"I Want Jesus to Walk with Me" (Job, Pss)
  B465, C627, EL325, G775, N490, P363, UM521
"Children of the Heavenly Father" (Pss, Heb, Mark)
  B55, EL781, F89, L474, N487, UM141
"Holy God, We Praise Thy Name" (Heb)
  E366, F385, EL414 (PD), G4, L535, N276, P460, UM79,
  VU894 (Fr.), W524
"The Head That Once Was Crowned" (Heb) (C)
  E483, EL432, L173, P149, UM326 (PD), VU190, W464
"I Love Thy Kingdom, Lord" (Heb)
  B354, C274, E524, F545, G310, L368, N312, P441, UM540
"O Splendor of God's Glory Bright" (Heb)
  E5, G666, N87, P474, UM679, VU413
"Jesus Loves Me" (Mark)
  B344 (PD), C113, EL595 (PD), F226, G188, N327, P304,
  UM191, VU365
"Our Parent, by Whose Name" (Mark)
  E587, EL640, L357, UM447, VU555, W570
"Jesus, Lover of My Soul" (Mark)
  B180 (PD), C542, E699, F222, G440, N546, P303, UM479
  (PD), VU669
"Draw Us in the Spirit's Tether" (Mark, Comm.)
  C392, EL470, G529, N337, P504, UM632, VU479
"When Love Is Found" (Mark, Comm.)
  C499, N362, UM643, VU489, W745
"Lord of All Hopefulness" (Mark)
  E482, EL765, G683, L469, S2197, SF2197, W568
"Bread of the World" (World Comm.)
  C387, E301, G499, N346, P502, UM624, VU461

Additional Contemporary Suggestions

"Blessed Be the Name" (Job)
  M12, S2034, SF2034, UM63

"Blessed Be Your Name" (Job)
  WS3002, M163
"My Redeemer Lives" (Job)
  M73
"How Can I Keep from Singing" (Job)
  M177
"Desert Song" (Job)
  M262
"Amazing Grace" ("My Chains Are Gone") (Job, Pss)
  M205, WS3104
"In Christ Alone" ("My Hope Is Found") (Job, Pss)
  M138, WS3105
"My Tribute" ("To God Be the Glory") (Job, Heb)
  B153, C39, F365, N14, UM99. V-8 p. 5. Vocal Solo
"Holy Ground" (Pss)
  B224, C112, G406, S2272, SF2272, SP86
"Purify My Heart" (Pss)
  M90, WS3103
"The Family Prayer Song" ("As for Me and My House") (Pss,
Mark)
  M54, S2188, SF2188
"How Majestic Is Your Name" (Heb)
  C63, G613, S2023, SF2023, SP14
"Agnus Dei" (Heb)
  M15
"Blessing, Honour, and Glory" (Heb)
  EL433, M21
"Most Holy Lord" (Heb)
  M44
"There Is None Like You" (Mark)
  M104
"Make Us One" (World Comm.)
  S2224, SF2224, SP137
"Bind Us Together" (World Comm.)
  S2226, SF2226, SP140
"We Are the Body of Christ" (World Comm.)
  G768, S2227, SF2227

Vocal Solos

"A Contrite Heart" (Pss)
  V-4   p. 10
"One Bread, One Body" (World Comm.)
  V-3 (2)   p. 40

Anthems

"As This Broken Bread" (Heb, World Comm.)
Wayne Wold; AEC-1 p.5
2-part mixed with organ (bit.ly/AEC-1-5)

"The Kingdom of God" (Mark)
David Conte; EC Schirmer 8182
SATB and keyboard (bit.ly/ECS8182)

Other Suggestions

Visuals:
  O   Hand, sores, suffering, potsherd, ashes, man/woman
  P   Walking, heart, washing hands, singing, foot
  E   Jesus, angels, crown, cross, pioneer
  G   Divorce decree, marriage (wedding rings, certificate),
       children, Mark 10:14, blessing
Call to Worship: WSL68 (World Comm.) or N824 (Heb)
Prayers: WSL67, C394, WSL116, and WSL171 (World Comm.)
Prayer of Confession: WSL89 (Job, Pss)
Prayer: UM639. Bread and Justice (Mark, World Comm.)
Sung Response: S2257 or WS3172. "Communion Setting"
Closing Prayer: WSL171 (World Comm.)
Alternate Lessons: Gen 2:18-24; Ps 8 (see p. 4)

Job 23:1-9, 16-17

Job answered:

²Today my complaint is again bitter;
  my strength is weighed down because of my groaning.
³Oh, that I could know how to find him—
  come to his dwelling place;
  ⁴I would lay out my case before him,
    fill my mouth with arguments,
  ⁵know the words with which he would answer,
    understand what he would say to me.
⁶Would he contend with me through brute force?
  No, he would surely listen to me.
⁷There those who do the right thing can argue with him;
  I could escape from my judge forever.
⁸Look, I go east; he's not there,
  west, and don't discover him;
  ⁹north in his activity, and I don't grasp him;
he turns south, and I don't see.
. . . .
¹⁶God has weakened my mind;
  the Almighty has frightened me.
¹⁷Still I'm not annihilated by darkness;
  he has hidden deep darkness from me.

Psalm 22:1-15 (G210/631, N632, P168, UM752)

My God! My God,
  why have you left me all alone?
  Why are you so far from saving me—
    so far from my anguished groans?
²My God, I cry out during the day,
  but you don't answer;
  even at nighttime I don't stop.
³You are the holy one, enthroned.
You are Israel's praise.
⁴Our ancestors trusted you—
  they trusted you and you rescued them;
  ⁵they cried out to you and they were saved;
  they trusted you and they weren't ashamed.
⁶But I'm just a worm, less than human;
  insulted by one person, despised by another.
⁷All who see me make fun of me—
  they gape, shaking their heads:
  ⁸"He committed himself to the LORD,
    so let God rescue him;
    let God deliver him
    because God likes him so much."
⁹But you are the one who pulled me from the womb,
  placing me safely at my mother's breasts.
¹⁰I was thrown on you from birth;
  you've been my God
  since I was in my mother's womb.
¹¹Please don't be far from me,
  because trouble is near
    and there's no one to help.
¹²Many bulls surround me;
  mighty bulls from Bashan encircle me.
¹³They open their mouths at me
  like a lion ripping and roaring!
¹⁴I'm poured out like water.
  All my bones have fallen apart.
    My heart is like wax;
    it melts inside me.

¹⁵My strength is dried up
  like a piece of broken pottery.
My tongue sticks to the roof of my mouth;
  you've set me down in the dirt of death.

Hebrews 4:12-16

¹²[B]ecause God's word is living, active, and sharper than any two-edged sword. It penetrates to the point that it separates the soul from the spirit and the joints from the marrow. It's able to judge the heart's thoughts and intentions. ¹³No creature is hidden from it, but rather everything is naked and exposed to the eyes of the one to whom we have to give an answer.

¹⁴Also, let's hold on to the confession since we have a great high priest who passed through the heavens, who is Jesus, God's Son; ¹⁵because we don't have a high priest who can't sympathize with our weaknesses but instead one who was tempted in every way that we are, except without sin.

¹⁶Finally, let's draw near to the throne of favor with confidence so that we can receive mercy and find grace when we need help.

Mark 10:17-31

¹⁷As Jesus continued down the road, a man ran up, knelt before him, and asked, "Good Teacher, what must I do to obtain eternal life?"

¹⁸Jesus replied, "Why do you call me good? No one is good except the one God. ¹⁹You know the commandments: *Don't commit murder. Don't commit adultery. Don't steal. Don't give false testimony.* Don't cheat. *Honor your father and mother.*"

²⁰"Teacher," he responded, "I've kept all of these things since I was a boy."

²¹Jesus looked at him carefully and loved him. He said, "You are lacking one thing. Go, sell what you own, and give the money to the poor. Then you will have treasure in heaven. And come, follow me." ²²But the man was dismayed at this statement and went away saddened, because he had many possessions.

²³Looking around, Jesus said to his disciples, "It will be very hard for the wealthy to enter God's kingdom!" ²⁴His words startled the disciples, so Jesus told them again, "Children, it's difficult to enter God's kingdom! ²⁵ It's easier for a camel to squeeze through the eye of a needle than for a rich person to enter God's kingdom."

²⁶They were shocked even more and said to each other, "Then who can be saved?"

²⁷Jesus looked at them carefully and said, "It's impossible with human beings, but not with God. All things are possible for God."

²⁸Peter said to him, "Look, we've left everything and followed you."

²⁹Jesus said, "I assure you that anyone who has left house, brothers, sisters, mother, father, children, or farms because of me and because of the good news ³⁰ will receive one hundred times as much now in this life—houses, brothers, sisters, mothers, children, and farms (with harassment)—and in the coming age, eternal life. ³¹ But many who are first will be last. And many who are last will be first."

Primary Hymns and Songs for the Day

"Lord, Speak to Me" (Job, Mark) (O)
B568, EL676, F625, G722, L403, N531, P426, UM463 (PD), VU589
  H-3   Hbl-75; Chr-131; Desc-22; Org-18
  S-1   #52. Descant

"O God, Our Help in Ages Past" (Job, Pss) (O)
B74, C67, E680, EL632, F370, G687, L320, N25, P210, UM117 (PD), VU806, W579

"Precious Lord, Take My Hand" (Job, Pss)
B456, C628, EL773, G834, N472, P404, UM474, VU670
  H-3   Chr-164; Org-116

"Out of the Depths I Cry to You" (Job, Pss)
EL600, G424, L295, N483, P240, UM515

"O Jesus, I Have Promised" (Mark)
B276, C612, E655, EL810, F402, G724/725, L503, N493, P388/389, UM396 (PD), VU120
  S-2   #9. Descant

"Lord, I Want to Be a Christian" (Mark)
B489, C589, F421, G729, N454, P372 (PD), UM402

"Take My Life, and Let It Be" (Mark) (C)
B277/283, C609, E707, EL583/685, G697, L406, P391, N448, UM399 (PD), VU506

Additional Hymn Suggestions

"Immortal, Invisible, God Only Wise" (Job)
B6, C66, E423, EL834, F319, G12, L526, N1, P263, UM103 (PD), VU264, W512

"My Faith Looks Up to Thee" (Job, Pss)
B416, C576, E691, EL759, F84, G829, L479, P383, UM452 (PD), VU663

"Precious Lord, Take My Hand" (Job, Pss)
B456, C628, EL773, G834, N472, P404, UM474, VU670

"Why Stand So Far Away, My God?" (Job, Pss)
C671, G786, S2180, SF2180

"By the Babylonian Rivers" (Job, Pss)
G72, P246, S2217, VU859, W426

"O God, My God" (Pss)
N515

"Come, Thou Fount of Every Blessing" (Heb)
B15, C16, E686, EL807, F318, G475, L499, N459, P356, UM400 (PD), VU559

"God of Grace and God of Glory" (Heb)
B395, C464, E594/595, EL705, F528, G307, L415, N436, P420, UM577, VU686

"O Word of God Incarnate" (Heb)
C322, E632, EL514, G459, L231, N315, P327, UM598 (PD), VU499

"For All the Saints" (Heb)
B355, C637, E287, EL422, F614, G326, L174, N299, P526, UM711 (PD), VU705, W705

"I Sing a Song of the Saints of God" (Heb)
E293, G730, N295, P364, UM712 (PD)

"Take Up Thy Cross" (Mark)
B494, E675, EL667, G718, L398, N204, P393, UM415, VU561, W634

"The Summons" (Mark)
EL798, G726, S2130, SF2130, VU567

Additional Contemporary Suggestions

"Goodness Is Stronger than Evil" (Job)
EL721, G750, S2219, SF2219

"Shout to the North" (Job)
G319, M99, WS3042

"Breathe" (Job, Pss)
M61, WS3112

"Word of God, Speak" (Job, Pss, Heb)
M148, WS3184

"Thy Word Is a Lamp" (Heb)
C326, G458, SP183, UM601

"He Came Down" (Heb)
EL253, G137, S2085, SF2085

"You Are My All in All" (Heb, Mark)
G519, SP220, WS3040

"You Are Mine" (Mark)
EL581, G177, S2218, SF2218

"Humble Thyself in the Sight of the Lord" (Mark)
S2131, SF2131, SP223

"Make Me a Servant" (Mark)
S2176, SF2176, SP193

"Cry of My Heart" (Mark)
M39, S2165, SF2165

"Step by Step" (Mark)
G743, M51, WS3004

"Purify My Heart" (Mark)
M90, WS3103

"Love the Lord"
WS3116, M270

"All Things are Possible" (Mark)
M92

"Take This Life" (Mark)
M98

"Every Move I Make" (Mark)
M122

"Surrender" (Mark)
M157

Vocal Solos

"Steal Away to Heaven" (Job, Pss)
V-3 (1)   p. 17

"Here I Am" (Mark)
V-11   p. 19

Anthems

"Step By Step (Job)
Arr. Larry Shackley; Hope C5290
SATB and piano (bit.ly/C5290)

"Mothering God, You Gave Me Birth" (Heb)
Arr. Tom Trenney; Augsburg 978-1-4514-9254-5
SATB and piano (bit.ly/9254-5)

Other Suggestions

Visuals:
  O   Briefcase, Job 23:3, courtroom, judge, scales, darkness
  P   Crying, worm, birth, nursing, bulls, lion, water, melted wax, dust
  E   Heb 4:12, open Bible, sword, scales, heart, Christ
  G   Kneeling, Jesus, ten commandments, rich/poor, camel/needle

Introit: S2265, SF2265. "Time Now to Gather" (Heb, Comm.)
Call to Confession and Assurance: N833 and N840 (Heb)
Response: C299, S2277, SF2277. "Lord, Have Mercy" (Heb)
Alternate Lessons: Amos 5:6-7, 10-15; Ps 90:12-17 (see p. 4)

Job 38:1-7, (34-41)

Then the LORD answered Job from the whirlwind:
²Who is this darkening counsel
    with words lacking knowledge?
³Prepare yourself like a man;
    I will interrogate you, and you will respond to me.
⁴Where were you when I laid the earth's foundations?
    Tell me if you know.
⁵Who set its measurements? Surely you know.
    Who stretched a measuring tape on it?
⁶On what were its footings sunk;
    who laid its cornerstone,
        ⁷while the morning stars sang in unison
            and all the divine beings shouted?
. . . .
³⁴Can you issue an order to the clouds
    so their abundant waters cover you?
³⁵Can you send lightning so that it goes
    and then says to you, "I'm here"?
³⁶Who put wisdom in remote places,
    or who gave understanding to a rooster?
³⁷Who is wise enough to count the clouds,
        and who can tilt heaven's water containers
            ³⁸so that dust becomes mud
                and clods of dirt adhere?
³⁹Can you hunt prey for the lion
    or fill the cravings of lion cubs?
⁴⁰They lie in their den,
    lie in ambush in their lair.
⁴¹Who provides food for the raven
    when its young cry to God,
        move about without food?

Psalm 104:1-9, 24, 35c (G34, N889/890, P224 UM826)

Let my whole being bless the LORD!
    LORD my God, how fantastic you are!
    You are clothed in glory and grandeur!
²You wear light like a robe;
    you open the skies like a curtain.
³You build your lofty house on the waters;
    you make the clouds your chariot,
    going around on the wings of the wind.
⁴You make the winds your messengers;
    you make fire and flame your ministers.
⁵You established the earth on its foundations
    so that it will never ever fall.
⁶You covered it with the watery deep like a piece of clothing;
    the waters were higher than the mountains!
⁷But at your rebuke they ran away;
    they fled in fear at the sound of your thunder.
⁸They flowed over the mountains,
    streaming down the valleys
    to the place you established for them.
⁹You set a boundary they cannot cross
    so they'll never again cover the earth.
. . . .
²⁴LORD, you have done so many things!
    You made them all so wisely!
The earth is full of your creations!
. . . .
³⁵ᶜ Praise the LORD!

Hebrews 5:1-10

Every high priest is taken from the people and put in charge of things that relate to God for their sake, in order to offer gifts and sacrifices for sins. ²The high priest is able to deal gently with the ignorant and those who are misled since he himself is prone to weakness. ³Because of his weakness, he must offer sacrifices for his own sins as well as for the people. ⁴No one takes this honor for themselves but takes it only when they are called by God, just like Aaron.

⁵In the same way Christ also didn't promote himself to become high priest. Instead, it was the one who said to him,
    You are my Son.
        Today I have become your Father,
⁶as he also says in another place,
    You are a priest forever,
        according to the order of Melchizedek.
⁷During his days on earth, Christ offered prayers and requests with loud cries and tears as his sacrifices to the one who was able to save him from death. He was heard because of his godly devotion. ⁸Although he was a Son, he learned obedience from what he suffered. ⁹After he had been made perfect, he became the source of eternal salvation for everyone who obeys him.¹⁰He was appointed by God to be a high priest according to the order of Melchizedek.

Mark 10:35-45

³⁵James and John, Zebedee's sons, came to Jesus and said, "Teacher, we want you to do for us whatever we ask."

³⁶"What do you want me to do for you?" he asked.

³⁷They said, "Allow one of us to sit on your right and the other on your left when you enter your glory."

³⁸Jesus replied, "You don't know what you're asking! Can you drink the cup I drink or receive the baptism I receive?"

³⁹"We can," they answered.

Jesus said, "You will drink the cup I drink and receive the baptism I receive, ⁴⁰ but to sit at my right or left hand isn't mine to give. It belongs to those for whom it has been prepared."

⁴¹Now when the other ten disciples heard about this, they became angry with James and John. ⁴²Jesus called them over and said, "You know that the ones who are considered the rulers by the Gentiles show off their authority over them and their high-ranking officials order them around. ⁴³ But that's not the way it will be with you. Whoever wants to be great among you will be your servant. ⁴⁴ Whoever wants to be first among you will be the slave of all, ⁴⁵ for the Human One didn't come to be served but rather to serve and to give his life to liberate many people."

Primary Hymns and Songs for the Day

"I Sing the Almighty Power of God" (Job) (O)
    C64, G32, N12, P288 (PD)
        H-3   Hbl-16, 22, 68; Chr-101; Desc-37
        S-1   #115. Harm.
    B42, E398, UM152 (PD)
        H-3   Hbl-44; Chr-21; Desc-40; Org-40
        S-1   #131-132. Intro. and descant
    VU231 (PD), W502 (PD)
"O God, in a Mysterious Way" (Job, Pss)
    B73, E677, F603, G30, L483, N412, P270
"*Jesu, Jesu*" (Mark)
    B501, C600, E602, EL708, G203, N498, P367, UM432,
    VU593, W431, S-1 #63. Vocal part
        H-3   Chr-114; Org-19
        S-1   #63. Vocal part
"The Servant Song" (Mark)
    C490, EL659, G727, N539, S2222, SF2222, VU595
"Lord, Whose Love Through Humble Service" (Mark) (C)
    C461, E610, EL712, L423, P427, UM581, W630

Additional Hymn Suggestions

"How Great Thou Art" (Job)
    B10, C33, EL856, G625, N35, P467, UM77, VU238
"For the Beauty of the Earth" (Job)
    B44, C56, E416, EL879, F1, G14, L561, P473, N28, UM92
    (PD), VU226, W557
"God of the Sparrow, God of the Whale" (Job)
    C70, EL740, G22, N32, P272, UM122, VU229
"Eternal Father, Strong to Save" (Job, Mark)
    B69, C85, E608, EL756, F679, G8, L467, P562 (PD), S2191,
    VU659
"Joyful, Joyful, We Adore Thee" (Job, Pss)
    B7, C2, E376, EL836, F377, G611, L551, N4, P464, UM89
    (PD), VU232, W525
"Immortal, Invisible, God Only Wise" (Heb)
    B6, C66, E423, EL834, F319, G12, L526, N1, P263, UM103
    (PD), VU264, W512
"O Sing a Song of Bethlehem" (Heb)
    B120, F208, G159, N51, P308, UM179 (PD)
"Ah, Holy Jesus" (John)
    C210, E158, EL349, G218, N218, P93, UM289, VU138
"Glorious Things of Thee are Spoken" (Heb)
    B398, C709, E522/523, EL647, F376, G81, L358, N307, P446,
    UM731 (PD)
"My Song Is Love Unknown" (Heb)
    E458, EL343, G209, L94, N222, P76, S2083, SF2083, VU143,
    W439
"Ye Servants of God" (Heb, Mark)
    B589, C110, E535, EL825 (PD), F360, G299, N305, P477,
    UM181 (PD), VU342
"By All Your Saints Still Striving" (Mark)
    EL420/421, G325, W706
"Take Up Thy Cross" (Mark)
    B494, E675, EL667, G718, N204, P393, UM415, VU561
"By Gracious Powers" (Mark)
    E695/696, G818, N413, P342, UM517, W577
"The Church of Christ, in Every Age" (Mark)
    B402, C475, EL729, G320, L433, N306, P421, UM589,
    VU601, W626
"Together We Serve" (Mark)
    G767, S2175, SF2175

Additional Contemporary Suggestions

"God of Wonders" (Job, Pss)
    M80, WS3034
"Indescribable" (Job, Pss)
    M127
"Desert Song" (Job, Pss)
    M262
"My Redeemer Lives" (Job, Heb)
    M73
"Bless the Lord, O My Soul" (Pss)
    SP32
"Beautiful Savior" (Pss, Heb)
    M243
"Once Again" (Heb)
    M78
"Amazing Love" (Heb)
    M81
"You Are My All in All" (Heb)
    G519, SP220, WS3040
"You Are My King" ("Amazing Love") (Heb)
    M82, WS3102
"That's Why We Praise Him" (Heb)
    M94
"I Come to the Cross" (Heb)
    M106
"We Bring the Sacrifice of Praise" (Heb)
    S2031, SF2031, SP1
"Humble Thyself in the Sight of the Lord" (Mark)
    S2131, SF2131, SP223
"Make Me a Servant" (Mark)
    S2176, SF2176, SP193
"They'll Know We Are Christians" (Mark)
    C494, G300, S2223, SF2223
"More Love, More Power" (Mark)
    M40
"Let It Be Said of Us" (Mark)
    M53
"Take This Life" (Mark)
    M98

Vocal Solos

"Holy Is the Lamb" (Heb)
    V-5(1)   p. 5
"Ah, Holy Jesus" (Heb)
    V-6   p. 24

Anthems

"For the Beauty of the Earth" (Job)
Hal H. Hopson; Augsburg 978-1-5064-2204-6
SATB and piano (bit.ly/2204-6)

"By All Your Saints Still Striving" (Mark)
Arr. Joel Martinson; AEC-2 p. 23
SATB and organ

Other Suggestions

Visuals:
    O   Whirlwind, creation, cornerstone, stars, storm
    P   Light, tent, clouds, wind, fire, sea, mountains
    E   Priest/sacrifice, Christ, Heb 5:5a, Jesus praying, cross
    G   Hands, chalice, baptism, cross, servant
Prayers: N851 and C68 (Job) and UM570 (Mark)
Alternate Lessons: Isa 53:4-12; Ps 91:9-16 (see p. 4)

Job 42:1-6, 10-17

Job answered the LORD:

²I know you can do anything;
   no plan of yours can be opposed successfully.
³You said, "Who is this darkening counsel without knowledge?"
   I have indeed spoken about things I didn't understand,
   wonders beyond my comprehension.
⁴You said, "Listen and I will speak;
   I will question you and you will inform me."
⁵My ears had heard about you,
   but now my eyes have seen you.
⁶Therefore, I relent and find comfort
   on dust and ashes.

. . . .

¹⁰Then the LORD changed Job's fortune when he prayed for his friends, and the LORD doubled all Job's earlier possessions. ¹¹All his brothers, sisters, and acquaintances came to him and ate food with him in his house. They comforted and consoled him concerning all the disaster theLORD had brought on him, and each one gave him a qesitah and a gold ring. ¹²Then the LORD blessed Job's latter days more than his former ones. He had fourteen thousand sheep, six thousand camels, one thousand yoke of oxen, and one thousand female donkeys. ¹³He also had seven sons and three daughters. ¹⁴He named one Jemimah, a second Keziah, and the third Keren-happuch. ¹⁵No women in all the land were as beautiful as Job's daughters; and their father gave an inheritance to them along with their brothers. ¹⁶After this, Job lived 140 years and saw four generations of his children. ¹⁷Then Job died, old and satisfied.

Psalm 34:1-8, (19-22) (G520, N644, P187, UM769)

I will bless the LORD at all times;
   his praise will always be in my mouth.
²I praise the LORD—
   let the suffering listen and rejoice.
³Magnify the LORD with me!
   Together let us lift his name up high!
⁴I sought the LORD and he answered me.
   He delivered me from all my fears.
⁵Those who look to God will shine;
   their faces are never ashamed.
⁶This suffering person cried out:
   the LORD listened and saved him from every trouble.
⁷On every side, the LORD's messenger protects those who honor
         God; and he delivers them.
⁸Taste and see how good the LORD is!
   The one who takes refuge in him is truly happy!

. . . .

¹⁹The righteous have many problems,
   but the LORD delivers them from every one.
²⁰He protects all their bones;
   not even one will be broken.
²¹But just one problem will kill the wicked,
   and those who hate the righteous will be held responsible.
²²The LORD saves his servants' lives;
   all those who take refuge in him
   won't be held responsible for anything.

Hebrews 7:23-28

²³The others who became priests are numerous because death prevented them from continuing to serve. ²⁴In contrast, he holds the office of priest permanently because he continues to serve forever. ²⁵This is why he can completely save those who are approaching God through him, because he always lives to speak with God for them.

²⁶It's appropriate for us to have this kind of high priest: holy, innocent, incorrupt, separate from sinners, and raised high above the heavens. ²⁷He doesn't need to offer sacrifices every day like the other high priests, first for their own sins and then for the sins of the people. He did this once for all when he offered himself. ²⁸The Law appoints people who are prone to weakness as high priests, but the content of the solemn pledge, which came after the Law, appointed a Son who has been made perfect forever.

Mark 10:46-52

⁴⁶Jesus and his followers came into Jericho. As Jesus was leaving Jericho, together with his disciples and a sizable crowd, a blind beggar named Bartimaeus, Timaeus' son, was sitting beside the road. ⁴⁷When he heard that Jesus of Nazareth was there, he began to shout, "Jesus, Son of David, show me mercy!" ⁴⁸Many scolded him, telling him to be quiet, but he shouted even louder, "Son of David, show me mercy!"

⁴⁹Jesus stopped and said, "Call him forward."

They called the blind man, "Be encouraged! Get up! He's calling you."

⁵⁰Throwing his coat to the side, he jumped up and came to Jesus.

⁵¹Jesus asked him, "What do you want me to do for you?"

The blind man said, "Teacher, I want to see."

⁵²Jesus said, "Go, your faith has healed you." At once he was able to see, and he began to follow Jesus on the way.

Primary Hymns and Songs for the Day

"Wonderful Words of Life" (Job, Heb) (O)
    B261, C323, F29, N319, UM600 (PD)
        H-3   Chr-221; Org-186

"Pass Me Not, O Gentle Savior" (Mark)
    B308, F416, N551, UM351 (PD), VU665
        H-3   Chr-159

"My Faith Looks Up to Thee" (Mark)
    B416, C576, E691, EL759, F84, G829, L479, P383, UM452
    (PD), VU663
        H-3   Hbl-77; Chr-138; Org-108
        S-2   #142. Flute/violin descant

"Open My Eyes, That I May See" (Mark)
    B502, C586, F486, G451, P324, UM454, VU371
        H-3   Chr-157; Org-108

"Open Our Eyes, Lord" (Mark)
    B499, S2086, SF2086, SP199

"A Mighty Fortress Is Our God" (Job, Reformation) (C)
    B8, C65, E687/688, EL503/504/505, F118, G275, L228/229,
    N439/440, P259/260, UM110 (PD), VU261/262/263,
    W575/576
        H-3   Chr-19; Desc-35; Org-34
        S-1   #111-113. Various treatments

Additional Hymn Suggestions

"From All That Dwell Below the Skies" (Job)
    B13, C49, E380, G327, L550, N27, P229, UM101 (PD)

"My Life Flows On" (Job)
    C619, EL763, G821, N476, S2212, SF2212, VU716

"I Bind unto Myself Today" (Job)
    E370, EL450 (PD), G6, L188, VU317

"O God, in a Mysterious Way" (Job)
    B73, E677, F603, G30, L483, N412, P270

"If Thou But Suffer God to Guide Thee" (Job, Mark)
    B57, C565, E635, EL769, G816, L453, N410, P282, UM142
    (PD), VU285 (Fr.) and VU286

"God of the Sparrow, God of the Whale" (Pss)
    C70, EL740, G22, N32, P272, UM122, VU229

"Christ, Whose Glory Fills the Skies" (Heb)
    EL553, F293, G662, L265, P462/463, UM173 (PD), VU336

"O Love, How Deep" (Heb)
    E448/449, EL322, G618, L88, N209, P83, UM267, VU348

"My Hope Is Built" (Heb)
    B406, C537, EL596/597, F92, G353, L293/ 294, N368, P379,
    UM368 (PD)

"God, How Can We Forgive" (Heb)
    G445, S2169, SF2169

"O For a Thousand Tongues to Sing" (Mark)
    B216, C5, E493, EL886, F349, G610, L559, N42, P466, UM57
    (PD), VU326

"O Christ, the Healer" (Mark)
    C503. EL610, G793, L360, N175, P380, UM265, W747

"Softly and Tenderly Jesus Is Calling" (Mark)
    B312, C340, EL608 (PD), F432, G418, N449, UM348

"Be Thou My Vision" (Mark)
    B60, C595, E488, EL793, F468, G450, N451, P339, UM451,
    VU642

"The Summons" (Mark)
    EL798, G726, S2130, SF2130, VU567

"O For a Thousand Tongues to Sing" (Mark)
    WS3001

Additional Contemporary Suggestions

"Through It All" (Job)
    C555, F43, UM507

"Blessed Be Your Name" (Job)
    WS3002, M163

"In His Time" (Job)
    B53, S2203, SF2203, SP39

"Goodness Is Stronger than Evil" (Job)
    EL721, G750, S2219, SF2219

"My Redeemer Lives" (Job)
    M73

"How Can I Keep from Singing" (Job)
    M177

"I Exalt You" (Pss)
    SP18

"O Magnify the Lord" (Pss)
    SP77

"How Majestic Is Your Name" (Pss)
    C63, G613, S2023, SF2023, SP14

"Jesus, Name above All Names" (Heb)
    S2071, SF2071, SP76

"Amazing Grace" ("My Chains Are Gone") (Heb)
    M205, WS3104

"In Christ Alone" ("My Hope Is Found") (Heb)
    M138, WS3105

"Before the Throne of God Above" (Heb)
    M65

"That's Why We Praise Him" (Heb)
    M94

"Turn Your Eyes upon Jesus" (Mark)
    B320, F621, SP218, UM349

"The Power of Your Love" (Mark)
    M26

"Good to Me"
    M164

"Open the Eyes of My Heart" (Mark)
    G452, M57, WS3008

Vocal Solos

"This Is My Father's World" (Job, Pss)
    V-6   p. 42

"Softly and Tenderly" (Mark)
    V-5(3)   p. 52

Anthems

"Taste and See the Goodness of the Lord" (Pss, Comm.)
Thomas Keesecker; AEC-3 p. 71
Unison or 2-part and keyboard (bit.ly/AEC-3-71)

"Be Thou My Vision" (Mark)
Arr. Daniel Musselman; MorningStar MSM-50-5814
SATB and piano (bit.ly/50-5814)

Other Suggestions

Visuals:
    O   Dust/ashes, gold coins, rings, boys/girls
    P   Praise, Ps 34:8, taste: fruits, vegetables, sweets
    E   Christ, vestments on the altar
    G   Tattered cloak, blind man: dramatize, dance, mime
Opening Prayer: N831 (Job, Pss)
Response: EL152, S2275, SF2275, WS3133. "Kyrie" (Mark)
Litany: C488. A Litany of the Saints (Reformation)
Blessing: C268. A Sarum Blessing (Mark)
Alternate Lessons: Jer 31:7-9, Ps 126 (see p. 4)

Isaiah 25:6-9

6On this mountain,
    the LORD of heavenly forces will prepare for all peoples
      a rich feast, a feast of choice wines,
      of select foods rich in flavor,
      of choice wines well refined.
7He will swallow up on this mountain the veil that is veiling all
      peoples,
    the shroud enshrouding all nations.
8He will swallow up death forever.
The LORD God will wipe tears from every face;
    he will remove his people's disgrace from off the whole
      earth,
      for the LORD has spoken.
9They will say on that day,
"Look! This is our God,
    for whom we have waited—
    and he has saved us!
This is the LORD, for whom we have waited;
    let's be glad and rejoice in his salvation!"

Psalm 24 (G364, N634, P176/177, UM755)

The earth is the LORD's and everything in it,
    the world and its inhabitants too.
2Because God is the one who established it on the seas;
    God set it firmly on the waters.
3Who can ascend the LORD's mountain?
    Who can stand in his holy sanctuary?
4Only the one with clean hands and a pure heart;
    the one who hasn't made false promises,
    the one who hasn't sworn dishonestly.
5That kind of person receives blessings from the LORD
    and righteousness from the God who saves.
6And that's how things are
    with the generation that seeks him—
    that seeks the face of Jacob's God.   *[Selah]*
7Mighty gates: lift up your heads!
    Ancient doors: rise up high!
      So the glorious king can enter!
8Who is this glorious king?
    The LORD—strong and powerful!
    The LORD—powerful in battle!
9Mighty gates: lift up your heads!
    Ancient doors: rise up high!
      So the glorious king can enter!
10Who is this glorious king?
    The LORD of heavenly forces—
    he is the glorious king!   *[Selah]*

Revelation 21:1-6a

Then I saw a new heaven and a new earth, for the former heaven and the former earth had passed away, and the sea was no more. 2I saw the holy city, New Jerusalem, coming down out of heaven from God, made ready as a bride beautifully dressed for her husband. 3I heard a loud voice from the throne say, "Look! God's dwelling is here with humankind. He will dwell with them, and they will be his peoples. God himself will be with them as their God. 4He will wipe away every tear from their eyes. Death will be no more. There will be no mourning, crying, or pain anymore, for the former things have passed away." 5Then the one seated on the throne said, "Look! I'm making all things new." He also said, "Write this down, for these words are trustworthy and true." 6aThen he said to me, "All is done. I am the Alpha and the Omega, the beginning and the end."

John 11:32-44

32When Mary arrived where Jesus was and saw him, she fell at his feet and said, "Lord, if you had been here, my brother wouldn't have died."

33When Jesus saw her crying and the Jews who had come with her crying also, he was deeply disturbed and troubled. 34He asked, "Where have you laid him?"

They replied, "Lord, come and see."

35Jesus began to cry. 36The Jews said, "See how much he loved him!" 37But some of them said, "He healed the eyes of the man born blind. Couldn't he have kept Lazarus from dying?"

38Jesus was deeply disturbed again when he came to the tomb. It was a cave, and a stone covered the entrance. 39Jesus said, "Remove the stone."

Martha, the sister of the dead man, said, "Lord, the smell will be awful! He's been dead four days."

40Jesus replied, "Didn't I tell you that if you believe, you will see God's glory?" 41So they removed the stone. Jesus looked up and said, "Father, thank you for hearing me. 42I know you always hear me. I say this for the benefit of the crowd standing here so that they will believe that you sent me." 43Having said this, Jesus shouted with a loud voice, "Lazarus, come out!"44The dead man came out, his feet bound and his hands tied, and his face covered with a cloth. Jesus said to them, "Untie him and let him go."

Primary Hymns and Songs for the Day

"Lift Up Your Heads, Ye Mighty Gates" (Pss) (O)
　　B128, C129, F239, G93, N117, P8, UM213 (PD), W363
　　　　H-3　　Hbl-50; Chr-47; Desc-101; Org-167
　　　　S-1　　#334-5. Desc. and Harm.
　　　　V-10　p. 38. Vocal Solo

"For All the Saints" (Pss, Rev, All Saints)
　　B355, C637, E287, EL422, F614, G326, L174, N299, P526,
　　UM711 (PD), VU705, W705
　　　　H-3　　Hbl-58; Chr-65; Org-152
　　　　S-1　　#314-318. Various treatments

"Joy Comes with the Dawn" (Isa, Rev, John)
　　S2210, SF2210, VU166

"Holy Ground" (Pss, All Saints)
　　B224, C112, G406, S2272, SF2272, SP86

"Marching to Zion" (Isa, Rev) (C)
　　B524, C707, EL625, F550, N382, UM733 (PD), VU714
　　　　H-3　　Chr-298

Additional Hymn Suggestions

"O What Their Joy and Glory Must Be" (Isa, Rev)
　　E623, L337, N385, UM727 (PD)

"O Day of Peace That Dimly Shines" (Isa, Rev)
　　C711, E597, EL711, G373, P450, UM729, VU682, W654

"All Who Hunger" (Isa, Comm.)
　　C419, EL461, G509, S2126, SF2126, VU460

"The Trumpets Sound, the Angels Sing" (Isa)
　　EL531, G505

"Glorious Things of Thee Are Spoken" (Pss, Rev)
　　B398, C709, E522/523, EL647, F376, G81, L358, N307, P446,
　　UM731 (PD)

"Of the Father's Love Begotten" (Rev)
　　B251, C104, E82, EL295, F172 (PD), G108, L42, N118, P309,
　　UM184, VU61, W398

"Come, Ye Disconsolate" (Rev)
　　B67, C502, EL607, SF2132, UM510 (PD)

"Rejoice! Rejoice, Believers" (Rev)
　　E68, EL244, G362, L25, P15

"Here, O My Lord, I See Thee" (Rev, Comm.)
　　C416, E318, F567, G517, N336, P520, UM623, VU459

"O Holy City, Seen of John" (Rev)
　　E582/583, G374, N613, P453, UM726, VU709

"Blessed Quietness" (Rev)
　　F145, C267, N284, S2142, SF2142

"I Sing a Song of the Saints of God" (Rev, John)
　　E293, G730, N295, P364, UM712 (PD)

"Awake, O Sleeper" (John, All Saints)
　　E547, EL452, UM551, VU566, W586

"How Blest Are They" (John, All Saints)
　　C646, N365, UM654

"Father, We Praise Thee" (All Saints)
　　E1/2, EL558 (PD), L267, N90, P459, UM680

"Rejoice in God's Saints" (All Saints)
　　C476, EL418, G732, UM708

"When Jesus Wept" (John)
　　C199, E715, G194, P312, S2106, SF2106, VU146

"For All the Faithful Women" (All Saints)
　　EL419, G324

"By All Your Saints Still Striving" (All Saints)
　　EL420/421, G325, W706

"How Lovely, Lord, How Lovely" (All Saints)
　　C285, G402, P207, S2042, VU801

"Blest Are They" (All Saints)
　　EL728, G172, S2155, SF2155, VU896

"Deep in the Shadows of the Past" (All Saints)
　　G50, N320, P330, S2246

"As We Gather at Your Table" (All Saints, Comm.)
　　EL522, N332, S2268, SF2268, VU457

Additional Contemporary Suggestions

"The King of Glory Comes" (Pss)
　　B127, S2091, SF2091, W501

"Sing to the King" (Pss)
　　M141

"Hosanna" (Pss, Rev)
　　M268, WS3188

"Spirit Song" (Rev)
　　C352, SP134, UM347

"Soon and Very Soon" (Rev)
　　B192, EL439, G384, UM706, S-2 #187. Piano arr.

"We Will Glorify" (Rev)
　　B213, S2087, SF2087, SP68

"There's Something About That Name" (Rev)
　　B177, C115, F227, SP89, UM171

"Blessing, Honour and Glory" (Rev)
　　EL433, M21

"How Great Is Our God" (Rev)
　　WS3003, M117

"All Who Are Thirsty" (Rev)
　　M159

"I Will Rise" (Rev, John)
　　M260

"Praise the Name of Jesus" (John)
　　S2066, SF2066, SP87

"We Fall Down" (All Saints)
　　G368, M66, WS3187

Vocal Solos

"Marchin' On Up" (Isa, Rev)
　　V-3 (3)　　　p. 57

"In Bright Mansions Above" (All Saints)
　　V-4　　　　　p. 39

Anthems

"Sing with All the Saints in Glory" (Rev, All Saints)
William Bradley Roberts; AEC-2 p. 63
Unison/mixed and organ

"Blest Are the Pure in Heart" (Rev, All Saints)
Hugh Benham; FitzSimons F2384 (Hal Leonard)
SATB and organ (bit.ly/F2384)

Other Suggestions

These scriptures and suggestions may also be used on Nov. 4.
Visuals:
　　O　　Banquet, sheet, handkerchief, rejoicing
　　P　　Sea, river, hill, washing hands, heart, Ps 24:7, gates/
　　　　　　doors
　　E　　Wedding, alpha/omega, joy, tears/handkerchief
　　G　　Woman weeping, open tomb, white linen, strips of
　　　　　　cloth
Prayer for Illumination: WSL75 (Rev)
Litany: C488. A Litany of the Saints (All Saints)
Prayer: N856, UM713, UM461, UM656 (All Saints Day)
Benediction: WSL46 (All Saints)

Ruth 1:1-18

During the days when the judges ruled, there was a famine in the land. A man with his wife and two sons went from Bethlehem of Judah to dwell in the territory of Moab. [2] The name of that man was Elimelech, the name of his wife was Naomi, and the names of his two sons were Mahlon and Chilion. They were Ephrathites from Bethlehem in Judah. They entered the territory of Moab and settled there.

[3] But Elimelech, Naomi's husband, died. Then only she was left, along with her two sons. [4] They took wives for themselves, Moabite women; the name of the first was Orpah and the name of the second was Ruth. And they lived there for about ten years.

[5] But both of the sons, Mahlon and Chilion, also died. Only the woman was left, without her two children and without her husband.

[6] Then she arose along with her daughters-in-law to return from the field of Moab, because while in the territory of Moab she had heard that the LORD had paid attention to his people by providing food for them. [7] She left the place where she had been, and her two daughters-in-law went with her. They went along the road to return to the land of Judah.

[8] Naomi said to her daughters-in-law, "Go, turn back, each of you to the household of your mother. May the LORD deal faithfully with you, just as you have done with the dead and with me. [9] May the LORD provide for you so that you may find security, each woman in the household of her husband." Then she kissed them, and they lifted up their voices and wept.

[10] But they replied to her, "No, instead we will return with you, to your people."

[11] Naomi replied, "Turn back, my daughters. Why would you go with me? Will there again be sons in my womb, that they would be husbands for you? [12] Turn back, my daughters. Go. I am too old for a husband. If I were to say that I have hope, even if I had a husband tonight, and even more, if I were to bear sons— [13] would you wait until they grew up? Would you refrain from having a husband? No, my daughters. This is more bitter for me than for you, since the LORD's will has come out against me."

[14] Then they lifted up their voices and wept again. Orpah kissed her mother-in-law, but Ruth stayed with her. [15] Naomi said, "Look, your sister-in-law is returning to her people and to her gods. Turn back after your sister-in-law."

[16] But Ruth replied, "Don't urge me to abandon you, to turn back from following after you. Wherever you go, I will go; and wherever you stay, I will stay. Your people will be my people, and your God will be my God. [17] Wherever you die, I will die, and there I will be buried. May the LORD do this to me and more so if even death separates me from you." [18] When Naomi saw that Ruth was determined to go with her, she stopped speaking to her about it.

Psalm 146:1-10 (G806, N719, P253/254, UM858)

Praise the LORD!
> Let my whole being praise the LORD!
[2] I will praise the LORD with all my life;
> I will sing praises to my God as long as I live.
[3] Don't trust leaders;
> don't trust any human beings—
> there's no saving help with them!
[4] Their breath leaves them,
> then they go back to the ground.
> On that very same day, their plans die too.
[5] The person whose help is the God of Jacob—
> the person whose hope rests on the LORD their God—
> is truly happy!

[6] God: the maker of heaven and earth,
> the sea, and all that is in them,
God: who is faithful forever,
> [7] who gives justice to people who are oppressed,
> who gives bread to people who are starving!
The LORD: who frees prisoners.
> [8] The LORD: who makes the blind see.
> The LORD: who straightens up those who are bent low.
> The LORD: who loves the righteous.
> [9] The LORD: who protects immigrants,
> who helps orphans and widows,
> but who makes the way of the wicked twist and turn!
[10] The LORD will rule forever!
> Zion, your God will rule from one generation to the next!
Praise the LORD!

Hebrews 9:11-14

[11] But Christ has appeared as the high priest of the good things that have happened. He passed through the greater and more perfect meeting tent, which isn't made by human hands (that is, it's not a part of this world). [12] He entered the holy of holies once for all by his own blood, not by the blood of goats or calves, securing our deliverance for all time. [13] If the blood of goats and bulls and the sprinkled ashes of cows made spiritually contaminated people holy and clean, [14] how much more will the blood of Jesus wash our consciences clean from dead works in order to serve the living God? He offered himself to God through the eternal Spirit as a sacrifice without any flaw.

Mark 12:28-34

[28] One of the legal experts heard their dispute and saw how well Jesus answered them. He came over and asked him, "Which commandment is the most important of all?"

[29] Jesus replied, "The most important one is *Israel, listen! Our God is the one Lord,* [30] *and you must love the Lord your God with all your heart, with all your being, with all your mind, and with all your strength.* [31] The second is this, *You will love your neighbor as yourself.* No other commandment is greater than these."

[32] The legal expert said to him, "Well said, Teacher. You have truthfully said that God is one and there is no other besides him. [33] And to love God with all of the heart, a full understanding, and all of one's strength, and to love one's neighbor as oneself is much more important than all kinds of entirely burned offerings and sacrifices."

[34] When Jesus saw that he had answered with wisdom, he said to him, "You aren't far from God's kingdom." After that, no one dared to ask him any more questions.

Primary Hymns and Songs for the Day

"O For a Thousand Tongues to Sing" (Pss) (O)
    B216, C5, E493, EL886, F349, G610, L559, N42, P466, UM57
    (PD), VU326
         H-3   Hbl-79; Chr-142; Desc-17; Org-12
         S-1   #33-38. Various Treatments

"Hope of the World" (Heb)
    C538, E472, G734, L493, N46, P360, UM178, VU215

"More Love to Thee, O Christ" (Mark)
    B473, C527, F476, G828, N456, P359, UM453 (PD)

"Lord of All Hopefulness" (Mark)
    E482, EL765, G683, L469, S2197, SF2197, W568

"I'll Praise My Maker While I've Breath" (Pss) (C)
    B35, C20, E429 (PD), G806, P253, UM60, VU867
         H-3   Chr-109; Org-105
         S-2   #141. Harm.

Additional Hymn Suggestions

"For All the Faithful Women" (Ruth)
    EL419, G324

"How Like a Gentle Spirit" (Ruth)
    C69, N443, UM115

"When God Restored Our Common Life" (Ruth, Pss)
    G74, S2182, SF2182

"In the Singing" (Pss, Comm.)
    EL466, G533, S2255, SF2255

"My Hope Is Built" (Heb)
    B406, C537, EL596/597, F92, G353, L293/ 294, N368, P379,
    UM368 (PD)

"Like a Mother Who Has Borne Us" (Heb, Mark)
    G44, N583

"The Gift of Love" (Mark)
    B423, C526, G693, P335, UM408, VU372

"Jesu, Jesu" (Mark)
    B501, C600, E602, EL708, G203, N498, P367, UM432,
    VU593, W431, S-1 #63. Vocal part

"Lord, Speak to Me" (Mark)
    B568, EL676, F625, G722, L403, N531, P426, UM463 (PD),
    VU589

"Blest Be the Dear Uniting Love" (Mark)
    B387, C433, EL656, F560, G306, L370, N393, P438, UM557
    (PD), VU602

"We've a Story to Tell to the Nations" (Mark)
    B586, C484, F659, UM569 (PD)

"Love the Lord Your God" (Mark)
    G62, S2168, SF2168

"Make Me a Channel of Your Peace" (Mark)
    G753, S2171, SF2171, VU684

"In Remembrance of Me" (Mark, Comm.)
    B365, C403, G521, S2254

Additional Contemporary Suggestions

"The Family Prayer Song" ("As for Me and My House") (Ruth,
Mark)
    M54, S2188, SF2188

"God of Wonders" (Pss)
    M80, WS3034

"Desert Song" (Pss)
    M262

"Forever Reign" (Pss)
    M256

"Beautiful Savior" (Pss, Heb)
    M243

"Amazing Grace" ("My Chains Are Gone") (Heb)
    M205, WS3104

"In Christ Alone" ("My Hope Is Found") (Heb)
    M138, WS3105

"O How He Loves You and Me!" (Heb)
    B146, F622, S2108, SF2108, SP113

"Holy Ground" (Heb)
    B224, C112, G406, S2272, SF2272, SP86

"They'll Know We Are Christians" (Mark)
    C494, G300, S2223, SF2223

"More Like You" (Mark)
    S2167, SF2167

"Love the Lord" (Mark)
    WS3116, M270

"More Love, More Power" (Mark)
    M40

"With All of My Heart" (Mark)
    M86, SP187

Vocal Solos

"Whither Thou Goest" (Ruth)
    V-8   p. 117

"O For a Thousand Tongues to Sing" (Pss)
    V-1   p. 32
    V-6   p. 28

"He Died for Me" (Heb)
    V-8   p. 220

"Make Me a Channel of Your Peace" (Mark)
    V-3 (2)   p. 25
    V-3 (3)   p. 28

"This Is My Commandment" (Mark)
    V-8   p. 284

Anthems

"There Will I Be" (Ruth)
Craig Courtney; Beckenhorst BP2031
SATB and piano (bit.ly/BP2031)

"How Blest Are They" (Pss)
Claude L. Bass; MorningStar 50-5201
SATB and piano (bit.ly/50-5201)

Other Suggestions

The scriptures and service ideas from Nov. 1 may also be used on this
    day.
Visuals:
    O   3 women walking, 2 women talking, weeping,
             embracing
    P   praise, singing, :5, Creation, justice, healing, etc.
    E   Christ, Crucifixion
    G   mezuzah, heart, ministry to variety of people
Prayer: UM401. For Holiness of Heart (Mark)
Response: C523, EL642, G205, S2179, SF2179, W604."Live in
    Charity" ("*Ubi Caritas*")
Blessing: WSL177 (Mark)
Alternate Lessons: Deuteronomy 6:1-9; Psalm 119:1-8 (see p. 4)

Ruth 3:1-5; 4:13-17

Naomi her mother-in-law said to her, "My daughter, shouldn't I seek security for you, so that things might go well for you? [2]Now isn't Boaz, whose young women you were with, our relative? Tonight he will be winnowing barley at the threshing floor. [3]You should bathe, put on some perfume, wear nice clothes, and then go down to the threshing floor. Don't make yourself known to the man until he has finished eating and drinking. [4]When he lies down, notice the place where he is lying. Then go, uncover his feet, and lie down. And he will tell you what to do."

[5]Ruth replied to her, "I'll do everything you are telling me." . . .

4 [13]So Boaz took Ruth, and she became his wife. He was intimate with her, the LORD let her become pregnant, and she gave birth to a son. [14]The women said to Naomi, "May the LORD be blessed, who today hasn't left you without a redeemer. May his name be proclaimed in Israel. [15]He will restore your life and sustain you in your old age. Your daughter-in-law who loves you has given birth to him. She's better for you than seven sons." [16]Naomi took the child and held him to her breast, and she became his guardian. [17]The neighborhood women gave him a name, saying, "A son has been born to Naomi." They called his name Obed. He became Jesse's father and David's grandfather.

Psalm 127 (G46, N708, P238)

Unless it is the LORD who builds the house,
　　the builders' work is pointless.
Unless it is the LORD who protects the city,
　　the guard on duty is pointless.
[2]It is pointless that you get up early and stay up late,
　　eating the bread of hard labor
　　because God gives sleep to those he loves.
[3]No doubt about it: children are a gift from the LORD;
　　the fruit of the womb is a divine reward.
[4]The children born when one is young
　　are like arrows in the hand of a warrior.
[5]The person who fills a quiver full with them is truly happy!
　　They won't be ashamed when arguing with their enemies in
　　　　the gate.

Hebrews 9:24-28

[24]Christ didn't enter the holy place (which is a copy of the true holy place) made by human hands, but into heaven itself, so that he now appears in God's presence for us. [25]He didn't enter to offer himself over and over again, like the high priest enters the earthly holy place every year with blood that isn't his. [26]If that were so, then Jesus would have to suffer many times since the foundation of the world. Instead, he has now appeared once at the end of the ages to get rid of sin by sacrificing himself.[27]People are destined to die once and then face judgment.[28]In the same way, Christ was also offered once to take on himself the sins of many people. He will appear a second time, not to take away sin but to save those who are eagerly waiting for him.

Mark 12:38-44

[38]As he was teaching, he said, "Watch out for the legal experts. They like to walk around in long robes. They want to be greeted with honor in the markets. [39]They long for places of honor in the synagogues and at banquets. [40]They are the ones who cheat widows out of their homes, and to show off they say long prayers. They will be judged most harshly."

[41]Jesus sat across from the collection box for the temple treasury and observed how the crowd gave their money. Many rich people were throwing in lots of money. [42]One poor widow came forward and put in two small copper coins worth a penny. [43]Jesus called his disciples to him and said, "I assure you that this poor widow has put in more than everyone who's been putting money in the treasury. [44]All of them are giving out of their spare change. But she from her hopeless poverty has given everything she had, even what she needed to live on."

Primary Hymns and Songs for the Day

"Love Divine, All Loves Excelling" (Ruth, Heb) (O)
  B208, C517, E657, EL631, F21, G366, N43, P376, UM384
  (PD), VU333, W588
    H-3   Chr-134; Desc-18; Org-13
    S-1   #41-42. Desc. and Harm.
"Take My Life, and Let It Be" (Mark, Stewardship)
  B277/283, C609, E707, EL583/685, G697, L406, P391, N448,
  UM399 (PD), VU506
"O Master, Let Me Walk with Thee" (Mark) (C)
  B279, C602, E659/660, EL818, F442, G738, L492, N503,
  P357, UM430 (PD), VU560
    H-3   Hbl-81; Chr-147; Desc-74; Org-87
    S-2   #118. Descant
"We Give Thee But Thine Own" (Mark) (C)
  B609, C382, EL686, F515, G708, N785, P428, VU543
    H-3   Chr-207; Org-149

Additional Hymn Suggestions

"For the Fruits of This Creation" (Ruth)
  B643, C714, E424, EL679, G36, L563, N425, P553, UM97,
  VU227, W562
"Guide Me, O Thou Great Jehovah" (Ruth)
  B56, C622, E690, EL618, F608, G65, L343, N18/19, P281,
  UM127 (PD), VU651 (Fr.)
"When Love Is Found" (Ruth)
  C499, N362, UM643, VU489, W745
"The Care the Eagle Gives Her Young" (Ruth, Pss)
  C76, N468, UM118, VU269
"Blest Be the Tie That Binds" (Ruth, Mark)
  B387, C433, EL656, F560, G306, L370, N393, P438, UM557
  (PD), VU602
"Your Love, O God, Has Called Us Here" (Ruth, Mark)
  B509, E353, N361, UM647
"Savior of the Nations, Come" (Heb)
  E54, EL263, G102, P14 (PD), UM214, W372
"Rejoice, the Lord Is King" (Heb)
  B197, C699, E481, EL430, F374, G363, L171, N303, P155,
  UM715 (PD), VU213, W493
"I'm So Glad Jesus Lifted Me" (Heb)
  C529, EL860 (PD), N474, S2151, SF2151
"Alleluia! Sing to Jesus!" (Heb)
  C233, E460/461, EL392, G260, N257, P144 (PD)
"What Gift Can We Bring" (Mark)
  N370, UM87
"All My Hope Is Firmly Grounded" (Mark)
  C88, E665, EL757, N408, UM132, VU654 and VU655
"The Gift of Love" (Mark)
  B423, C526, G693, P335, UM408, VU372
"Where Cross the Crowded Ways of Life" (Mark)
  C665, E609, EL719, F665, G343, L429, N543, P408, UM427
  (PD), VU681
"Jesu, Jesu" (Mark)
  B501, C600, E602, EL708, G203, N498, P367, UM432,
  VU593, W431, S-1 #63. Vocal part
"Cuando El Pobre" ("When the Poor Ones") (Mark)
  C662, EL725, G762, P407, UM434, VU702
"What Does the Lord Require" (Mark)
  C659, E605, P405, UM441, W624
"Where Charity and Love Prevail" (Mark)
  E581, EL359, G316, L126, N396, UM549
"I'm Gonna Live So God Can Use Me" (Stewardship)
  C614, G700, P369, S2153, VU575

Additional Contemporary Suggestions

"Blessed Be the Name" (Ruth)
  M12, S2034, SF2034, UM63
"The Family Prayer Song" (Ruth, Pss)
  M54, S2188, SF2188
"You Are My All in All" (Heb)
  G519, SP220, WS3040
"The Power of the Cross" (Heb)
  M222, WS3085
"You Are My King" ("Amazing Love") (Heb)
  M82, WS3102
"How Deep the Father's Love for Us" (Heb)
  M137
"Oh, How He Loves You and Me" (Heb)
  B146, F622, S2108, SF2108, SP113
"Holy Ground" (Heb)
  B224, C112, G406, S2272, SF2272, SP86
"Praise You" (Mark, Stewardship)
  M84, S2003, SF2003
"Give Thanks" (Mark, Stewardship)
  C528, G647, S2036, SF2036, SP170
"More Precious than Silver" (Mark, Stewardship)
  S2065, SF2065, SP99
"Lord, Be Glorified" (Mark, Stewardship)
  B457, EL744, G468, S2150, SF2150, SP196
"Love the Lord Your God" (Mark)
  G62, S2168, SF2168
"What Does the Lord Require of You" (Mark)
  C661, G70, S2174, SF2174, VU701
"Your Grace Is Enough" (Mark)
  M191, WS3106
"These Hands" (Mark, Stewardship)
  M101

Vocal Solos

"Whither Thou Goest" (Ruth)
  V-8   p. 117
"Take My Life" (Mark, Stewardship)
  V-3 (3)   p. 17
  V-8   p. 262

Anthems

"I Love You, Lord" (Ruth)
Arr. Arnold Sherman; Hope C5474
SATB and keyboard, opt. handbells (bit.ly/C-5474)

"Author of Faith, Eternal Word" (Heb)
Howard Helvey; MorningStar 50-5006
SATB and organ (bit.ly/50-5006)

Other Suggestions

Consider the Mark reading for a stewardship emphasis today.
Visuals:
    O   Threshing, marriage, nursing woman, Jesse tree
    P   Building church, rising/sleeping, newborns, arrow/
         quiver
    E   Ascension, Crucifixion, Second Coming
    G   Long robe, greeting, banquet, widow, 2 coins
Offertory Prayer: WSL99 or WSL123 (Mark)
Prayers: WSL99, N842 and N845 (Mark, Stewardship)
Alternate Lessons: 1 Kgs 17:8-16, Ps 146 (see p. 4)

1 Samuel 1:4-20

[4]Whenever he sacrificed, Elkanah would give parts of the sacrifice to his wife Peninnah and to all her sons and daughters. [5]But he would give only one part of it to Hannah, though he loved her, because the LORD had kept her from conceiving. [6]And because the LORD had kept Hannah from conceiving, her rival would make fun of her mercilessly, just to bother her. [7]So that is what took place year after year. Whenever Hannah went to the LORD's house, Peninnah would make fun of her. Then she would cry and wouldn't eat anything.

[8]"Hannah, why are you crying?" her husband Elkanah would say to her. "Why won't you eat? Why are you so sad? Aren't I worth more to you than ten sons?"

[9]One time, after eating and drinking in Shiloh, Hannah got up and presented herself before the LORD. (Now Eli the priest was sitting in the chair by the doorpost of the LORD's temple.) [10]Hannah was very upset and couldn't stop crying as she prayed to the LORD. [11]Then she made this promise: "LORD of heavenly forces, just look at your servant's pain and remember me! Don't forget your servant! Give her a boy! Then I'll give him to the LORDfor his entire life. No razor will ever touch his head."

[12]As she kept praying before the LORD, Eli watched her mouth.[13]Now Hannah was praying in her heart; her lips were moving, but her voice was silent, so Eli thought she was drunk.

[14]"How long will you act like a drunk? Sober up!" Eli told her.

[15]"No sir!" Hannah replied. "I'm just a very sad woman. I haven't had any wine or beer but have been pouring out my heart to the LORD. [16]Don't think your servant is some good-for-nothing woman. This whole time I've been praying out of my great worry and trouble!"

[17]Eli responded, "Then go in peace. And may the God of Israel give you what you've asked from him."

[18]"Please think well of me, your servant," Hannah said. Then the woman went on her way, ate some food, and wasn't sad any longer.

[19]They got up early the next morning and worshipped the LORD. Then they went back home to Ramah. Elkanah had sex with his wife Hannah, and the LORD remembered her. [20]So in the course of time, Hannah conceived and gave birth to a son. She named him Samuel, which means "I asked the LORD for him."

1 Samuel 2:1-10

Then Hannah prayed:
My heart rejoices in the LORD.
    My strength rises up in the LORD!
    My mouth mocks my enemies
        because I rejoice in your deliverance.
[2]No one is holy like the LORD—
    no, no one except you!
    There is no rock like our God!
[3]Don't go on and on, talking so proudly,
    spouting arrogance from your mouth,
    because the LORD is the God who knows,
        and he weighs every act.
[4]The bows of mighty warriors are shattered,
    but those who were stumbling now dress themselves in
        power!
[5]Those who were filled full now sell themselves for bread,
    but the ones who were starving are now fat from food!
    The woman who was barren has birthed seven children,
        but the mother with many sons has lost them all!
[6]The LORD!
    He brings death, gives life,
        takes down to the grave, and raises up!
[7]The LORD!

He makes poor, gives wealth,
    brings low, but also lifts up high!
[8]God raises the poor from the dust,
    lifts up the needy from the garbage pile.
    God sits them with officials,
        gives them the seat of honor!
The pillars of the earth belong to the LORD;
    he set the world on top of them!
[9]God guards the feet of his faithful ones,
    but the wicked die in darkness
        because no one succeeds by strength alone.
[10]The LORD!
His enemies are terrified!
    God thunders against them from heaven!
    The LORD!
    He judges the far corners of the earth!
May God give strength to his king
    and raise high the strength of his anointed one.

Hebrews 10:11-14 (15-18) 19-25

[11]Every priest stands every day serving and offering the same sacrifices over and over, sacrifices that can never take away sins. [12]But when this priest offered one sacrifice for sins for all time, he sat down at the right side of God. [13]Since then, he's waiting until his enemies are made into a footstool for his feet,[14]because he perfected the people who are being made holy with one offering for all time.

[15]The Holy Spirit affirms this when saying,
    [16]*This is the covenant that I will make with them.*
        After these days, says the LORD,
        I will place my laws in their hearts
        and write them on their minds.
    [17]*And I won't remember their sins*
        and their lawless behavior anymore.

[18]When there is forgiveness for these things, there is no longer an offering for sin.

[19]Brothers and sisters, we have confidence that we can enter the holy of holies by means of Jesus' blood, [20]through a new and living way that he opened up for us through the curtain, which is his body, [21]and we have a great high priest over God's house.

[22]Therefore, let's draw near with a genuine heart with the certainty that our faith gives us, since our hearts are sprinkled clean from an evil conscience and our bodies are washed with pure water.

[23]Let's hold on to the confession of our hope without wavering, because the one who made the promises is reliable.

[24]And let us consider each other carefully for the purpose of sparking love and good deeds. [25]Don't stop meeting together with other believers, which some people have gotten into the habit of doing. Instead, encourage each other, especially as you see the day drawing near.

Mark 13:1-8

As Jesus left the temple, one of his disciples said to him, "Teacher, look! What awesome stones and buildings!"

[2]Jesus responded, "Do you see these enormous buildings? Not even one stone will be left upon another. All will be demolished."

[3]Jesus was sitting on the Mount of Olives across from the temple. Peter, James, John, and Andrew asked him privately,[4]"Tell us, when will these things happen? What sign will show that all these things are about to come to an end?"

[5]Jesus said, "Watch out that no one deceives you. [6]Many people will come in my name, saying, 'I'm the one!' They will deceive many people. [7]When you hear of wars and reports of wars, don't be alarmed. These things must happen, but this isn't the end yet. [8]Nations and kingdoms will fight against each other, and there will be earthquakes and famines in all sorts of places. These things are just the beginning of the sufferings associated with the end."

Primary Hymns and Songs for the Day

"O God, Our Help in Ages Past" (1 Sam) (O)
  B74, C67, E680, EL632, F370, G687, L320, N25, P210,
  UM117 (PD), VU806, W579
        H-3   Hbl-33, 80; Chr-143; Desc-93; Org-132
        S-1   #293-296. Various treatments
"My Soul Gives Glory to My God" (1 Sam 1)
  C130, EL251, G99, N119, P600, UM198, VU899
        H-3   Chr-139, 145; Desc-77
        S-1   #241-242. Orff arr. and descant
"My Lord, What a Morning" (Heb, Mark)
  C708, EL438 (PD), G352, P449, UM719, VU708
        H-3   Chr-139
"How Firm a Foundation" (Mark)
  B338, C618, E636/637, EL796, F32, G463, L507, N407, P361,
  UM529 (PD), VU660, W585
        H-3   Hbl-27, 69; Chr-102; Desc-41; Org-41
        S-1   #133. Harm.
               #134. Performance note
"O Day of God, Draw Nigh" (Mark) (C)
  B623, C700, E601, N611, P452, UM730 (PD), VU688/689
        H-3   Hbl-79; Chr-141; Desc-95; Org-143
        S-1   #306-308. Various treatments

Additional Hymn Suggestions

"I'll Praise My Maker While I've Breath" (1 Sam) (O)
  B35, C20, E429 (PD), G806, P253, UM60, VU867
"O Worship the King" (1 Sam)
  B16, C17, E388, EL842, F336, G41, L548, N26, P476, UM73
  (PD), VU235
"Praise to the Lord, the Almighty" (1 Sam)
  B14, C25, E390, EL858 (PD) and 859, F337, G35, L543, N22,
  P482, UM139, VU220 (Fr.) and VU221, W547
"Give to the Winds Thy Fears" (1 Sam)
  G815, N404, P286, UM129 (PD), VU636
"Rock of Ages, Cleft for Me" (1 Sam)
  B342, C214, E685, EL623, F108, G438, N596, UM361
"Sweet Hour of Prayer" (1 Sam)
  B445, C570, F439, N505, UM496 (PD)
"Wonder of Wonders" (1 Sam, Heb, Baptism)
  C378, G489, N328, P499, S2247
"Great Is Thy Faithfulness" (1 Sam 1, Heb)
  B54, C86, EL733, F98, G39, N423, P276, UM140, VU288
"Jesus, the Very Thought of Thee" (Heb)
  B225, C102, E642, EL754, F465, G629, L316, N507, P310,
  UM175 (PD)
"Near to the Heart of God" (Heb)
  B295, C581, F35, G824, P527, UM472 (PD)
"Wash, O God, Our Sons and Daughters" (Heb, Baptism)
  C365, EL445, G490, UM605, VU442
"Fight the Good Fight" (Heb)
  E552, F613, G846, L461, P307 (PD), VU674
"As We Gather at Your Table" (Heb, Comm.)
  EL522, N332, S2268, SF2268, VU457
"Swing Low, Sweet Chariot" (Heb, Mark)
  C643, G825, UM703
"Steal Away to Jesus" (Heb, Mark)
  C644, G358, N599, UM704
"Wake, Awake, for Night Is Flying" (Heb, Mark)
  E61, EL436, G349, L31, P17, UM720 (PD), VU711
"What Wondrous Love Is This" (Mark)
  B143 (PD), C200, E439, EL666, F283, G215, L385, N223,
  P85, UM292, VU147 (Fr.), W600
"O Love, How Deep" (Mark)
  E448/449, EL322, G618, L88, N209, P83, UM267, VU348

Additional Contemporary Suggestions

"Praise to the Lord" (1 Sam 2)
  EL844, S2029, SF2029, VU835
"Give Thanks" (1 Sam 2)
  C528, G647, S2036, SF2036, SP170
"The Family Prayer Song" ("As for Me and My House") (1 Sam)
  M54, S2188, SF2188
"Shout to the North" (1 Sam 2)
  G319, M99, WS3042
"Your Grace Is Enough" (1 Sam 2)
  M191, WS3106
"You Are My All in All" (1 Sam 2, Heb)
  G519, SP220, WS3040
"The Power of the Cross" (Heb)
  M222, WS3085
"You Are My King" ("Amazing Love") (Heb)
  M82, WS3102
"Grace Like Rain" (Heb)
  M251
"Freedom Is Coming" (Mark)
  G359, S2192, SF2192
"Lead Me, Guide Me" (Mark)
  C583, EL768, G740, S2214, SF2214
"Days of Elijah" (Mark)
  M139, WS3186
"Refiner's Fire" (Mark)
  M50
"Did You Feel the Mountains Tremble?" (Mark)
  M69

Vocal Solos

"Come, Thou Fount of Every Blessing" (1 Sam)
  V-3 (3)   p. 22
  V-6   p. 4
"My Lord, What a Mornin'" (Mark)
  V-7   p. 68

Anthems

"There Is None Like You" (1 Sam)
Arr. Jack Schrader; Hope C5229
SATB with piano (bit.ly/C5229)

"My Lord, What a Morning" (Heb, Mark)
Arr. Robert A. Hobby; MorningStar MSM-50-6059
SATB and piano (bit.ly/50-6059)

Other Suggestions

For Thanksgiving Sunday, see Thanksgiving Day Suggestions.
Visuals:
  O   Woman weeping/praying, old man, couple
        worshiping, newborn
  P   Praying, rock, broken bow, 4 pillars, scales
  E   Cross, footstool, curtain, water, baptism, worship
  G   Scattered stones, war, earthquake, famine, dawn
Introit: C590, G472, P338, UM494. "*Kum Ba Yah*" (1 Sam)
Canticle: C131, N15, UM199. (1 Sam 2)
Sung Benediction: B660, C437, UM665, VU964. "Go Now in
    Peace" or C438, E714, G540, P537, UM667. "Shalom"
    (1 Sam 1)
Alternate Lessons: Dan 12:1-3, Ps 16 (see p. 4)

Joel 2:21-27

²¹Don't fear, fertile land;
     rejoice and be glad,
     for the LORD is about to do great things!
²²Don't be afraid, animals of the field,
          for the meadows of the wilderness will turn green;
     the tree will bear its fruit;
          the fig tree and grapevine will give their full yield.
²³Children of Zion,
          rejoice and be glad in the LORD your God,
     because he will give you the early rain as a sign of
               righteousness;
          he will pour down abundant rain for you,
               the early and the late rain, as before.
²⁴The threshing floors will be full of grain;
          the vats will overflow with new wine and fresh oil.
²⁵I will repay you for the years
          that the cutting locust,
     the swarming locust, the hopping locust, and the devouring
               locust have eaten—
          my great army, which I sent against you.
²⁶You will eat abundantly and be satisfied,
          and you will praise the name of the LORD your God,
     who has done wonders for you;
          and my people will never again be put to shame.
²⁷You will know that I am in the midst of Israel,
          and that I am the LORD your God—no other exists;
     never again will my people be put to shame.

Psalm 126 (G73/74, N707, P237, UM847)

When the LORD changed Zion's circumstances for the better,
     it was like we had been dreaming.
²Our mouths were suddenly filled with laughter;
     our tongues were filled with joyful shouts.
It was even said, at that time, among the nations,
     "The LORD has done great things for them!"
³Yes, the LORD has done great things for us,
     and we are overjoyed.
⁴LORD, change our circumstances for the better,
     like dry streams in the desert waste!
⁵Let those who plant with tears
     reap the harvest with joyful shouts.
⁶Let those who go out,
     crying and carrying their seed,
     come home with joyful shouts,
     carrying bales of grain!

1 Timothy 2:1-7

First of all, then, I ask that requests, prayers, petitions, and thanksgiving be made for all people. ²Pray for kings and everyone who is in authority so that we can live a quiet and peaceful life in complete godliness and dignity. ³This is right and it pleases God our savior, ⁴who wants all people to be saved and to come to a knowledge of the truth. ⁵There is one God and one mediator between God and humanity, the human Christ Jesus, ⁶who gave himself as a payment to set all people free. This was a testimony that was given at the right time. ⁷I was appointed to be a preacher and apostle of this testimony—I'm telling the truth and I'm not lying! I'm a teacher of the Gentiles in faith and truth.

Matthew 6:25-33

²⁵"Therefore, I say to you, don't worry about your life, what you'll eat or what you'll drink, or about your body, what you'll wear. Isn't life more than food and the body more than clothes? ²⁶Look at the birds in the sky. They don't sow seed or harvest grain or gather crops into barns. Yet your heavenly Father feeds them. Aren't you worth much more than they are? ²⁷Who among you by worrying can add a single moment to your life? ²⁸And why do you worry about clothes? Notice how the lilies in the field grow. They don't wear themselves out with work, and they don't spin cloth. ²⁹But I say to you that even Solomon in all of his splendor wasn't dressed like one of these. ³⁰If God dresses grass in the field so beautifully, even though it's alive today and tomorrow it's thrown into the furnace, won't God do much more for you, you people of weak faith? ³¹Therefore, don't worry and say, 'What are we going to eat?' or 'What are we going to drink?' or 'What are we going to wear?' ³²Gentiles long for all these things. Your heavenly Father knows that you need them. ³³Instead, desire first and foremost God's kingdom and God's righteousness, and all these things will be given to you as well."

Primary Hymns and Songs for the Day

"Come, Ye Thankful People, Come" (Joel, Thanks.) (O)
   B637, C718, E290, EL693, F392, G367, L407, N422, P551,
   UM694 (PD), VU516, W759
      H-3   Hbl-54; Chr-58; Desc-94; Org-137
      S-1   #302-303. Desc. and Harm.

"We Gather Together" (Joel, Matt, Thanks.)
   B636, C276, E433, F387, G336, N421, P559, UM131 (PD)
      H-3   Chr-206; Desc-61; Org-68
      S-1   #192-#194. Various treatments

"Now Thank We All Our God" (Joel, Matt, Thanks.)
   B638, C715, E396/397, EL839/840, F525, G643, L533 or
   L534, N419, P555, UM102 (PD), VU236 (Fr.), W560
      H-3   Hbl-78; Chr-140; Desc-81; Org-98
      S-1   #252-254. Various treatments

"God Will Take Care of You" (Matt)
   B64, F56, N460, UM130 (PD)

"His Eye Is on the Sparrow" (Matt)
   C82, G661, N475, S2146, SF2146

"Great Is Thy Faithfulness" (Pss, Matt) (C)
   B54, C86, EL733, F98, G39, N423, P276, UM140, VU288
      H-3   Chr-87; Desc-39; Org-39
      S-2   #59. Piano Arr.

Additional Hymn Suggestions

"All Creatures of Our God and King" (Joel, Thanks.)
   B27, C22, E400, EL835, F347, G15, L527, N17, P455, UM62,
   VU217 (Fr.), W520

"*Una Espiga*" ("Sheaves of Summer") (Joel, Comm.)
   C396, G532, N338, UM637

"Hail to the Lord's Anointed" (Pss)
   C140, EL311, G149, L87, P205 N104, UM203, VU30

"To God Be the Glory" (Pss)
   B4, C72, F363, G634, P485, UM98 (PD)

"Let Us with a Joyful Mind" (Pss)
   E389, G31, L521. N16, P244, S2012, SF2012, VU234

"Baptized in Water" (1 Tim, Baptism)
   B362, EL456, G482, P492, S2248, W720

"Dear Lord and Father of Mankind" (1 Tim)
   B267, C594, E652/563, F422, G169, L506, N502, P345,
   UM358 (PD), VU608

"For the Healing of the Nations" (1 Tim)
   C668, G346, N576, UM428, VU678, W643

"God of the Ages" ("God of Our Fathers") (1 Tim)
   B629, C725, E718, F687, G331, L567, N592, P262, UM698
   (PD), W764

"O Savior, in This Quiet Place" (1 Tim)
   G794, P390, N555

"For the Fruits of This Creation" (Matt)
   B643, C714, E424, EL679, G36, L563, N425, P553, UM97,
   VU227, W562

"The King of Love My Shepherd Is" (Matt)
   E645, EL502, G802, L456, P171, UM138 (PD), VU273

"All Things Bright and Beautiful" (Matt
   C61, E405, G20, N31, P267, UM147 (PD), VU291

"You Satisfy the Hungry Heart" (Matt, Comm.)
   C429, EL484, G523, P521, UM629, VU478, W736

"God Be with You till We Meet Again" (Matt)
   C434, EL536, F523, G541/542, N81, P540, UM672/673,
   VU422/423

"How Lovely, Lord, How Lovely" (Matt)
   C285, G402, P207, S2042, VU801

"Lord of All Hopefulness" (Matt)
   E482, EL765, G683, L469, S2197, SF2197, W568

"Joyful, Joyful, We Adore Thee" (Thanks.)
   B7, C2, E376, EL836, F377, G611, L551, N4, P464, UM89
   (PD), VU232, W525

Additional Contemporary Suggestions

"Open Our Eyes, Lord" (Joel)
   B499, S2086, SF2086, SP199

"Open the Eyes of My Heart" (Joel)
   G452, M57, WS3008

"Trading My Sorrows" (Pss)
   M75, WS3108

"From the Inside Out" (Pss)
   M263

"Seek Ye First" (Matt)
   B478, C354, E711, G175, P333, UM405, SP182, VU356

"God Is So Good" (Matt)
   B23, G658, S2056, SF2056

"Someone Asked the Question" (Matt)
   N523, S2144

"Cares Chorus" (Matt)
   S2215, SF2215, SP221

"God Is Good All the Time" (Matt)
   WS3026, M45

"Today Is the Day" (Matt)
   M223

"Give Thanks" (Thanks.)
   C528, G647, S2036, SF2036, SP170

"I Thank You, Jesus" (Thanks.)
   AH4079, C116, N41, WS3037

Vocal Solos

"Now Thank We All Our God" (Joel, Thanks.)
   V-6   p. 8

"Bright and Beautiful" (Matt)
   V-3 (3)   p. 10

"Great Is Thy Faithfulness" (Matt, Thanks.)
   V-8   p. 48

"His Eye Is on the Sparrow" (Matt)
   V-8   p. 166

Anthems

"Jubilate Deo" (Joel, Thanks.)
Dale Wood; AEC-1 p.36
2-part mixed and organ (SATB ISBN 9780800645779)

"Lord, Fill My Heart with Thankfulness" (Thanks.)
Arr. Walter Krueger; AEC-3 p. 26
Unison and keyboard, opt. Instr.

Other Suggestions

Visuals: cornucopia, fruit, vegetables, etc.
   O   Farm animals, green pastures, fruit trees, grapes
   P   Laughter, bounty, river, weeping/joy, sheaves
   E   Praying hands, one, Christ, cross, ransom note
   G   Food, clothing, birds, lilies, grass, water
Introit: WS3152. "Welcome" (Pss, Thanks.)
Call to Worship: WSL58 (Matt)
Prayer: N858. Providence of God (Matt, Thanks.)
Litany: C716. A Thanksgiving (Matt, Thanks.)
Response: S2195, SF2195 or S2081, SF2081 (Thanks.)
Sung Benediction: G80, S2279, SF2279, SP128, VU884. "The
   Trees of the Field" (Pss)

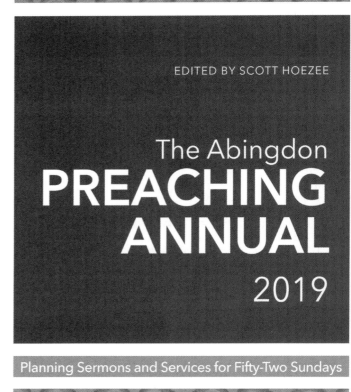

The Bible Is Our Story. Help Tell it.

The CEB
STORYTELLERS
BIBLE

Stories convey truths through plot, character, and point of view. Nowhere is that more true than in the Bible. Jesus and the prophets taught through story, and **The CEB Storytellers Bible** helps readers see the big themes and important truths of the Bible while also guiding them in how to tell these stories in contemporary language.

KEY FEATURES

- Articles about reading and telling Bible stories
- Extensive commentary on all the best-known (and many of the less common) stories of the Bible, including Jesus' parables
- Multiple indexes
- "Learning to Tell Bible Stories," a self-directed, nine-step workshop to help speakers learn to tell stories to make them come alive for listeners

Improve sermons with better storytelling and with better understanding of the Bible's stories.

9781609262082 | $39.99

The WESLEY
STUDY BIBLE

Experience the depth of John Wesley's perspectives on scripture presented for the 21st century disciple.

- More than 150 contributors from ten denominations and from six countries in the Wesleyan family bring their ministry and scholarship to this project.
- Notes are set with corresponding scripture in easy-to-read type.
- Holiness of Heart & Life articles provide relevant lessons for today's Christians.
- Wesleyan Core Terms notes give context and history of the theology of Wesleyan faith.

CEB Wesley Study Bible
9781609262105 | $59.99

2 Samuel 23:1-7

These are David's last words:
This is the declaration of Jesse's son David,
    the declaration of a man raised high,
    a man anointed by the God of Jacob,
    a man favored by the strong one of Israel.
[2]The LORD's spirit speaks through me;
    his word is on my tongue.
[3]Israel's God has spoken,
    Israel's rock said to me:
"Whoever rules rightly over people,
    whoever rules in the fear of God,
[4]is like the light of sunrise
    on a morning with no clouds,
        like the bright gleam after the rain
        that brings grass from the ground."
[5]Yes, my house is this way with God!
    He has made an eternal covenant with me,
        laid out and secure in every detail.
Yes, he provides every one of my victories
    and brings my every desire to pass.
[6]But despicable people are like thorns,
    all of them good for nothing,
        because they can't be carried by hand.
[7]No one can touch them,
except with iron bar or the shaft of a spear.
    They must be burned up with fire right on the spot!

Psalm 132:1-12 (G381, N711, UM849)

LORD, remember David—
    all the ways he suffered
    [2]and how he swore to the LORD,
        how he promised the strong one of Jacob:
[3]"I won't enter my house,
won't get into my bed.
[4]I won't let my eyes close,
won't let my eyelids sleep,
    [5]until I find a place for the LORD,
        a dwelling place for the strong one of Jacob."
[6]Yes, we heard about it in Ephrathah;
    we found it in the fields of Jaar.
[7]Let's enter God's dwelling place;
    let's worship at the place God rests his feet!
[8]Get up, LORD, go to your residence—
    you and your powerful covenant chest!
[9]Let your priests be dressed in righteousness;
    let your faithful shout out with joy!
[10]And for the sake of your servant David,
    do not reject your anointed one.
[11]The LORD swore to David
    a true promise that God won't take back:
        "I will put one of your own children on your throne.
[12]And if your children keep my covenant
        and the laws that I will teach them,
    then their children too will rule on your throne forever."

Revelation 1:4b-8

[4b]Grace and peace to you from the one who is and was and is coming, and from the seven spirits that are before God's throne,[5]and from Jesus Christ—the faithful witness, the firstborn from among the dead, and the ruler of the kings of the earth.

To the one who loves us and freed us from our sins by his blood, [6]who made us a kingdom, priests to his God and Father—to him be glory and power forever and always. Amen.

[7]Look, he is coming with the clouds! Every eye will see him, including those who pierced him, and all the tribes of the earth will mourn because of him. This is so. Amen. [8]"I am the Alpha and the Omega," says the Lord God, "the one who is and was and is coming, the Almighty."

John 18:33-37

[33]Pilate went back into the palace. He summoned Jesus and asked, "Are you the king of the Jews?"

[34]Jesus answered, "Do you say this on your own or have others spoken to you about me?"

[35]Pilate responded, "I'm not a Jew, am I? Your nation and its chief priests handed you over to me. What have you done?"

[36]Jesus replied, "My kingdom doesn't originate from this world. If it did, my guards would fight so that I wouldn't have been arrested by the Jewish leaders. My kingdom isn't from here."

[37]"So you are a king?" Pilate said.

Jesus answered, "You say that I am a king. I was born and came into the world for this reason: to testify to the truth. Whoever accepts the truth listens to my voice."

Primary Hymns and Songs for the Day

"Rejoice, the Lord Is King" (Rev, Christ the King) (O)
  B197, C699, E481, EL430, F374, G363, L171, N303, P155,
  UM715 (PD), VU213, W493
    H-3   Hbl-8, 53, 90; Chr-37; Desc-27; Org-24
    S-1   #78-80. Various treatments
"Lo, He Comes with Clouds Descending" (2 Sam, Rev)
  B199, E57/58, EL435, F306, G348, L27, P6, UM718, VU25
    H-3   Hbl-93; Chr-129; Desc-50; Org-53
    S-1   #157. Descant
"He Is Exalted" (Rev, Christ the King)
  S2070, SF2070, SP66
"Jesus Shall Reign" (2 Sam, Rev) (C)
  B587, C95, E544, EL434, F238, G265, L530, N157, P423,
  UM157 (PD), VU330, W492
    H-3   Hbl-29, 58; Chr-117; Desc-31; Org-31
    S-1   #100-103. Various treatments

Additional Hymn Suggestions

"Crown Him with Many Crowns" (2 Sam)
  B161, C234, E494, EL855, F345, G268, L170, N301, P151,
  UM327 (PD), VU211
"Hail to the Lord's Anointed" (2 Sam, Pss, Rev) (O)
  C140, EL311, G149, L87, P205 N104, UM203, VU30
"Holy, Holy, Holy" (Rev)
  B2, C4, E362, F323, EL413, G1, L165, N277, P138, UM64/65,
  VU315, W485
"Immortal, Invisible, God Only Wise" (Rev)
  B6, C66, E423, EL834, F319, G12, L526, N1, P263, UM103
  (PD), VU264, W512
"Praise to the Lord, the Almighty" (Rev)
  B14, C25, E390, EL858 (PD) and 859, F337, G35, L543, N22,
  P482, UM139, VU220 (Fr.) and VU221, W547
"When Morning Gilds the Skies" (Rev)
  B221, C100, E427, EL853 (PD), F322, G667, L546, N86,
  P487, UM185, VU339 (Fr.), W675
"This Is the Feast of Victory" (Rev, Comm.)
  E417/418, G513, P594, UM638, VU904, W458
"Rejoice, the Lord Is King" (Rev, Christ the King)
  B197, C699, E481, EL430, F374, G363, L171, N303, P155,
  UM715 (PD), VU213, W493
"At the Name of Jesus" (Rev, John)
  B198, E435, EL416, F351, G264, L179, P148, UM168, VU335,
  W499
"You, Lord, Are Both Lamb and Shepherd" (John)
  G274, SF2102, VU210, WS3043
"God of Grace and God of Glory" (John)
  B395, C464, E594/595, EL705, F528, G307, L415, N436,
  P420, UM577, VU686
"Lead On, O King Eternal" (John)
  B621, C632, E555, EL805, F595, G269, L495, N573, P447/
  P448, UM580
"Let All Mortal Flesh Keep Silence" (John, Comm.)
  B80, C124, E324, EL490, F166, G347, L198, N345, P5,
  UM626 (PD), VU473 (Fr.), W523
"O God Beyond All Praising" (Christ King, Thanks.)
  EL880, S2009, SF2009, VU256, W541

Additional Contemporary Suggestions

"Rock of Ages" (2 Sam)
  M93
"I Will Call upon the Lord" (2 Sam)
  G621, S2002, SF2002, SP224
"Praise the Name of Jesus" (2 Sam, Christ the King)
  S2066, SF2066, SP87

"In the Lord I'll Be Ever Thankful" (2 Sam)
  G654, S2195, SF2195
"Surely the Presence of the Lord" (Pss)
  C263, SP243, UM328; S-2 #200. Stanzas for soloist
"Turn Your Eyes upon Jesus" (Rev)
  B320, F621, SP218, UM349
"You Are Holy" ("Prince of Peace") (Rev)
  G705, M129
"Soon and Very Soon" (Rev, Christ the King)
  B192, EL439, G384, UM706, S-2 #187. Piano Arr.
"Awesome God" (Rev, John, Christ the King)
  G616, S2040, SF2040, SP11
"King of Kings" (Rev, Christ the King)
  B234, S2075, SF2075, SP94, VU167
"We Will Glorify the King of Kings" (Rev, Christ the King)
  B213, S2087, SF2087, SP68
"How Great Is Our God" (Rev, Christ the King)
  WS3003, M117
"Blessing, Honor and Glory" (Rev, Christ the King)
  EL433, M21
"Jesus, We Crown You with Praise" (Rev, Christ the King)
  M24
"Jehovah Reigns" (Rev, Christ the King)
  M55
"All Hail King Jesus" (John, Christ the King)
  S2069, SF2069, SP63
"Our God Reigns" (Christ the King)
  SP64
"Crown Him King of Kings" (Christ the King)
  M22
"He Reigns" (Christ the King)
  M168
"The Highest and the Greatest" (Christ the King)
  M230
"Prepare Ye the Way" ("You Reign on High") (Christ the King)
  M275

Vocal Solos

"Jesus Is Lord of All" (Christ the King)
  V-8   p. 254
"King of Glory, King of Peace" (Christ the King)
  V-9   p. 24

Anthems

"Sit Down, Servant" (Pss)
Arr. Larry Shackley, Lorenz 10/4290L
SATB and piano 4-hands (bit.ly/10-4290L)

"All Hail the Power" (Rev)
Arr. Mark Hayes; Lorenz 10/4122L
SATB and piano, opt. brass (bit.ly/4122L)

Other Suggestions

Visuals: Cross/crown, lamb/cross
  O   Speaking, rock, sunrise, rain/grass, thorns, spear, fire
  P   Empty bed, ark, crown, throne, scepter
  E   Crown, scepter, cross, royal robe, fabric (gold/purple)
  G   Jesus/Pilate, shackles, John 18:36a, crown, listening
Introit: EL819, G388, S2274, SF2274. "Come, All You People"
  ("*Uyai Mose*") (Pss)
Greeting and Opening Prayer: N820 and N827 (John)
Prayers: WSL91 and UM721 (John, Christ the King)

Jeremiah 33:14-16

[14]The time is coming, declares the LORD, when I will fulfill my gracious promise with the people of Israel and Judah. [15]In those days and at that time, I will raise up a righteous branch from David's line, who will do what is just and right in the land.[16]In those days, Judah will be saved and Jerusalem will live in safety. And this is what he will be called: The LORD Is Our Righteousness.

Psalm 25:1-10 (G420, N635, P178, UM756)

I offer my life to you, LORD.
  [2]My God, I trust you.
Please don't let me be put to shame!
  Don't let my enemies rejoice over me!
[3]For that matter,
  don't let anyone who hopes in you
    be put to shame;
  instead, let those who are treacherous without excuse be put
    to shame.
[4]Make your ways known to me, LORD;
  teach me your paths.
[5]Lead me in your truth—teach it to me—
  because you are the God who saves me.
    I put my hope in you all day long.
[6]LORD, remember your compassion and faithful love—
  they are forever!
[7]But don't remember the sins of my youth or my wrongdoing.
  Remember me only according to your faithful love
    for the sake of your goodness, LORD.
[8]The LORD is good and does the right thing;
  he teaches sinners which way they should go.
[9]God guides the weak to justice,
  teaching them his way.
[10]All the LORD's paths are loving and faithful
  for those who keep his covenant and laws.

1 Thessalonians 3:9-13

[9]How can we thank God enough for you, given all the joy we have because of you before our God? [10]Night and day, we pray more than ever to see all of you in person and to complete whatever you still need for your faith. [11]Now may our God and Father himself guide us on our way back to you. [12]May the LORD cause you to increase and enrich your love for each other and for everyone in the same way as we also love you. [13]May the love cause your hearts to be strengthened, to be blameless in holiness before our God and Father when our LORD Jesus comes with all his people. Amen.

Luke 21:25-36

[25]"There will be signs in the sun, moon, and stars. On the earth, there will be dismay among nations in their confusion over the roaring of the sea and surging waves. [26] The planets and other heavenly bodies will be shaken, causing people to faint from fear and foreboding of what is coming upon the world. [27]Then they will see the Human One coming on a cloud with power and great splendor. [28] Now when these things begin to happen, stand up straight and raise your heads, because your redemption is near."

[29]Jesus told them a parable: "Look at the fig tree and all the trees. [30]When they sprout leaves, you can see for yourselves and know that summer is near. [31]In the same way, when you see these things happening, you know that God's kingdom is near. [32]I assure you that this generation won't pass away until everything has happened. [33]Heaven and earth will pass away, but my words will certainly not pass away.

[34]"Take care that your hearts aren't dulled by drinking parties, drunkenness, and the anxieties of day-to-day life. Don't let that day fall upon you unexpectedly, [35] like a trap. It will come upon everyone who lives on the face of the whole earth. [36] Stay alert at all times, praying that you are strong enough to escape everything that is about to happen and to stand before the Human One."

Primary Hymns and Songs for the Day

"O Come, O Come, Emmanuel" (Jer) (O)
  B76, C119, E56, EL257, F169, G88, L34 (PD), N116, P9,
  UM211, VU1(Fr.), W357
      H-3   Hbl-14, 79; Chr-141; Org-168
      S-1   #342. Handbell accompaniment
"There's Something About That Name" (Luke)
  B177, C115, F227, SP89, UM171
"My Lord, What a Morning" (Luke)
  C708, EL438 (PD), G352, P449, UM719, VU708
      H-3   Chr-139
"O Day of God, Draw Nigh" (Luke)
  B623, C700, E601, N611, P452, UM730 (PD), VU688/689
      H-3   Hbl-79; Chr-141; Desc-95; Org-143
      S-1   #306-308. Various treatments
"Lift Up Your Heads, Ye Mighty Gates" (Jer, Pss, 1 Thess) (C)
  B128, C129, F239, G93, N117, P8, UM213 (PD), W363
      H-3   Hbl-50; Chr-47; Desc-101; Org-167
      S-1   #334-5. Desc. and Harm.

Additional Hymn Suggestions

"Come, Thou Long-Expected Jesus" (Jer, Luke)
  B77, C125, E66, EL254, F168, G82/83, L30, N122, P1/2,
  UM196 (PD), VU2, W364
"Hail to the Lord's Anointed" (Jer)
  C140, EL311, G149, L87, P205 N104, UM203, VU30
"Prepare the Way of the Lord" (Jer, Advent)
  C121, G95, UM207, W369
"Blessed Be the God of Israel" (Jer)
  C135, E444, EL250/552, G109, P602, UM209, VU901
"Lo, How a Rose E'er Blooming" (Jer)
  B78, C160, E81, EL272, F174, G129, L58, N127, P48 (PD),
  UM216, VU8, W374
"This Is the Day the Lord Hath Made" (Jer)
  B358, G681, P230, UM658
"Lead Me, Lord" (Jer, Pss)
  C593, N774, UM473 (PD), VU662
"Lord, I Want to Be a Christian" (1 Thess)
  B489, C589, F421, G729, N454, P372 (PD), UM402
"Where Charity and Love Prevail" (1 Thess)
  E581, EL359, G316, L126, N396, UM549
"Creator of the Stars of Night" (1 Thess)
  C127, E60, EL245, G84, L323, N111, P4, UM692 (PD)
"Come Now, O Prince of Peace" ("O-So-So") (1 Thess)
  EL247, G103, S2232, SF2232
"Lord, Make Us More Holy" (1 Thess)
  G313, N75 (PD), P536
"I Want to Walk as a Child of the Light" (1 Thess, Luke)
  E490, EL815, G377, UM206, W510
"Lo, He Comes with Clouds Descending" (1 Thess, Luke)
  B199, E57/58, EL435, G348, L27, P6, UM718, VU25
"People, Look East" (Luke)
  C142, EL248, G105, P12, UM202, VU9, W359
"In the Bleak Midwinter" (Luke)
  E112, EL294, G144, N128, P36, UM221 (PD), VU55
"How Firm a Foundation" (Luke)
  B338, C618, E636/637, EL796, F32, G463, L507, N407, P361,
  UM529 (PD), VU660, W585
"Wake, Awake, for Night Is Flying" (Luke)
  E61, EL436, G349, L31, P17, UM720 (PD), VU711
"Here, O My Lord, I See Thee" (Luke, Comm.)
  C416, E318, F567, G517, L211, N336, P520, UM623, VU459

Additional Contemporary Suggestions

"The King of Glory Comes" (Jer)
  B127, S2091, SF2091, W501

"You Are Holy" ("Prince of Peace") (Jer, Advent)
  G705, M129
"Sing to the King" (Jer)
  M141
"My Life Is in You, Lord" (Pss)
  S2032, SF2032, SP204
"Cry of My Heart" (Pss)
  M39, S2165, SF2165
"Falling on My Knees" (Pss)
  M155, WS3099
"Purify My Heart" (Pss)
  M90, WS3103
"I Could Sing of Your Love Forever" (Pss)
  M63
"Lead Me, Lord" (Pss)
  M108
"All Who Are Thirsty" (Pss, Advent)
  M159
"He Came Down" (1 Thess)
  EL253, G137, S2085, SF2085
"Hosanna" (1 Thess, Luke)
  WS3188, M268
"Freedom Is Coming" (Luke)
  G359, S2192, SF2192
"The Battle Belongs to the Lord" (Luke)
  SP158
"Ancient of Days" (Luke)
  M1
"My Savior Lives" (Advent)
  M237

Vocal Solos

"God Will Make a Way" (with "He Leadeth Me") (Pss, Advent)
  V-3 (2)   p. 9
"Lo, He Comes with Clouds Descending" (Luke)
  V-1   p. 54
"My Lord, What a Mornin'" (Luke, Advent)
  V-3 (1)   p. 39
  V-7   p. 68

Anthems

"Alleluia! Rejoice! The Lord Shall Come" (Jer)
Arr. Patrick Liebergen; Choristers Guild CGA1283
SATB and piano, opt handbells (bit.ly/CGA1283)

"Once He Came in Blessing" (Luke)
Arr. Mark Sedio; AEC-1 p. 40
2-part mixed with keyboard and flute

Other Suggestions

Visuals:
  O   Branch, Jesse tree, new buds
  P   Teaching, leading, path, open Bible
  E   Joy, praying hands, Jesus, Second Coming
  G   Sun, moon, earth, clouds, Christ descending, fig tree,
           budding tree, guard, praying, weights, Luke 21:36a
Introit: WS3048. "View the Present through the Promise" (Luke)
Greeting: N819 (Pss)
Advent Wreath Responses: C128, S2090, SF2090, UM206
Prayers: WSL10, N816, C19, UM211, C120, WSL115 (Advent)
Response: EL152, S2275, SF2275, WS3133. "Kyrie" (Pss)
See The Abingdon Worship Annual 2018 *for more ideas.*

Malachi 3:1-4

Look, I am sending my messenger who will clear the path before
    me;
    suddenly the Lord whom you are seeking will come to his
      temple.
    The messenger of the covenant in whom you take delight is
      coming,
    says the Lord of heavenly forces.
²Who can endure the day of his coming?
    Who can withstand his appearance?
He is like the refiner's fire or the cleaner's soap.
³He will sit as a refiner and a purifier of silver.
    He will purify the Levites
      and refine them like gold and silver.
    They will belong to the Lord,
      presenting a righteous offering.
⁴The offering of Judah and Jerusalem will be pleasing to the
    Lord
    as in ancient days and in former years.

Luke 1:68-79

⁶⁸"Bless the Lord God of Israel
    because he has come to help and has delivered his people.
⁶⁹He has raised up a mighty savior for us in his servant David's
    house,
      ⁷⁰just as he said through the mouths of his holy prophets
      long ago.
⁷¹He has brought salvation from our enemies
    and from the power of all those who hate us.
⁷²He has shown the mercy promised to our ancestors,
    and remembered his holy covenant,
      ⁷³the solemn pledge he made to our ancestor Abraham.
He has granted ⁷⁴that we would be rescued
    from the power of our enemies
so that we could serve him without fear,
      ⁷⁵in holiness and righteousness in God's eyes,
      for as long as we live.
⁷⁶You, child, will be called a prophet of the Most High,
    for you will go before the Lord to prepare his way.
⁷⁷You will tell his people how to be saved
    through the forgiveness of their sins.
⁷⁸Because of our God's deep compassion,
    the dawn from heaven will break upon us,
      ⁷⁹to give light to those who are sitting in darkness
    and in the shadow of death,
      to guide us on the path of peace."

Philippians 1:3-11

³I thank my God every time I mention you in my prayers. ⁴I'm thankful for all of you every time I pray, and it's always a prayer full of joy. ⁵I'm glad because of the way you have been my partners in the ministry of the gospel from the time you first believed it until now. ⁶I'm sure about this: the one who started a good work in you will stay with you to complete the job by the day of Christ Jesus. ⁷I have good reason to think this way about all of you because I keep you in my heart. You are all my partners in God's grace, both during my time in prison and in the defense and support of the gospel. ⁸God is my witness that I feel affection for all of you with the compassion of Christ Jesus.

⁹This is my prayer: that your love might become even more and more rich with knowledge and all kinds of insight. ¹⁰I pray this so that you will be able to decide what really matters and so you will be sincere and blameless on the day of Christ. ¹¹I pray that you will then be filled with the fruit of righteousness, which comes from Jesus Christ, in order to give glory and praise to God.

Luke 3:1-6

In the fifteenth year of the rule of the emperor Tiberius—when Pontius Pilate was governor over Judea and Herod was ruler over Galilee, his brother Philip was ruler over Ituraea and Trachonitis, and Lysanias was ruler over Abilene, ²during the high priesthood of Annas and Caiaphas—God's word came to John son of Zechariah in the wilderness. ³John went throughout the region of the Jordan River, calling for people to be baptized to show that they were changing their hearts and lives and wanted God to forgive their sins. ⁴This is just as it was written in the scroll of the words of Isaiah the prophet,
A voice crying out in the wilderness:
    "Prepare the way for the Lord;
      make his paths straight.
    ⁵*Every valley will be filled,*
      and every mountain and hill will be leveled.
    The crooked will be made straight
      and the rough places made smooth.
    ⁶*All humanity will see God's salvation."*

Primary Hymns and Songs for the Day

"Come, Thou Long-Expected Jesus" (Mal, Luke) (O)
  B77, C125, E66, EL254, F168, G82/83, L30, N122, P1/2,
  UM196 (PD), VU2, W364
       H-3   Hbl-46; Chr-26, 134; Desc-53; Org-56
       S-1   #168-171. Various treatments
"Prepare the Way of the Lord" (Luke 3, Advent)
  C121, G95, UM207, W369
"Blessed Be the God of Israel" (Mal, Luke 1)
  C135, E444, EL250/552, G109, P602, UM209, VU901
"Refiner's Fire" (Mal)
  M50
"He Who Began a Good Work in You" (Phil)
  S2163, SF2163, SP180
"Angels from the Realms of Glory" (Mal) (C)
  B94, C149, E93, EL275, F190, G143, L50, N126, P22, UM220
  (PD), VU36, W377
       H-3   Chr-30, 48, 62; Desc-89; Org-121
       S-1   #280. Desc. and Harm.

Additional Hymn Suggestions

"Isaiah the Prophet Has Written of Old" (Mal)
  G77, N108, P337, VU680
"Soon and Very Soon" (Mal)
  B192, EL439, G384, UM706, S-2 #187. Piano arr.
"Spirit Divine, Attend Our Prayers" (Mal)
  E509, G407, P325, VU385, W476
"Love Divine, All Loves Excelling" (Mal, Phil)
  B208, C517, E657, EL631, F21, G366, N43, P376, UM384
  (PD), VU333, W588
"Come Down, O Love Divine" (Mal, Phil)
  C582, E516, EL804, G282, N289, P313, UM475, VU367
"Guide My Feet" (Luke 1)
  G741, N497, P354, S2208
"Lead Me, Guide Me" (Luke 1)
  C583, EL768, G740, S2214, SF2214
"Prepare the Way, O Zion" (Luke 1, Luke 3)
  EL264, G106, L26, P13, VU882
"O Come, O Come, Emmanuel" (Mal, Luke)
  B76, C119, E56, EL257, F169, G88, L34 (PD), N116, P9,
  UM211, VU1(Fr.), W357
"I Want to Walk as a Child of the Light" (Luke 1)
  E490, EL815, G377, UM206, W510
"Lo, How a Rose E'er Blooming" (Mal, Luke 1)
  B78, C160, E81, EL272, F174, G129, L58, N127, P48 (PD),
  UM216, VU8, W374
"Lift Up Your Heads, Ye Mighty Gates" (Phil, Advent)
  B128, C129, F239, G93, N117, P8, UM213 (PD), W363
"More Love to Thee, O Christ" (Phil)
  B473, C527, F476, G828, N456, P359, UM453 (PD)
"Deck Thyself, My Soul, with Gladness" (Phil, Comm.)
  E339, EL488/489, G514, P506, UM612 (PD), VU463
"Called as Partners in Christ's Service" (Phil)
  C453, G761, N495, P343
"People, Look East" (Luke)
  C142, EL248, G105, P12, UM202, VU9, W359
"Come, Let Us Eat" (Luke, Comm.)
  EL491, G528, L214, UM625
"Wild and Lone the Prophet's Voice" (Luke 3)
  G163, P409, S2089, SF2089

Additional Contemporary Suggestions

"Shout to the North" (Mal, Advent)
  G319, M99, WS3042

"Purify My Heart" (Mal)
  M90, WS3103
"Move Me Again" (Mal)
  M145
"Prepare Ye the Way" ("You Reign") (Mal, Luke)
  M275
"Give Thanks" (Luke)
  C528, G647, S2036, SF2036, SP170
"We Are Marching" ("Siyahamba") (Luke 1)
  C442, EL866, G853, N526, S2235, SF2235, VU646
"How Great Is Our God" (Luke 1, Advent)
  WS3003, M117
"God Is Good All the Time" (Luke 1)
  WS3026, M45
"Here I Am To Worship" (Luke 1, Advent)
  M116, WS3177
"Shine on Us" (Luke 1, Advent)
  M19
"Everyday" (Luke 1, Advent)
  M150
"I Will Enter His Gates" (Phil)
  S2270, SF2270, SP168
"Alleluia" (Luke 3, Comm.)
  B223, C106, F361, N765, SP108, UM186, S-2 #3-4. Desc. and
  Harm.
"Rise Up and Praise Him" (Luke 3)
  M62

Vocal Solos

"And He Shall Purify, " "But Who May Abide," and
"Thus Saith the Lord" from *Messiah* (Mal)
"Every Valley" from *Messiah* (Mal, Luke)
  V-2
"God Will Make a Way" (with "He Leadeth Me") (Mal, Luke)
  V-3 (2)   p. 9
"Alleluia, Sing to Jesus" (Mal, Luke)
  V-3 (3)   p. 50
"Come, Thou Long-Expected Jesus" (Luke, Advent)
  V-10   p. 11

Anthems

"Stir Up Your Power" (Phil, Advent)
Linda Cable Shute; AEC-1 p. 59
2-part mixed and keyboard, opt. cong. (bit.ly/AEC-1-59)

"Arise! Sing Forth!" (Luke, Advent)
Purcell/arr. Hopson; Augsburg AEC-2 p. 5
SAB and piano

Other Suggestions

Visuals:
  O   Fire, soap, silver, gold, refining, silver polish
  P   Christ, child, dawn breaking, light/darkness
  E   Prayer, open Bible, heart, shackles, letter, robe, harvest
  G   John, baptism, Luke 3:4b, straight path, level ground,
           all nations
Introit: S2005, SF2005. "Arise, Shine" (Luke, Advent)
Introit: WS3185, stanza 1. "Send Us Your Spirit" (Luke 1)
Call to Worship: WSL4 or N822 (Luke, Phil, Advent)
Canticles: C137, F191, N733, UM205, UM208, VU900 (Luke 1)
Litany: N880. A Litany of Darkness and Light (Luke 1)
Prayers: N826, N853, C31, UM201, WSL125, WSL152 (Luke)

Zephaniah 3:14-20

[14]Rejoice, Daughter Zion! Shout, Israel!
> Rejoice and exult with all your heart, Daughter Jerusalem.

[15]The LORD has removed your judgment;
> he has turned away your enemy.

The LORD, the king of Israel, is in your midst;
> you will no longer fear evil.

[16]On that day, it will be said to Jerusalem:
> Don't fear, Zion.
> Don't let your hands fall.

[17]The LORD your God is in your midst—a warrior bringing victory.
> He will create calm with his love;
> he will rejoice over you with singing.
> > [18]I will remove from you those worried about the appointed feasts.
> They have been a burden for her, a reproach.

[19]Watch what I am about to do to all your oppressors at that time.
> I will deliver the lame;
> I will gather the outcast.
> I will change their shame into praise and fame throughout the earth.

[20]At that time, I will bring all of you back,
> at the time when I gather you.
> I will give you fame and praise among all the neighboring peoples
> > when I restore your possessions and you can see them— says the LORD.

Isaiah 12:2-6

[2]God is indeed my salvation;
> I will trust and won't be afraid.

Yah, the LORD, is my strength and my shield;
> he has become my salvation."

[3]You will draw water with joy from the springs of salvation.

[4]And you will say on that day:

"Thank the LORD; call on God's name;
> proclaim God's deeds among the peoples;
> declare that God's name is exalted.

[5]Sing to the LORD, who has done glorious things;
> proclaim this throughout all the earth."

[6]Shout and sing for joy, city of Zion,
> because the holy one of Israel is great among you.

Philippians 4:4-7

[4]Be glad in the LORD always! Again I say, be glad! [5]Let your gentleness show in your treatment of all people. The LORD is near. [6]Don't be anxious about anything; rather, bring up all of your requests to God in your prayers and petitions, along with giving thanks. [7]Then the peace of God that exceeds all understanding will keep your hearts and minds safe in Christ Jesus.

Luke 3:7-18

[7]Then John said to the crowds who came to be baptized by him, "You children of snakes! Who warned you to escape from the angry judgment that is coming soon? [8]Produce fruit that shows you have changed your hearts and lives. And don't even think about saying to yourselves, Abraham is our father. I tell you that God is able to raise up Abraham's children from these stones. [9]The ax is already at the root of the trees. Therefore, every tree that doesn't produce good fruit will be chopped down and tossed into the fire."

[10]The crowds asked him, "What then should we do?"

[11]He answered, "Whoever has two shirts must share with the one who has none, and whoever has food must do the same."

[12]Even tax collectors came to be baptized. They said to him, "Teacher, what should we do?"

[13]He replied, "Collect no more than you are authorized to collect."

[14]Soldiers asked, "What about us? What should we do?"

He answered, "Don't cheat or harass anyone, and be satisfied with your pay."

[15]The people were filled with expectation, and everyone wondered whether John might be the Christ. [16]John replied to them all, "I baptize you with water, but the one who is more powerful than me is coming. I'm not worthy to loosen the strap of his sandals. He will baptize you with the Holy Spirit and fire.[17]The shovel he uses to sift the wheat from the husks is in his hands. He will clean out his threshing area and bring the wheat into his barn. But he will burn the husks with a fire that can't be put out." [18]With many other words John appealed to them, proclaiming good news to the people.

Primary Hymns and Songs for the Day

"Hail to the Lord's Anointed" (Zeph) (O)
 C140, EL311, G149, L87, P205 N104, UM203, VU30

"The First Song of Isaiah" (Isa)
 G71, S2030, SF2030

"Good Christian Friends, Rejoice" (Phil, Luke)
 B96, C164, E107 (PD), EL288, F177, G132, L55, N129, P28,
 UM224, VU35, W391
   H-3 Hbl-19, 30, 65; Chr-83; Desc-55; Org-62
   S-1 #180. Rhythm Instr. accomp,

"Wild and Lone the Prophet's Voice" (Luke)
 G163, P409, S2089, SF2089

"Come, Thou Long-Expected Jesus" (Zeph) (C)
 B77, C125, E66, EL254, F168, G82/83, L30, N122, P1/2,
 UM196 (PD), VU2, W364
   H-3 Hbl-46; Chr-26, 134; Desc-53; Org-56
   S-1 #168-171. Various treatments

Additional Hymn Suggestions

"Sing Praise to God Who Reigns Above" (Zeph)
 B20, C6, E408, EL871, F343, G645, N6, P483, UM126 (PD),
 VU216, W528

"O God of Every Nation" (Zeph)
 C680, E607, EL713, G756, L416, P289, UM435, VU677

"Tell Out, My Soul" (Zeph, Isa, Phil, Luke)
 B81, E437/438, UM200, W534

"Blessed Be the God of Israel" (Zeph, Luke)
 C135, E444, EL250/552, G109, P602, UM209, VU901

Toda la Tierra" ("All Earth Is Waiting") (Zeph, Luke 3)
 C139, EL266, N121, UM210, VU5

"To God Be the Glory" (Phil)
 B4, C72, F363, G634, P485, UM98 (PD)

"When Morning Gilds the Skies" (Phil)
 B221, C100, E427, EL853 (PD), F322, G667, L546, N86,
 P487, UM185, VU339 (Fr.), W675

"Near to the Heart of God" (Phil)
 B295, C581, F35, G824, P527, UM472 (PD)

"What a Friend We Have in Jesus" (Phil)
 B182, C585, EL742, F466, G465, L439, N506, P403, UM526
 (PD), VU661

"Rise to Greet the Sun" (Matt)
 EL852, G668, N470, UM678

"Rejoice, the Lord Is King" (Phil)
 B197, C699, E481, EL430, F374, G363, L171, N303, P155,
 UM715 (PD), VU213, W493

"O Day of Peace That Dimly Shines" (Phil, Luke)
 C711, E597, EL711, G373, P450, UM729, VU682, W654

"Lord of All Hopefulness" (Phil, Advent)
 E482, EL765, G683, L469, S2197, SF2197, W568

"In the Bleak Midwinter" (Luke)
 E112, EL294, G144, N128, P36, UM221 (PD), VU55

"Open Now Thy Gates of Beauty" (Luke)
 EL533 (PD), G403, L250, N67, P489

Cuando El Pobre" ("When the Poor Ones") (Luke)
 C662, EL725, G762, P407, UM434, VU702

"What Does the Lord Require" (Luke)
 C659, E605, P405, UM441, W624

"God the Sculptor of the Mountains" (Luke)
 EL736, G5, S2060, SF2060

"On Jordan's Bank the Baptist's Cry" (Luke)
 E76, EL249, G96, L36, N115, P10, W356, VU20

"Crashing Waters at Creation" (Luke)
 EL455, G476, N326, SF2247, VU449

Additional Contemporary Suggestions

"Shout to the Lord" (Zeph, Isa)
 EL821, S2074, SF2074, M16; V-3 (2) p. 32 Vocal Solo

"The King of Glory Comes" (Zeph)
 B127, S2091, W501

"Mighty to Save" (Zeph)
 M246, WS3038

"Forever" (Isa)
 M68, WS3023

"He Is Exalted" (Isa)
 S2070, SF2070, SP66

"Someone Asked the Question" (Isa, Phil)
 N523, S2144

"In the Lord I'll Be Ever Thankful" (Isa, Phil)
 G654, S2195, SF2195

"I Will Enter His Gates" (Isa, Phil)
 S2270, SF2270, SP168

"I've Got Peace Like a River" (Phil)
 B418, C530, G623, N478, P368, S2145, VU577

"Come and Fill Our Hearts" ("*Confitemini Domino*") (Phil)
 EL538, G466, S2157, SF2157, W561

"Sanctuary" (Phil)
 G701, M52, S2164, SF2164

"Jesus, Name above All Names" (Luke)
 S2071, SF2071, SP76

"I Will Never Be (the Same Again)" (Luke)
 M34

"Refiner's Fire" (Luke, Advent)
 M50

Vocal Solos

"Rejoice Greatly, O Daughter of Zion" (Zeph)
 V-2

"Prepare Thyself, Zion" (Zeph)
 V-9   p. 2

"A Song of Trust" (Phil)
 V-4   p. 20

Anthems

"Come, Thou Long-Expected Jesus" (Zeph)
Mark Shepperd; MorningStar MSM-50-0047
SATB divisi and organ, opt. Instr. (bit.ly/50-0047)

"Prepare the Way, O Zion" (Luke)
Sheldon Curry; Alfred Music 24388
SATB and piano (bit.ly/Alfred24388)

Other Suggestions

Visuals:
 O Rejoicing, singing, festival, clock, saving
 P Races/nations, singing, shouting, water/well
 E Rejoicing, praying hands, Phil 4:4, 5*b*, 6*a, b*, peace
 G Snakes, axe/root, Holy Spirit, fir, water, 2 coats, tax
   form, fruit, winnowing fork, wheat, service, trees
   bearing fruit and barren

Introit: C215, E199, EL363, G234, L132, N230, P115, UM315
 (PD), VU165, W456, stanza 1. "Come, Ye Faithful, Raise the
 Strain" (Zeph)

Call to Worship: WSL9 (Zeph) or N823 (Advent)

Call to Prayer: EL538, G466, S2157, SF2157, W561. "Come and
 Fill Our Hearts" (Phil)

Prayers: UM201, UM366, UM597, VU880, N872 (Luke)

Micah 5:2-5a

[2]As for you, Bethlehem of Ephrathah,
> though you are the least significant of Judah's forces,
>> one who is to be a ruler in Israel on my behalf will come
>>> out from you.
> His origin is from remote times, from ancient days.

[3]Therefore, he will give them up
> until the time when she who is in labor gives birth.
> The rest of his kin will return to the people of Israel.

[4]He will stand and shepherd his flock in the strength of the
> LORD,
> in the majesty of the name of the LORD his God.
> They will dwell secure,
> because he will surely become great throughout the earth;

[5a]he will become one of peace.

Luke 1:47-55

[47]In the depths of who I am I rejoice in God my savior.
[48]He has looked with favor on the low status of his servant.
> Look! From now on, everyone will consider me highly
>> favored
[49]because the mighty one has done great things for me.
Holy is his name.
[50]He shows mercy to everyone,
> from one generation to the next,
> who honors him as God.
[51]He has shown strength with his arm.
> He has scattered those with arrogant thoughts and proud
>> inclinations.
[52]He has pulled the powerful down from their thrones
> and lifted up the lowly.
[53]He has filled the hungry with good things
> and sent the rich away empty-handed.
[54]He has come to the aid of his servant Israel,
> remembering his mercy,
[55]just as he promised to our ancestors,
> to Abraham and to Abraham's descendants forever."

Hebrews 10:5-10

[5]Therefore, when he comes into the world he says,
> *You didn't want a sacrifice or an offering,*
>> *but you prepared a body for me;*
> [6]*you weren't pleased with entirely burned offerings or a sin offering.*
> [7]*So then I said,*
> *"Look, I've come to do your will, God.*
> *This has been written about me in the scroll."*

[8]He says above, *You didn't want* and *you weren't pleased with a sacrifice or an offering* or *with entirely burned offerings or a purification offering*, which are offered because the Law requires them. [9]Then he said, *Look, I've come to do your will.* He puts an end to the first to establish the second. [10]We have been made holy by God's will through the offering of Jesus Christ's body once for all.

Luke 1:39-45

[39]Mary got up and hurried to a city in the Judean highlands. [40]She entered Zechariah's home and greeted Elizabeth. [41]When Elizabeth heard Mary's greeting, the child leaped in her womb, and Elizabeth was filled with the Holy Spirit. [42]With a loud voice she blurted out, "God has blessed you above all women, and he has blessed the child you carry. [43]Why do I have this honor, that the mother of my Lord should come to me? [44]As soon as I heard your greeting, the baby in my womb jumped for joy. [45]Happy is she who believed that the Lord would fulfill the promises he made to her."

Primary Hymns and Songs for the Day

"O Come, All Ye Faithful" (Luke) (O)
> B89, C148, E83, EL283, F193, G133, L45, N135, P41, UM234 (PD), VU60 (Fr.), W392
>> H-3   Hbl-78; Desc-12; Org-2
>> S-1   #7-13. Various treatments

"O Little Town of Bethlehem" (Mic)
> B86, C144, E78/79, EL279, F178, G121, L41, N133, P43/44, UM230, VU64, W386
>> H-3   Hbl-81; Chr-145; Desc-95; Org-141
>> S-1   #304. Harm.

"My Soul Gives Glory to My God" (Luke)
> C130, EL251, G99, N119, P600, UM198, VU899
>> H-3   Chr-139, 145; Desc-77
>> S-1   #241-242. Orff arr. and descant

"Give Thanks" (Luke)
> C528, G647, S2036, SF2036, SP170

"Hark! the Herald Angels Sing" (Mic, Luke)
> B88, C150, E87, EL270, F184, G119, L60, N144, P31, UM240 (PD), VU48, W387

"Joy to the World" (Mic, Luke) (C)
> B87, C143, E100, EL267, F171, G134/ G266, L39, N132, P40, UM246 (PD), VU59, W399
>> H-3   Hbl-8, 29, 73; Chr-119; Desc-15; Org-6
>> S-1   #19-20. Trumpet Desc.

Additional Hymn Suggestions

"O Sing a Song of Bethlehem" (Mic)
> B120, F208, G159, N51, P308, UM179 (PD)

"Once in Royal David's City" (Mic)
> C165, EL269, G140, N45, P49, UM250 (PD), VU62, W402

"Hark! the Herald Angels Sing" ("Jesus, the Light of the World") (Mic, Luke)
> G127, N160

"That Boy-Child of Mary" (Mic, Luke)
> B110, EL293, G139, P55, UM241

"We Walk by Faith" (Heb)
> E209, EL635, G817, N256, P399, S2196, SF2196, W572

"Called as Partners in Christ's Service" (Heb)
> C453, G761, N495, P343

"Tell Out, My Soul" (Luke)
> B81, E437/438, UM200, W534

"Canticle of the Turning" ("My Soul Cries Out with a Joyful Shout") (Luke)
> EL723, G100

"Sing Out, My Song" ("Magnificat") (Luke)
> EL236, G646, W553

"To a Maid Engaged to Joseph" (Luke)
> G98, P19, UM215, VU14

"Lo, How a Rose E'er Blooming" (Luke)
> B78, C160, E81, EL272, F174, G129, L58, N127, P48 (PD), UM216, VU8, W374

"Sing of Mary, Pure and Lowly" (Luke)
> C184, E277, UM272, W404

"Like a Child" (Luke)
> C133, S2092, SF2092, VU366

"The Snow Lay on the Ground" (Luke)
> E110, G116, S2093, P57

"Joseph Dearest, Joseph Mine" (Luke)
> N105, S2099, SF2099

"Love Has Come" (Luke, Advent, Christmas)
> EL292, G110, WS3059

"Come, Let Us Dream" (Luke)
> WS3157

Additional Contemporary Suggestions

"Gentle Shepherd" (Mic, Advent)
> WS3096

"Ancient of Days" (Mic)
> M1

"Good to Me" (Mic, Luke)
> M164

"Shout to the North" (Mic, Luke)
> G319, M99, WS3042

"You Are My All in All" (Mic, Heb, Luke)
> G519, SP220, WS3040

"The King of Glory Comes" (Mic, Luke)
> B127, S2091, SF2091, W501

"Praise to the Lord" (Luke)
> EL844, S2029, SF2029, VU835

"Glory to God" ("Gloria a Dios") (Luke)
> EL164, G585, S2033, SF2033

"The Virgin Mary Had a Baby Boy" (Luke)
> S2098, VU73

"Holy Ground" (Luke)
> B224, C112, G406, S2272, SF2272, SP86

"God Is So Good" (Luke)
> B23, G658, S2056, SF2056

"How Great You Are" (Luke)
> WS3015

"Make Way" (Luke)
> WS3044

"Your Grace Is Enough" (Luke)
> M191, WS3106

"Mary Had a Little Lamb" (Luke)
> WS3190

"O Magnify the Lord" (Luke)
> SP77

Vocal Solos

"He Shall Feed His Flock" (Mic)
> V-2
> V-8   p. 334

"To Touch His Tiny Hand" (Luke)
> V-10   p. 22

Anthems

"Come, My Light" (Mic, Luke)
Anne Krentz Organ; AEC-2 p. 30
2-part mixed and piano (bit.ly/AEC-2-30)

"Joy to the World" (Mic, Luke)
Arr. Mark Patterson; Choristers Guild CGA1258
Unison/2-part and piano (bit.ly/CGA1258)

Other Suggestions

Visuals:
> **O**   Bethlehem, Christ feeding sheep, globe
> **P**   Mary, arm, toppled throne, feed, full/empty bowls
> **E**   Scroll, open Bible, cross/manger
> **G**   Pregnant women, greeting, Luke 1:42b

Call to Worship or Litany: N825 (Luke)
Canticle: C131, N732, UM199. "Magnificat" (Luke)
Words of Assurance: N840 (Luke)
Response: N192, UM300. "O the Lamb" (Heb)
Prayers: WSL6, WSL148, and N873 (Luke)

Isaiah 9:2-7

2 The people walking in darkness have seen a great light.
 On those living in a pitch-dark land, light has dawned.
3You have made the nation great;
 you have increased its joy.
They rejoiced before you as with joy at the harvest,
 as those who divide plunder rejoice.
4As on the day of Midian, you've shattered the yoke that burdened them,
 the staff on their shoulders,
 and the rod of their oppressor.
5Because every boot of the thundering warriors,
 and every garment rolled in blood
 will be burned, fuel for the fire.
6A child is born to us, a son is given to us,
 and authority will be on his shoulders.
He will be named
Wonderful Counselor, Mighty God,
Eternal Father, Prince of Peace.
7There will be vast authority and endless peace
 for David's throne and for his kingdom,
 establishing and sustaining it
 with justice and righteousness
 now and forever.
The zeal of the LORD of heavenly forces will do this.

Psalm 96 (G304/639, N684, P216/217, UM815)

Sing to the LORD a new song!
 Sing to the LORD, all the earth!
2Sing to the LORD! Bless his name!
 Share the news of his saving work every single day!
3Declare God's glory among the nations;
 declare his wondrous works among all people
 4because the LORD is great and so worthy of praise.
He is awesome beyond all other gods
 5because all the gods of the nations are just idols,
 but it is the LORD who created heaven!
6Greatness and grandeur are in front of him;
 strength and beauty are in his sanctuary.
7Give to the LORD, all families of the nations—
 give to the LORD glory and power!
8Give to the LORD the glory due his name!
 Bring gifts!
 Enter his courtyards!
9Bow down to the LORD in his holy splendor!
 Tremble before him, all the earth!
10Tell the nations, "The LORD rules!
 Yes, he set the world firmly in place;
 it won't be shaken.
 He will judge all people fairly."
11Let heaven celebrate! Let the earth rejoice!
 Let the sea and everything in it roar!
 12Let the countryside and everything in it celebrate!
 Then all the trees of the forest too
  will shout out joyfully
  13before the LORD because he is coming!
He is coming to establish justice on the earth!
 He will establish justice in the world rightly.
 He will establish justice among all people fairly.

Titus 2:11-14

11The grace of God has appeared, bringing salvation to all people. 12It educates us so that we can live sensible, ethical, and godly lives right now by rejecting ungodly lives and the desires of this world. 13At the same time we wait for the blessed hope and the glorious appearance of our great God and savior Jesus Christ. 14He gave himself for us in order to rescue us from every kind of lawless behavior, and cleanse a special people for himself who are eager to do good actions.

Luke 2:1-20

In those days Caesar Augustus declared that everyone throughout the empire should be enrolled in the tax lists. 2This first enrollment occurred when Quirinius governed Syria.3Everyone went to their own cities to be enrolled. 4Since Joseph belonged to David's house and family line, he went up from the city of Nazareth in Galilee to David's city, called Bethlehem, in Judea. 5He went to be enrolled together with Mary, who was promised to him in marriage and who was pregnant. 6While they were there, the time came for Mary to have her baby. 7She gave birth to her firstborn child, a son, wrapped him snugly, and laid him in a manger, because there was no place for them in the guestroom.

8Nearby shepherds were living in the fields, guarding their sheep at night. 9The Lord's angel stood before them, the Lord's glory shone around them, and they were terrified.

10The angel said, "Don't be afraid! Look! I bring good news to you—wonderful, joyous news for all people. 11Your savior is born today in David's city. He is Christ the Lord. 12This is a sign for you: you will find a newborn baby wrapped snugly and lying in a manger." 13Suddenly a great assembly of the heavenly forces was with the angel praising God. They said, 14"Glory to God in heaven, and on earth peace among those whom he favors."

15When the angels returned to heaven, the shepherds said to each other, "Let's go right now to Bethlehem and see what's happened. Let's confirm what the Lord has revealed to us."16They went quickly and found Mary and Joseph, and the baby lying in the manger. 17When they saw this, they reported what they had been told about this child. 18Everyone who heard it was amazed at what the shepherds told them. 19Mary committed these things to memory and considered them carefully. 20The shepherds returned home, glorifying and praising God for all they had heard and seen. Everything happened just as they had been told.

Primary Hymns and Songs for the Day

"Angels We Have Heard on High" (Luke) (O)
    B100, C155, E96, EL289, F192, G113, L71, P23, N125,
    UM238, VU38 (Fr.), W376
        H-3   Hbl-47; Chr-31; Desc-43; Org-45
"Born in the Night, Mary's Child" (Isa)
    G158, N152, P30, VU95
"Hark! the Herald Angels Sing" (Isa)
    B88, C150, E87, EL270, F184, G119, L60, N144, P31, UM240
    (PD), VU48, W387
"It Came Upon the Midnight Clear" (Isa, Luke)
    B93, C153, E89, EL282, F197, G123, L54, N131, P38, UM218
    (PD), VU44, W400
        H-3   Hbl-72; Chr-113; Desc-22; Org-19
        S-2   #39. Descant
"Silent Night" (Luke) (C)
    B91, C145, E111, EL281, F195, G122, L65, N134, P60,
    UM239 (PD), VU67 (Fr.), W379
        H-3   Hbl-92; Chr-171; Desc-99; Org-159
        S-1   #322. Descant
               #323. Guitar/Autoharp chords
        S-2   #167. Handbell Arr.

Additional Hymn Suggestions

"Angels from the Realms of Glory" (Isa)
    B94, C149, E93, EL275, F190, G143, L50, N126, P22, UM220
    (PD), VU36, W377
"Break Forth, O Beauteous Heavenly Light" (Isa)
    B114 (PD), E91, F207, G130, N140, P26, UM223, VU83
"On Christmas Night" (Isa, Titus, Luke)
    EL274, G112, N143, WS3064
"Love Has Come" (Titus)
    EL292, G110, WS3059
"Good Christian Friends, Rejoice" (Luke)
    B96, C164, E107 (PD), EL288, F177, G132, L55, N129, P28,
    UM224, VU35, W391
"Infant Holy, Infant Lowly" (Luke)
    B106, C163, EL276, F194, G128, P37, UM229, VU58
"O Little Town of Bethlehem" (Luke)
    B86, C144, E78/79, EL279, F178, G121, L41, N133, P43/44,
    UM230, VU64, W386
"O Come, All Ye Faithful" (Luke)
    B89, C148, E83, EL283, F193, G133, L45, N135, P41, UM234
    (PD), VU60 (Fr.), W392
"While Shepherds Watched Their Flocks" (Luke)
    C154, E94/95, F175, G117/118, P58, UM236, VU75
"That Boy-Child of Mary" (Luke)
    B110, EL293, G139, P55, UM241
" 'Twas in the Moon of Wintertime" (Luke)
    C166, E114, EL284, G142, N151, P61, UM244, VU71
"The First Noel" (Luke)
    B85, C151, E109, EL300, F179, G147, L56, N139, P56,
    UM245 (PD), VU90 (Fr.) and VU91, W408
"The Snow Lay on the Ground" (Luke)
    E110, G116, S2093, P57
"Joseph Dearest, Joseph Mine" (Luke)
    N105, S2099, SF2099
"I Come with Joy" (Comm.)
    B371, C420, E304, EL482, G515, N349, P507, UM617,
    VU477, W726

Additional Contemporary Suggestions

"King of Kings" (Isa)
    B234, S2075, SF2075, SP94, VU167

"Song of Hope" (Isa)
    G765, P432, S2186, VU424
"How Majestic Is Your Name" (Isa)
    C63, G613, S2023, SF2023, SP14
"Jesus, Name above All Names" (Isa)
    S2071, SF2071, SP76
"His Name Is Wonderful" (Isa)
    B203, F230, SP90, UM174
"You Are Holy" ("Prince of Peace") (Isa)
    G705, M129
"Marvelous Light" (Isa)
    M249
"Here I Am to Worship" (Isa, Luke)
    M116, WS3177
"Jesus, Jesus, Oh, What a Wonderful Child" (Isa, Luke)
    AH4039, EL297, G126, N136, WS3060
"How Great Is Our God" (Pss)
    WS3003, M117
"Shout to the North" (Pss)
    G319, M99, WS3042
"Blessed Be the Name of the Lord" (Pss)
    M12, S2034, SF2034, UM63
"Shout to the Lord" (Pss)
    EL821, S2074, SF2074, M16; V-3 (2) p. 32 Vocal Solo
"Majesty" (Pss)
    B215, SP73, UM176
"Sing Alleluia to the Lord" (Titus, Comm.)
    B214, C32, S2258, SF2258, SP93
"Lord, I Lift Your Name on High" (Luke)
    EL857, M2, S2088, SF2088
"Glory in the Highest" (Luke)
    M231

Vocal Solos

"O Holy Night" (Luke)
    V-8   p. 93
"Sing Noel!" (Luke)
    V-11   p. 13

Anthems

"Before the Marvel of This Night" (Luke)
Carl Schalk; AEC-1 p. 14
2-part mixed and keyboard (bit.ly/AEC-1-14)

"While Shepherds Watched Their Flocks" (Luke)
John Carter; AEC-2 p. 90
3-part mixed and piano

Other Suggestions

Visuals:
    O   Light, yoke, rod, infant Jesus, Isa 9:6b, crown
    P   All nature, gifts and offerings, gold
    E   Gold cross, glory, sacrifice
    G   Infant Jesus, manger, nativity scene, shepherds, angels
Canticle: UM83. "Canticle of God's Glory" (Luke)
Prayer: WSL8, UM231, F188, WSL126 (Christmas, Luke, Titus)
Readings: C152, F186, F196, F204 (Luke)
Call to Communion: WS3055. "Come, Little Children" (Luke)
Response: EL164, G585, S2033, SF2033. "Glory to God" ("*Gloria
    a Dios*") (Luke)
*Alternate Scriptures for Christmas Day: Isa 52:7-10, Ps 98, Heb 1:1-4
    (5-12), John 1:1-14*

1 Samuel 2:18-20, 26

[18]Now Samuel was serving the LORD. He was a young boy, clothed in a linen priestly vest. [19]His mother would make a small robe for him and take it to him every year when she went up with her husband to offer the annual sacrifice. [20]Eli would bless Elkanah and his wife: "May the LORD replace the child of this woman that you gave back to the LORD." Then they would return home. . . .

[26]Meanwhile, the boy Samuel kept growing up and was more and more liked by both the LORD and the people.

Psalm 148 (G17/18/679, N721, P256, UM861)

Praise the LORD!
Praise the LORD from heaven!
    Praise God on the heights!
[2]Praise God, all of you who are his messengers!
    Praise God, all of you who comprise his heavenly forces!
[3]Sun and moon, praise God!
    All of you bright stars, praise God!
[4]You highest heaven, praise God!
    Do the same, you waters that are above the sky!
[5]Let all of these praise the LORD's name
    because God gave the command and they were created!
[6]God set them in place always and forever.
    God made a law that will not be broken.
[7]Praise the LORD from the earth,
    you sea monsters and all you ocean depths!
[8]Do the same, fire and hail, snow and smoke,
    stormy wind that does what God says!
[9]Do the same, you mountains, every single hill,
    fruit trees, and every single cedar!
[10]Do the same, you animals—wild or tame—
    you creatures that creep along and you birds that fly!
[11]Do the same, you kings of the earth and every single person,
    you princes and every single ruler on earth!
[12]Do the same, you young men—young women too!—
    you who are old together with you who are young!
[13]Let all of these praise the LORD's name
    because only God's name is high over all.
    Only God's majesty is over earth and heaven.
[14]God raised the strength of his people,
    the praise of all his faithful ones—
        that's the Israelites,
        the people who are close to him.
Praise the LORD!

Colossians 3:12-17

[12]Therefore, as God's choice, holy and loved, put on compassion, kindness, humility, gentleness, and patience. [13]Be tolerant with each other and, if someone has a complaint against anyone, forgive each other. As the LORD forgave you, so also forgive each other. [14]And over all these things put on love, which is the perfect bond of unity. [15]The peace of Christ must control your hearts—a peace into which you were called in one body. And be thankful people. [16]The word of Christ must live in you richly. Teach and warn each other with all wisdom by singing psalms, hymns, and spiritual songs. Sing to God with gratitude in your hearts. [17]Whatever you do, whether in speech or action, do it all in the name of the Lord Jesus and give thanks to God the Father through him.

Luke 2:41-52

[41]Each year his parents went to Jerusalem for the Passover Festival. [42]When he was 12 years old, they went up to Jerusalem according to their custom. [43]After the festival was over, they were returning home, but the boy Jesus stayed behind in Jerusalem. His parents didn't know it. [44]Supposing that he was among their band of travelers, they journeyed on for a full day while looking for him among their family and friends. [45]When they didn't find Jesus, they returned to Jerusalem to look for him. [46]After three days they found him in the temple. He was sitting among the teachers, listening to them and putting questions to them. [47]Everyone who heard him was amazed by his understanding and his answers. [48]When his parents saw him, they were shocked.

His mother said, "Child, why have you treated us like this? Listen! Your father and I have been worried. We've been looking for you!"

[49]Jesus replied, "Why were you looking for me? Didn't you know that it was necessary for me to be in my Father's house?" [50]But they didn't understand what he said to them.

[51]Jesus went down to Nazareth with them and was obedient to them. His mother cherished every word in her heart. [52]Jesus matured in wisdom and years, and in favor with God and with people.

Primary Hymns and Songs for the Day

"Once in Royal David's City" (Luke, Christmas) (O)
　　C165, EL269, G140, N45, P49, UM250 (PD), VU62
　　　　H-3　　Hbl-83; Chr-68, 156; Desc-57; Org-63
　　　　S-1　　#182-184. Various treatments
"O Sing a Song of Bethlehem" (Luke)
　　B120, F208, G159, N51, P308, UM179 (PD)
　　　　H-3　　Hbl-15, 20, 34, 84; Chr-150; Org-67
　　　　S-2　　#100-103. Various treatments
"Infant Holy, Infant Lowly" (Luke, Christmas)
　　B106, C163, EL276, F194, G128, P37, UM229, VU58
　　　　H-3　　Chr-113; Desc-102; Org-171
　　　　S-1　　#345. Handbell/keyboard Arr.
"That Boy-Child of Mary" (Luke, Christmas)
　　B110, EL293, G139, P55, UM241
　　　　H-3　　Chr-179
　　　　S-1　　#45. Guitar/autoharp chords
　　　　S-2　　#28. Flute descant
"Go, Tell It on the Mountain" (Christmas) (C)
　　B95, C167, E99, EL290, F205, G136, L70, N154, P29, UM251, VU43, W397
　　　　H-3　　Hbl-17, 28, 61; Chr-73; Desc-45; Org-46

Additional Hymn Suggestions

"O Splendor of God's Glory Bright" (1 Sam)
　　E5, G666, N87, P474, UM679, VU413
"For the Beauty of the Earth" (1 Sam, Pss)
　　B44, C56, E416, EL879, F1, G14, L561, P473, N28, UM92 (PD), VU226, W557
"Holy God, We Praise Thy Name" (Col)
　　E366, F385, EL414 (PD), G4, L535, N276, P460, UM79, VU894 (Fr.), W524
"Jesus Shall Reign" (Col)
　　B587, C95, E544, EL434, F238, G265, L530, N157, P423, UM157 (PD), VU330, W492
"At the Font We Start Our Journey" (Col, New Year)
　　N308, S2114, SF2114
"In the Lord I'll Be Ever Thankful" (Col)
　　G654, S2195, SF2195
"My Life Flows On" ("How Can I Keep from Singing") (Col)
　　C619, EL763, G821, N476, S2212, SF2212, VU716
"When the Morning Stars Together" (Col)
　　G689, N453, P486
"In the Midst of New Dimensions" (Col)
　　G315, N391, S2238, SF2238
"Hark! the Herald Angels Sing" (Luke)
　　B88, C150, E87, EL270, F184, G119, L60, N144, P31, UM240 (PD), VU48, W387
"Love Came Down at Christmas" (Luke, Christmas)
　　B109, E84, N165, UM242
"We Meet You, O Christ" (Luke)
　　C183, P311, UM257, VU183
"God the Sculptor of the Mountains" (Luke)
　　EL736, G5, S2060, SF2060
"Like a Child" (Luke)
　　C133, S2092, SF2092, VU366
"Hark! the Herald Angels Sing" ("Jesus, the Light of the World") (Luke)
　　G127, N160

Additional Contemporary Suggestions

"Praise to the Lord" (1 Sam)
　　EL844, S2029, SF2029, VU835
"Praise, Praise, Praise the Lord" (Pss)
　　EL875, G390, S2035, SF2035

"God of Wonders" (Pss)
　　M80, WS3034
"Let Everything That Has Breath" (Pss)
　　M59
"Indescribable" (Pss)
　　M127
"Glory in the Highest" (Pss, Christmas)
　　M231
"Dwell" (Col)
　　M154
"Give Thanks" (Col)
　　C528, G647, S2036, SF2036, SP170
"Make Me a Channel of Your Peace" (Col)
　　G753, S2171, SF2171, VU684
"Song of Hope" (Col)
　　G765, P432, S2186, VU424
"Make Us One" (Col)
　　S2224, SF2224, SP137
"Bind Us Together" (Col)
　　S2226, SF2226, SP140
"No Sweeter Name" (Col)
　　M245
"Jesus, Jesus, Oh, What a Wonderful Child" (Luke)
　　AH4039, EL297, G126, N136, WS3060
"Born in the Night, Mary's Child" (Luke)
　　G158, N152, P30, VU95

Vocal Solos

"Bright and Beautiful" (1 Sam, Pss)
　　V-3 (3)　　p. 10
"Because You Are God's Chosen Ones" (Col)
　　V-8　　p. 286
"Gentle Jesus, Meek and Mild" (Luke, Christmas)
　　V-1　　p. 11
"Jesus, What a Wonderful Child" (Luke, Christmas)
　　V-5(1)　　p. 48
"Welcome to Our World" (Luke, Christmas)
　　WS3067
　　V-5(1)　　p. 34

Anthems

"Beloved, God's Chosen" (Col)
Robert A. Hobby; MorningStar MSM-50-8707
2-part mixed and piano and flute (bit.ly/50-8707)

"Once in Royal David's City" (Luke)
Joseph Martin; Jubilate Music 9172236
SATB and piano (bit.ly/9172236)

Other Suggestions

Visuals:
　　O　　Twelve-year-old boy, growing children, graduated sizes (clothes)
　　P　　Stars, planets, moon; nature imagery, single horn
　　E　　Clothes, compassion, forgiveness, singing, Col 3:16, 17b
　　G　　Growing boy, parents, child with teachers, glue or cord
Introit: C575, S2128, SF2128, VU374. "Come and Find the Quiet Center" (Col)
Canticle: UM646. "Canticle of Love" (Col)
Confession and Assurance: N832, N837, and N839 (Christmas)

Ecclesiastes 3:1-13

There's a season for everything
and a time for every matter under the heavens:
²a time for giving birth and a time for dying,
a time for planting and a time for uprooting what was
planted,
³a time for killing and a time for healing,
a time for tearing down and a time for building up,
⁴a time for crying and a time for laughing,
a time for mourning and a time for dancing,
⁵a time for throwing stones and a time for gathering stones,
a time for embracing and a time for avoiding embraces,
⁶a time for searching and a time for losing,
a time for keeping and a time for throwing away,
⁷a time for tearing and a time for repairing,
a time for keeping silent and a time for speaking,
⁸a time for loving and a time for hating,
a time for war and a time for peace.

⁹What do workers gain from all their hard work? ¹⁰I have observed the task that God has given human beings. ¹¹God has made everything fitting in its time, but has also placed eternity in their hearts, without enabling them to discover what God has done from beginning to end.

¹²I know that there's nothing better for them but to enjoy themselves and do what's good while they live. ¹³Moreover, this is the gift of God: that all people should eat, drink, and enjoy the results of their hard work.

Psalm 8 (G25, N624, P162/163, UM743)

Lord, our Lord, how majestic
is your name throughout the earth!
You made your glory higher than heaven!
²From the mouths of nursing babies
you have laid a strong foundation
because of your foes,
in order to stop vengeful enemies.
³When I look up at your skies,
at what your fingers made—
the moon and the stars
that you set firmly in place—
⁴what are human beings
that you think about them;
what are human beings
that you pay attention to them?
⁵You've made them only slightly less than divine,
crowning them with glory and grandeur.
⁶You've let them rule over your handiwork,
putting everything under their feet—
⁷all sheep and all cattle,
the wild animals too,
⁸the birds in the sky,
the fish of the ocean,
everything that travels the pathways of the sea.
⁹Lord, our Lord, how majestic is your name throughout the
earth!

Revelation 21:1-6a

Then I saw a new heaven and a new earth, for the former heaven and the former earth had passed away, and the sea was no more. 2I saw the holy city, New Jerusalem, coming down out of heaven from God, made ready as a bride beautifully dressed for her husband. 3I heard a loud voice from the throne say, "Look! God's dwelling is here with humankind. He will dwell with them, and they will be his peoples. God himself will be with them as their God. ⁴He will wipe away every tear from their eyes. Death will be no more. There will be no mourning, crying, or pain anymore, for the former things have passed away."⁵Then the one seated on the throne said, "Look! I'm making all things new." He also said, "Write this down, for these words are trustworthy and true." ⁶ᵃThen he said to me, "All is done. I am the Alpha and the Omega, the beginning and the end."

Matthew 25:31-46

³¹"Now when the Human One comes in his majesty and all his angels are with him, he will sit on his majestic throne.³²All the nations will be gathered in front of him. He will separate them from each other, just as a shepherd separates the sheep from the goats. ³³He will put the sheep on his right side. But the goats he will put on his left.

³⁴"Then the king will say to those on his right, 'Come, you who will receive good things from my Father. Inherit the kingdom that was prepared for you before the world began. ³⁵I was hungry and you gave me food to eat. I was thirsty and you gave me a drink. I was a stranger and you welcomed me. ³⁶I was naked and you gave me clothes to wear. I was sick and you took care of me. I was in prison and you visited me.'

³⁷"Then those who are righteous will reply to him, 'Lord, when did we see you hungry and feed you, or thirsty and give you a drink? ³⁸When did we see you as a stranger and welcome you, or naked and give you clothes to wear? ³⁹When did we see you sick or in prison and visit you?'

⁴⁰"Then the king will reply to them, 'I assure you that when you have done it for one of the least of these brothers and sisters of mine, you have done it for me.'

⁴¹"Then he will say to those on his left, 'Get away from me, you who will receive terrible things. Go into the unending fire that has been prepared for the devil and his angels. ⁴²I was hungry and you didn't give me food to eat. I was thirsty and you didn't give me anything to drink. ⁴³I was a stranger and you didn't welcome me. I was naked and you didn't give me clothes to wear. I was sick and in prison, and you didn't visit me.'

⁴⁴"Then they will reply, 'Lord, when did we see you hungry or thirsty or a stranger or naked or sick or in prison and didn't do anything to help you?' ⁴⁵ Then he will answer, 'I assure you that when you haven't done it for one of the least of these, you haven't done it for me.' ⁴⁶ And they will go away into eternal punishment. But the righteous ones will go into eternal life."

Primary Hymns and Songs for the Day

"O God, Our Help in Ages Past" (Pss, Rev) (O)
  B74, C67, E680, EL632, F370, G687, L320, N25, P210,
  UM117 (PD), VU806, W579
          H-3   Hbl-33, 80; Chr-143; Desc-93; Org-132
          S-1   #293-296. Various treatments
"How Great Thou Art" (Pss)
  B10, C33, EL856, G625, N35, P467, UM77, VU238
          H-3   Chr-103; Org-105
          S-1   #163. Harm.
"This Is a Day of New Beginnings" (Rev)
  B370, C518, N417, UM383, W661
          H-3   Chr-196
"In Remembrance of Me" (Matt, Comm.)
  B365, C403, G521, S2254
"Hymn of Promise" (Eccl) (C)
  C638, G250. N433, UM707, VU703
          H-3   Chr-112; Org-117
          S-1   #270. Descant

Additional Hymn Suggestions

"O God, in a Mysterious Way" (Eccl)
  B73, E677, F603, G30, L483, N412, P270
"For the Beauty of the Earth" (Eccl)
  B44, C56, E416, EL879, F1, G14, L561, P473, N28, UM92
  (PD), VU226, W557
"Sing Praise to God Who Reigns Above" (Eccl)
  B20, C6, E408, EL871, F343, G645, N6, P483, UM126 (PD),
  VU216, W528
"Great Is Thy Faithfulness" (Eccl)
  B54, C86, EL733, G39, N423, P276, UM140, VU288
"Many and Great, O God" (Eccl)
  B49, C58, E385, EL837, G21, N3, N341, P271 (PD), UM148,
  VU308, W503
"Rejoice! Rejoice, Believers" (Rev)
  E68, EL244, G362, L25, P15
"We Shall Overcome" (Rev)
  C630, G379, N570, UM533
"O Holy City, Seen of John" (Rev)
  E582/583, G374, N613, P453, UM726, VU709
"There's a Spirit in the Air" (Rev, Matt)
  B393, C257, N294, P433, UM192, VU582, W531
"For the Healing of the Nations" (Rev, Matt)
  C668, G346, N576, UM428, VU678, W643
"We Praise You, O God, Our Redeemer" (Matt)
  B19, F334, EL870, G612, L241, N420, VU218
"If Thou But Suffer God to Guide Thee" (Matt)
  B57, C565, E635, EL769, G816, L453, N410, P282, UM142
  (PD), VU285 (Fr.) and VU286
"Morning Has Broken" (Matt)
  B48, C53, E8, EL556, F5, G664, P469, UM145, VU409
"Where Cross the Crowded Ways of Life" (Matt)
  C665, E609, EL719, G343, L429, N543, P408, UM427
"As We Gather at Your Table" (Matt, Comm.)
  EL522, N332, S2268, SF2268, VU457

Additional Contemporary Suggestions

"In His Time" (Eccl)
  B53, S2203, SF2203, SP39
"I Could Sing of Your Love Forever" (Eccl)
  M63
"We Will Dance" (Eccl)
  M140
"The Happy Song" (Eccl)
  M167

"God of Wonders" (Pss)
  M80, WS3034
"How Majestic Is Your Name" (Pss)
  C63, G613, S2023, SF2023, SP14
"God with Us" (Pss, Christmas)
  M252
"There's Something About That Name" (Rev)
  B177, C115, F227, SP89, UM171
"Spirit Song" (Rev)
  C352, SP134, UM347
"Soon and Very Soon" (Rev)
  B192, EL439, G384, UM706, S-2 #187. Piano arr.
"We Will Glorify" (Rev)
  B213, S2087, SF2087, SP68
"There Is a Higher Throne" (Rev)
  WS3189
"Blessing, Honour and Glory" (Rev)
  EL433, M21
"How Great Is Our God" (Rev)
  WS3003, M117
"You Are Holy" ("Prince of Peace") (Rev)
  G705, M129
"All Who Are Thirsty" (Rev)
  M159
"Happy Day" (Rev)
  M221
"Sing to the King" (Matt)
  M141
"People Need the Lord" (Matt)
  B557, S2244, SF2244

Vocal Solos

"I Will Sing of Thy Great Mercies" (Eccl)
  V-4   p. 43
"Reach Out to Your Neighbor" (Matt)
  V-8   p. 372
"A Covenant Prayer" (New Year)
  V-11   p. 6

Anthems

"To Everything a Season" (Eccl)
Taylor Davis; Choristers Guild CGA1347
SATB with piano, opt. oboe (bit.ly/CGA1347)

"In All These You Welcomed Me" (Matt)
William Bradley Roberts; AEC-2 p. 63
Unison/mixed and organ (bit.ly/AEC-2-63)

Other Suggestions

Visuals:
  O   Seasons, birth/death, workers, time piece, joy, gift
  P   Ps 8:1, infants, moon, stars, people, crown, sheep,
           birds, sea
  E   Heaven/earth, bride, handkerchief, newness, Alpha/
           Omega
  G   Christ, angels, nations, sheep/goats, ministry, fire,
Introit: M90, WS3103. "Purify My Heart" (Matt, New Year)
Prayer of Confession: N836 or WSL87 (Matt, New Year)
Readings: B617, C157, C473, F308, WSL80, and WSL98 (Matt)
Canticle: UM734. "Canticle of Hope" (Rev)

Isaiah 60:1-6

Arise! Shine! Your light has come;
    the LORD's glory has shone upon you.
[2]Though darkness covers the earth
    and gloom the nations,
    the LORD will shine upon you;
    God's glory will appear over you.
[3]Nations will come to your light
    and kings to your dawning radiance.
[4]Lift up your eyes and look all around:
    they are all gathered; they have come to you.
Your sons will come from far away,
    and your daughters on caregivers' hips.
[5]Then you will see and be radiant;
    your heart will tremble and open wide,
    because the sea's abundance will be turned over to you;
    the nations' wealth will come to you.
[6]Countless camels will cover your land,
    young camels from Midian and Ephah.
They will all come from Sheba,
    carrying gold and incense,
    proclaiming the LORD's praises.

Psalm 72:1-7, 10-14 (G149, N667, P204/205, UM795)

God, give your judgments to the king.
    Give your righteousness to the king's son.
[2]Let him judge your people with righteousness
    and your poor ones with justice.
[3]Let the mountains bring peace to the people;
    let the hills bring righteousness.
[4]Let the king bring justice to people who are poor;
    let him save the children of those who are needy,
        but let him crush oppressors!
[5]Let the king live as long as the sun,
    as long as the moon,
        generation to generation.
[6]Let him fall like rain upon fresh-cut grass,
    like showers that water the earth.
[7]Let the righteous flourish throughout their lives,
    and let peace prosper until the moon is no more.
. . . .
[10]Let the kings of Tarshish and the islands bring tribute;
    let the kings of Sheba and Seba present gifts.
[11]Let all the kings bow down before him;
    let all the nations serve him.
[12]Let it be so, because he delivers the needy who cry out,
    the poor, and those who have no helper.
[13]He has compassion on the weak and the needy;
    he saves the lives of those who are in need.
[14]He redeems their lives from oppression and violence;
    their blood is precious in his eyes.

Ephesians 3:1-12

This is why I, Paul, am a prisoner of Christ for you Gentiles.
[2]You've heard, of course, about the responsibility to distribute God's grace, which God gave to me for you, right? [3]God showed me his secret plan in a revelation, as I mentioned briefly before ([4]when you read this, you'll understand my insight into the secret plan about Christ). [5]Earlier generations didn't know this hidden plan that God has now revealed to his holy apostles and prophets through the Spirit. [6]This plan is that the Gentiles would be coheirs and parts of the same body, and that they would share with the Jews in the promises of God in Christ Jesus through the gospel. [7]I became a servant of the gospel because of the grace that God showed me through the exercise of his power.

[8]God gave his grace to me, the least of all God's people, to preach the good news about the immeasurable riches of Christ to the Gentiles. [9]God sent me to reveal the secret plan that had been hidden since the beginning of time by God, who created everything. [10]God's purpose is now to show the rulers and powers in the heavens the many different varieties of his wisdom through the church. [11]This was consistent with the plan he had from the beginning of time that he accomplished through Christ Jesus our Lord. [12]In Christ we have bold and confident access to God through faith in him.

Matthew 2:1-12

After Jesus was born in Bethlehem in the territory of Judea during the rule of King Herod, magi came from the east to Jerusalem. [2]They asked, "Where is the newborn king of the Jews? We've seen his star in the east, and we've come to honor him."

[3]When King Herod heard this, he was troubled, and everyone in Jerusalem was troubled with him. [4]He gathered all the chief priests and the legal experts and asked them where the Christ was to be born. [5]They said, "In Bethlehem of Judea, for this is what the prophet wrote:

  [6]*You, Bethlehem, land of Judah,*
    by no means are you least among the rulers of Judah,
      because from you will come one who governs,
      who will shepherd my people Israel."

[7]Then Herod secretly called for the magi and found out from them the time when the star had first appeared. [8]He sent them to Bethlehem, saying, "Go and search carefully for the child. When you've found him, report to me so that I too may go and honor him." [9]When they heard the king, they went; and look, the star they had seen in the east went ahead of them until it stood over the place where the child was. [10]When they saw the star, they were filled with joy. [11]They entered the house and saw the child with Mary his mother. Falling to their knees, they honored him. Then they opened their treasure chests and presented him with gifts of gold, frankincense, and myrrh. [12]Because they were warned in a dream not to return to Herod, they went back to their own country by another route.

Primary Hymns and Songs for the Day

"Angels from the Realms of Glory" (Matt) (O)
    B94, C149, E93, EL275, F190, G143, L50, N126, P22, UM220
    (PD), VU36, W377
        H-3   Chr-30, 48, 62; Desc-89; Org-121
        S-1   #280. Desc. and Harm.
"What Child Is This" (Matt)
    B118, C162, E115, EL296, F180, G145, L40, N148, P53,
    UM219 (PD), VU74, W411
        H-3   Hbl-102; Chr-210; Desc-46; Org-47
        S-1   #150. Guitar chords
"We Three Kings" (Matt)
    B113, C172, E128, F206, G151, P66, UM254 (PD), W406
        H-3   Chr-208; Org-65
        S-2   #97-98. Various treatments
"What Star Is This, with Beams So Bright" (Matt)
    E124, G152, P68, W407
"In Bethlehem a Newborn Boy" (Matt)
    E246, G153, P35 (PD), VU77
"The First Noel" (Matt) (C)
    B85, C151, E109, EL300, F179, G147, L56, N139, P56,
    UM245 (PD), VU90 (Fr.) and VU91, W408
        H-3   Hbl-95; Chr-182; Desc-100; Org-161
        S-1   #328-330. Various treatments

Additional Hymn Suggestions

"O Splendor of God's Glory Bright" (Isa)
    E5, G666, N87, P474, UM679, VU413
"Awake! Awake, and Greet the New Morn" (Isa)
    C138, EL242, G107, N107, W360
"Arise, Your Light Is Come" (Isa)
    B83, EL314, G744, N164, P411, VU79
"Jesus Shall Reign" (Isa, Pss, Eph)
    B587, C95, E544, EL434, F238, G265, L530, N157, P423,
    UM157 (PD), VU330, W492
"Christ, Whose Glory Fills the Skies" (Eph)
    EL553, G662, L265, P462/463, UM173 (PD), VU336
"Ye Servants of God" (Eph)
    B589, C110, E535, EL825 (PD), F360, G299, N305, P477,
    UM181 (PD), VU342
"O Love, How Deep" (Eph)
    E448/449, EL322, G618, L88, N209, P83, UM267, VU348
"What a Friend We Have in Jesus" (Eph)
    B182, C585, EL742, F466, G465, L439, N506, P403, UM526
    (PD), VU661
"Blessed Jesus, at Thy Word" (Eph)
    E440, EL520, G395, N74, P454, UM596 (PD), VU500
"I'm Gonna Live So God Can Use Me" (Eph)
    C614, G700, P369, S2153, VU575
"I Want to Walk as a Child of the Light" (Matt)
    E490, EL815, G377, UM206, W510
"Break Forth, O Beauteous Heavenly Light" (Isa, Matt)
    B114 (PD), E91, F207, G130, N140, P26, UM223, VU83
" 'Twas in the Moon of Wintertime" (Matt)
    C166, E114, EL284, G142, N151, P61, UM244, VU71
"O Morning Star, How Fair and Bright" (Eph, Matt)
    C105, E497, EL308, G827, N158, P69, UM247, VU98
"On This Day Earth Shall Ring" (Matt)
    E92, G141, P46, UM248 (PD)
"Now the Silence" (Matt, Comm.)
    C415, E333, EL460, G534, L205, UM619, VU475, W668
"Rise Up, Shepherd, and Follow" (Matt)
    G135, P50, S2096, SF2096, VU70
"As with Gladness Men of Old" (Matt)
    B117, C173, E119, EL302, G150, L82, N159, P63, VU81

"Who Would Think That What Was Needed" (Matt)
    G138, N153

Additional Contemporary Suggestions

"Shine, Jesus, Shine" (Epiphany)
    B579, EL671, G192, S2173, SF2173, SP142
"Beautiful Savior" (Epiphany)
    M243
"Shine on Us" (Isa, Epiphany)
    M19
"Let It Rise" (Isa)
    M4
"Here I Am to Worship" (Isa, Epiphany)
    M116, WS3177
"Mighty to Save" (Isa)
    M246, WS3038
"Arise Shine" (Isa)
    SP176
"Famous One" (Isa, Matt, Epiphany)
    M126
"We Are Singing" ("Siyahamba") (Isa, Pss, Epiphany)
    C442, EL866, G853, N526, S2235, SF2235, VU646
"Sing, Sing, Sing" (Pss, Matt)
    M235
"Grace Alone" (Eph)
    M100, S2162, SF2162
"We Worship and Adore You" (Matt)
    SP103
"O Praise Him" ("All This for a King") (Matt)
    M133
"Jesus, the Light of the World" (Isa, Matt, Epiphany)
    WS3056

Vocal Solos

"The People That Walked in Darkness" (Isa)
    V-2
"The Kings" (Matt, Epiphany)
    V-9   p. 13

Anthems

"With Wondering Awe" (Matt)
Arr. Neil Harmon; Hinshaw HMC2475
SATB and piano, opt. Instr. (bit.ly/HMC2475)

"The Silent Stars Shine Down on Us" (Matt)
Arr. Thomas Keesecker; AEC-1 p.76
2-part mixed and piano (bit.ly/AEC-1-76)

Other Suggestions

Visuals:
    O   Light/dark, nations, kings, dawn, babes in arms, gold/
         incense
    P   Scales, mountains/hills, poor, sun/moon, rain, grass,
         king
    E   Writing, Christ, all nations
    G   Wise men, star, Bethlehem, infant, Mary, gifts, escape
Introit: WS3185, stanza 1. "Send Us Your Spirit" (Matt)
Prayers: N826, UM255, C19, and WSL11 (Epiphany)
*Alternate scriptures for 2nd Sunday after Christmas: Jer 31:7-14, Ps
    147: 12-20, Eph 1:3-14, John 1:(1-9)10-18.*

Isaiah 43:1-7

But now, says the LORD—
>the one who created you, Jacob,
>the one who formed you, Israel:

Don't fear, for I have redeemed you;
>I have called you by name; you are mine.

²When you pass through the waters, I will be with you;
>when through the rivers, they won't sweep over you.

When you walk through the fire, you won't be scorched
>and flame won't burn you.

³I am the LORD your God,
>the holy one of Israel, your savior.

I have given Egypt as your ransom,
>Cush and Seba in your place.

⁴Because you are precious in my eyes,
>you are honored, and I love you.
>I give people in your place,
>>and nations in exchange for your life.

⁵Don't fear,
>I am with you.

From the east I'll bring your children;
>from the west I'll gather you.

⁶I'll say to the north, "Give them back!"
>and to the south, "Don't detain them."

Bring my sons from far away,
>and my daughters from the end of the earth,
>⁷everyone who is called by my name
>and whom I created for my glory,
>whom I have formed and made.

Psalm 29 (G10/259, N638, P180, UM761)

You, divine beings! Give to the LORD—
>give to the LORD glory and power!

²Give to the LORD the glory due his name!
>Bow down to the LORD in holy splendor!

³The LORD's voice is over the waters;
>the glorious God thunders;
>>the LORD is over the mighty waters.

⁴The LORD's voice is strong;
>the LORD's voice is majestic.

⁵The LORD's voice breaks cedar trees—
>yes, the LORD shatters the cedars of Lebanon.

⁶He makes Lebanon jump around like a young bull,
>makes Sirion jump around like a young wild ox.

⁷The LORD's voice unleashes fiery flames;
>⁸the LORD's voice shakes the wilderness—
>>yes, the LORD shakes the wilderness of Kadesh.

⁹The LORD's voice convulses the oaks,
>strips the forests bare,
>>but in his temple everyone shouts, "Glory!"

¹⁰The LORD sits enthroned over the floodwaters;
>the LORD sits enthroned—king forever!

¹¹Let the LORD give strength to his people!
>Let the LORD bless his people with peace!

Acts 8:14-17

¹⁴When word reached the apostles in Jerusalem that Samaria had accepted God's word, they commissioned Peter and John to go to Samaria. ¹⁵Peter and John went down to Samaria where they prayed that the new believers would receive the Holy Spirit. (¹⁶This was because the Holy Spirit had not yet fallen on any of them; they had only been baptized in the name of the Lord Jesus.) ¹⁷So Peter and John laid their hands on them, and they received the Holy Spirit.

Luke 3:15-17, 21-22

¹⁵The people were filled with expectation, and everyone wondered whether John might be the Christ. ¹⁶John replied to them all, "I baptize you with water, but the one who is more powerful than me is coming. I'm not worthy to loosen the strap of his sandals. He will baptize you with the Holy Spirit and fire.¹⁷The shovel he uses to sift the wheat from the husks is in his hands. He will clean out his threshing area and bring the wheat into his barn. But he will burn the husks with a fire that can't be put out." . . .

²¹When everyone was being baptized, Jesus also was baptized. While he was praying, heaven was opened ²²and the Holy Spirit came down on him in bodily form like a dove. And there was a voice from heaven: "You are my Son, whom I dearly love; in you I find happiness."

Primary Hymns and Songs for the Day

"Praise to the Lord, the Almighty" (Pss) (O)
   B14, C25, E390, EL858 (PD) and 859, F337, G35, L543, N22,
   P482, UM139, VU220 (Fr.) and VU221, W547
        H-3   Hbl-89; Chr-163; Desc-69; Org-79
        S-1   #218-222. Various treatments

"When Jesus Came to Jordan" (Luke)
   EL305, P72, UM252, W697

"Spirit Song" (Luke)
   C352, SP134, UM347

"Take Me to the Water" (Acts, Luke)
   C367, G480, N322, WS3165

"How Firm a Foundation" (Isa) (C)
   B338, C618, E636/637, EL796, F32, G463, L507, N407, P361,
   UM529 (PD), VU660, W585
        H-3   Hbl-27, 69; Chr-102; Desc-41; Org-41
        S-1   #133. Harm.
               #134. Performance note

Additional Hymn Suggestions

"If Thou But Suffer God to Guide Thee" (Isa)
   B57, C565, E635, EL769, G816, L453, N410, P282, UM142
   (PD), VU285 (Fr.) and VU286

"It Is Well with My Soul" (Isa)
   B410, C561, EL785, F495, G840, L346, N438, UM37

"Rejoice in God's Saints" (Isa)
   C476, EL418, G732, UM708

"You Are Mine" (Isa)
   EL581, G177, S2218, SF2218

"Gather Us In" (Isa)
   C284, EL532, G401, S2236, SF2236, W665

"Go, My Children, with My Blessing" (Isa)
   C431, EL543, G547, N82

"We Praise You, O God, Our Redeemer" (Isa)
   B19, F334, EL870, G612, L241, N420, VU218

"I Was There to Hear Your Borning Cry" (Isa, Luke)
   C75, EL732, G488, N351, S2051, SF2051, VU644

"Of the Father's Love Begotten" (Acts)
   B251, C104, E82, EL295, F172 (PD), G108, L42, N118, P309,
   UM184, VU61, W398

"Breathe on Me, Breath of God" (Acts, Luke, Baptism)
   B241, C254, E508, F161, G286, L488, N292, P316, UM420
   (PD), VU382 (Fr.), W725

"O Spirit of the Living God" (Acts)
   N263, UM539

"Wonder of Wonders" (Acts, Luke, Baptism)
   C378, G489, N328, P499, S2247

"Baptized in Water" (Acts, Luke, Baptism)
   B362, EL456, G482, P492, S2248, W720

"We Were Baptized in Christ Jesus" (Acts, Luke, Baptism)
   EL451, S2251, SF2251

"Sweet, Sweet Spirit" (Luke)
   B243, C261, F159, G408, N293, P398, SP136, UM334

"Spirit of God, Descend upon My Heart" (Luke)
   B245, C265, EL800, F147, G688, L486, N290, P326, UM500
   (PD), VU378

"Wash, O God, Our Sons and Daughters" (Luke, Baptism)
   C365, EL445, G490, UM605, VU442

"This Is the Spirit's Entry Now" (Luke, Baptism)
   EL448, L195, UM608, VU451, W722

"You Have Put On Christ" (Luke, Baptism)
   EL211, G491, UM609, VU452, W112

"We Know That Christ Is Raised" (Luke, Baptism)
   E296, EL449, G485, L189, P495, UM610, VU448, W721

"Child of Blessing, Child of Promise" (Luke, Baptism)
   G486, N325, P498. UM611, VU444

"God the Sculptor of the Mountains" (Luke)
   EL736, G5, S2060, SF2060

"She Comes Sailing on the Wind" (Luke)
   S2122, SF2122, VU380

"On Jordan's Bank the Baptist's Cry" (Luke)
   E76, EL249, G96, L36, N115, P10, W356, VU20

"O Holy Dove of God Descending" (Luke)
   N285

Additional Contemporary Suggestions

"Shout to the North" (Isa)
   G319, M99, WS3042

"Wade in the Water" (Acts, Luke, Baptism)
   C371, EL459 (PD), S2107, SF2107

"I've Just Come from the Fountain" (Acts, Luke)
   S2250, SF2250

"Water, River, Spirit, Grace" (Luke, Baptism)
   C366, N169, S2253, SF2253

"Jesus, Name above All Names" (Luke)
   S2071, SF2071, SP76

"I Know the Lord's Laid His Hands on Me" (Luke)
   S2139, SF2139

"Come, Holy Spirit" (Luke)
   WS3092

"Down to the River to Pray" (Luke, Baptism)
   WS3164

"I Will Never Be (the Same Again)" (Luke)
   M34

"Famous One" (Luke)
   M126

"Great and Mighty Is He" (Luke)
   SP4, M11

Vocal Solos

"Spirit of Faith Come Down" (Luke)
   V-1   p. 43

"Waterlife" (Acts, Luke, Baptism)
   V-5(3)   p. 17

"This Is De Healin' Water" (Acts, Luke)
   V-7   p. 52

Anthems

"Washed Anew" (Luke, Baptism)
Thomas Keesecker; AEC-2 p. 83
SATB and piano, opt. handbells (bit.ly/AEC-2-83)

"Carol of the Baptism" (Luke)
George Brandon; MorningStar MSM-50-2002
2-Part mixed or SAB and organ (bit.ly/50-2002)

Other Suggestions

Visuals:
   O   Clay, water (baptism), fire
   P   Nature images as described
   E   Water, symbols of the Holy Spirit
   G   Water, Holy Spirit, praying hands, dove, flames
Consider a congregational reaffirmation of baptismal covenant.
Introit: EL406, G281, S2118, SF2118, W473. "Holy Spirit, Come
   to Us" (Luke)
Prayers: WSL12, UM253, C364 (Luke, Baptism)

Isaiah 62:1-5

For Zion's sake I won't keep silent,
     and for Jerusalem's sake I won't sit still
     until her righteousness shines out like a light,
     and her salvation blazes like a torch.
[2]Nations will see your righteousness,
     all kings your glory.
You will be called by a new name,
     which the LORD's own mouth will determine.
[3]You will be a splendid garland in the LORD's hand,
     a royal turban in the palm of God's hand.
[4]You will no longer be called Abandoned,
     and your land will no longer be called Deserted.
Instead, you will be called My Delight Is in Her,
     and your land, Married.
     Because the LORD delights in you,
     your land will be cared for once again.
[5]As a young man marries a young woman,
     so your sons will marry you.
     With the joy of a bridegroom because of his bride,
     so your God will rejoice because of you.

Psalm 36:5-10 (G477, N645, P186, UM771)

[5]But your loyal love, LORD, extends to the skies;
     your faithfulness reaches the clouds.
[6]Your righteousness is like the strongest mountains;
     your justice is like the deepest sea.
     LORD, you save both humans and animals.
[7]Your faithful love is priceless, God!
     Humanity finds refuge in the shadow of your wings.
[8]They feast on the bounty of your house;
     you let them drink from your river of pure joy.
[9]Within you is the spring of life.
     In your light, we see light.
[10]Extend your faithful love to those who know you;
     extend your righteousness to those whose heart is right.

1 Corinthians 12:1-11

Brothers and sisters, I don't want you to be ignorant about spiritual gifts. [2]You know that when you were Gentiles you were often misled by false gods that can't even speak. [3]So I want to make it clear to you that no one says, "Jesus is cursed!" when speaking by God's Spirit, and no one can say, "Jesus is Lord," except by the Holy Spirit. [4]There are different spiritual gifts but the same Spirit; [5]and there are different ministries and the same Lord; [6]and there are different activities but the same God who produces all of them in everyone. [7]A demonstration of the Spirit is given to each person for the common good. [8]A word of wisdom is given by the Spirit to one person, a word of knowledge to another according to the same Spirit, [9]faith to still another by the same Spirit, gifts of healing to another in the one Spirit, [10]performance of miracles to another, prophecy to another, the ability to tell spirits apart to another, different kinds of tongues to another, and the interpretation of the tongues to another. [11]All these things are produced by the one and same Spirit who gives what he wants to each person.

John 2:1-11

On the third day there was a wedding in Cana of Galilee. Jesus' mother was there, and [2]Jesus and his disciples were also invited to the celebration. [3]When the wine ran out, Jesus' mother said to him, "They don't have any wine."

[4]Jesus replied, "Woman, what does that have to do with me? My time hasn't come yet."

[5]His mother told the servants, "Do whatever he tells you." [6]Nearby were six stone water jars used for the Jewish cleansing ritual, each able to hold about twenty or thirty gallons.

[7]Jesus said to the servants, "Fill the jars with water," and they filled them to the brim. [8]Then he told them, "Now draw some from them and take it to the headwaiter," and they did. [9]The headwaiter tasted the water that had become wine. He didn't know where it came from, though the servants who had drawn the water knew.

The headwaiter called the groom [10]and said, "Everyone serves the good wine first. They bring out the second-rate wine only when the guests are drinking freely. You kept the good wine until now." [11]This was the first miraculous sign that Jesus did in Cana of Galilee. He revealed his glory, and his disciples believed in him.

Primary Hymns and Songs for the Day

"Immortal, Invisible, God Only Wise" (Pss, 1 Cor) (O)
 B6, C66, E423, EL834, F319, G12, L526, N1, P263, UM103
 (PD), VU264, W512
"Many Gifts, One Spirit" (1 Cor) (O)
 N177, UM114
"Lift Every Voice and Sing" (Isa, MLK Day)
 B627, C631, E599, EL841, G339, L562, N593, P563, UM519
"Great Is Thy Faithfulness" (Isa, Pss)
 B54, C86, EL733, F98, G39, N423, P276, UM140, VU288
"We All Are One in Mission" (1 Cor, MLK Day)
 G733, P435, S2243, SF2243
"Forward Through the Ages" (1 Cor) (C)
 N355, UM555
        H-3   Hbl-59; Chr-156; Org-140

Additional Hymn Suggestions

"Holy God, We Praise Thy Name" (Isa)
 (See esp. Stanzas 5 and 7)
 E366, F385, EL414 (PD), G4, L535, N276, P460, UM79,
 VU894 (Fr.), W524
"Joyful, Joyful, We Adore Thee" (Isa)
 B7, C2, E376, EL836, F377, G611, L551, N4, P464, UM89
 (PD), VU232, W525
"All Hail the Power of Jesus' Name" (Isa)
 B200/201/202, C91/92, E450/451, EL634, F325/326/327,
 G263, L328/329, N304, P142/143, UM154/155, VU334
"Let All Mortal Flesh Keep Silence" (Isa)
 B80, C124, E324, EL490, F166, G347, L198, N345, P5,
 UM626 (PD), VU473 (Fr.), W523
"We've a Story to Tell to the Nations" (Isa, MLK Day)
 B586, C484, F659, UM569 (PD)
"My Lord, What a Morning" (Isa, MLK Day)
 C708, EL438 (PD), G352, P449, UM719, VU708
"Awake, O Sleeper" (1 Cor)
 E547, EL452, UM551, VU566, W586
"Help Us Accept Each Other" (1 Cor, MLK Day)
 C487, G754, N388, P358, UM560, W656
"Blest Be the Dear Uniting Love" (1 Cor, MLK Day)
 B387, C433, EL656, F560, G306, L370, N393, P438, UM557
 (PD), VU602
"*Una Espiga*" ("Sheaves of Summer") (1 Cor, Comm.)
 C396, G532, N338, UM637
"We Are the Body of Christ" (1 Cor)
 G768, S2227, SF2227
"As a Fire Is Meant for Burning" (1 Cor)
 S2237, SF2237, VU578
"We Meet You, O Christ" (John, MLK Day)
 C183, P311, UM257, VU183
"Jesus, Priceless Treasure" (John)
 E701, EL775, F277, G830, L457, N480 P365, UM532 (PD),
 VU667 and VU668 (Fr.)
"Blessed Jesus, at Thy Word" (John)
 E440, EL520, G395, N74, P454, UM596 (PD), VU500
"Jesus, Joy of Our Desiring" (John)
 UM644 (PD), VU328
"Your Love, O God, Has Called Us Here" (John)
 B509, E353, N361, UM647

Additional Contemporary Suggestions

"Mighty to Save" (Isa, Epiphany)
 M246, WS3038
"On Eagle's Wings" (Pss)
 B71, C77, EL787, G43, N775, UM143, VU807/808

"With You, O Lord" (Pss)
 WS3024
"Shine, Jesus, Shine" (Pss)
 B579, EL671, G192, S2173, SF2173, SP142
"The Steadfast Love of the Lord" (Pss)
 SP185
"I Could Sing of Your Love Forever" (Pss)
 M63
"There Is Joy in the Lord" (Pss)
 M74
"Your Love, Oh Lord" (Pss)
 M189
"Beautiful Savior" (Pss, Epiphany)
 M243
"One Bread, One Body" (1 Cor, Comm.)
 C393, EL496, G530, UM620, VU467
"Holy Spirit, Come to Us" (1 Cor)
 EL406, G281, S2118, SF2118, W473
"They'll Know We Are Christians" (1 Cor)
 C494, G300, S2223, SF2223
"Make Us One" (1 Cor)
 S2224, SF2224, SP137
"Bind Us Together" (1 Cor)
 S2226, SF2226, SP140
"We Are One in Christ Jesus" (1 Cor)
 C493, EL643, G322, S2229, SF2229
"The Family Prayer Song" (John)
 M54, S2188, SF2188

Vocal Solos

"Shine, Jesus, Shine" (Isa, John)
 V-3 (2)   p. 48
"On Eagle's Wings" (Pss)
 V-3 (2)   p. 2
 V-3 (3)   p. 4
"Spirit of Faith Come Down" (1 Cor)
 V-1   p. 43
"He Turned the Water into Wine" (John)
 V-8   p. 76

Anthems

"And the Father Will Dance" (Isa)
Mark Hayes; Hinshaw HMC1349 (SATB - HMC637)
SAB with piano (bit.ly/HMC1349)

"We All Are One in Mission" (1 Cor, MLK Day)
Arr. Joel Martinson; AEC-2 p. 23
SATB and organ

Other Suggestions

Consider observances of Martin Luther King Jr. Day.
Visuals:
 O   Crown, bride and groom, invitation, torch, sunrise
 P   Sky, clouds, mountains, wings, banquet, fountain
 E   "Many gifts, one spirit," ministries, unity
 G   Large clay water jars, water/wine/bread, wedding
Introit: E487, EL816, L513, N331, UM164 (PD), VU628, W569.
 "Come, My Way, My Truth, My Life" (John)
Prayers: N826 and WSL70 (Pss)
Litany: UM556. Litany for Christian Unity (1 Cor)
Prayers: N851, N861, WSL116, WSL192, C451 (1 Cor)

Nehemiah 8:1-3, 5-6, 8-10

When the seventh month came and the people of Israel were settled in their towns, all the people gathered together in the area in front of the Water Gate. They asked Ezra the scribe to bring out the Instruction scroll from Moses, according to which the Lord had instructed Israel.

²So on the first day of the seventh month, Ezra the priest brought the Instruction before the assembly. This assembly was made up of both men and women and anyone who could understand what they heard. ³Facing the area in front of the Water Gate, he read it aloud, from early morning until the middle of the day. He read it in the presence of the men and the women and those who could understand, and everyone listened attentively to the Instruction scroll. . . .

⁵Standing above all of the people, Ezra the scribe opened the scroll in the sight of all of the people. And as he opened it, all of the people stood up. ⁶Then Ezra blessed the Lord, the great God, and all of the people answered, "Amen! Amen!" while raising their hands. Then they bowed down and worshipped the Lord with their faces to the ground. . . .

⁸They read aloud from the scroll, the Instruction from God, explaining and interpreting it so the people could understand what they heard.

⁹Then Nehemiah the governor, Ezra the priest and scribe, and the Levites who taught the people said to all of the people, "This day is holy to the Lord your God. Don't mourn or weep." They said this because all the people wept when they heard the words of the Instruction.

¹⁰"Go, eat rich food, and drink something sweet," he said to them, "and send portions of this to any who have nothing ready! This day is holy to our Lord. Don't be sad, because the joy from the Lord is your strength!"

Psalm 19 (G61/690, N630, P166/167, UM750)

Heaven is declaring God's glory;
  the sky is proclaiming his handiwork.
²One day gushes the news to the next,
  and one night informs another what needs to be known.
³Of course, there's no speech, no words—
    their voices can't be heard—
⁴ but their sound extends throughout the world;
    their words reach the ends of the earth.
God has made a tent in heaven for the sun.
⁵The sun is like a groom
  coming out of his honeymoon suite;
  like a warrior, it thrills at running its course.
⁶It rises in one end of the sky;
  its circuit is complete at the other.
    Nothing escapes its heat.
⁷The Lord's Instruction is perfect,
  reviving one's very being.
The Lord's laws are faithful,
  making naive people wise.
⁸The Lord's regulations are right,
  gladdening the heart.
The Lord's commands are pure,
  giving light to the eyes.
⁹Honoring the Lord is correct,
  lasting forever.
The Lord's judgments are true.
  All of these are righteous!
¹⁰They are more desirable than gold—
  than tons of pure gold!
They are sweeter than honey—
  even dripping off the honeycomb!
¹¹No doubt about it:
  your servant is enlightened by them;
  there is great reward in keeping them.
¹²But can anyone know
  what they've accidentally done wrong?
  Clear me of any unknown sin
    ¹³and save your servant from willful sins.
  Don't let them rule me.
Then I'll be completely blameless;
  I'll be innocent of great wrongdoing.
¹⁴Let the words of my mouth
  and the meditations of my heart
  be pleasing to you,
  Lord, my rock and my redeemer.

1 Corinthians 12:12-31a

¹²Christ is just like the human body—a body is a unit and has many parts; and all the parts of the body are one body, even though there are many. ¹³We were all baptized by one Spirit into one body, whether Jew or Greek, or slave or free, and we all were given one Spirit to drink. ¹⁴Certainly the body isn't one part but many. ¹⁵If the foot says, "I'm not part of the body because I'm not a hand," does that mean it's not part of the body? ¹⁶If the ear says, "I'm not part of the body because I'm not an eye," does that mean it's not part of the body? ¹⁷If the whole body were an eye, what would happen to the hearing? And if the whole body were an ear, what would happen to the sense of smell? ¹⁸But as it is, God has placed each one of the parts in the body just like he wanted. ¹⁹If all were one and the same body part, what would happen to the body? ²⁰But as it is, there are many parts but one body. ²¹So the eye can't say to the hand, "I don't need you," or in turn, the head can't say to the feet, "I don't need you." ²²Instead, the parts of the body that people think are the weakest are the most necessary. ²³The parts of the body that we think are less honorable are the ones we honor the most. The private parts of our body that aren't presentable are the ones that are given the most dignity. ²⁴The parts of our body that are presentable don't need this. But God has put the body together, giving greater honor to the part with less honor ²⁵so that there won't be division in the body and so the parts might have mutual concern for each other. ²⁶If one part suffers, all the parts suffer with it; if one part gets the glory, all the parts celebrate with it. ²⁷You are the body of Christ and parts of each other. ²⁸In the church, God has appointed first apostles, second prophets, third teachers, then miracles, then gifts of healing, the ability to help others, leadership skills, different kinds of tongues. ²⁹All aren't apostles, are they? All aren't prophets, are they? All aren't teachers, are they? All don't perform miracles, do they? ³⁰All don't have gifts of healing, do they? All don't speak in different tongues, do they? All don't interpret, do they? ³¹ᵃUse your ambition to try to get the greater gifts.

Luke 4:14-21

¹⁴Jesus returned in the power of the Spirit to Galilee, and news about him spread throughout the whole countryside. ¹⁵He taught in their synagogues and was praised by everyone.

¹⁶Jesus went to Nazareth, where he had been raised. On the Sabbath he went to the synagogue as he normally did and stood up to read. ¹⁷The synagogue assistant gave him the scroll from the prophet Isaiah. He unrolled the scroll and found the place where it was written:
  ¹⁸*The Spirit of the Lord is upon me,*
    because the Lord has anointed me.
  He has sent me to preach good news to the poor,
    to proclaim release to the prisoners
    and recovery of sight to the blind,
    to liberate the oppressed,
      ¹⁹*and to proclaim the year of the Lord's favor.*
²⁰He rolled up the scroll, gave it back to the synagogue assistant, and sat down. Every eye in the synagogue was fixed on him. ²¹He began to explain to them, "Today, this scripture has been fulfilled just as you heard it."

Primary Hymns and Songs for the Day

"God Is Here" (Neh, 1 Cor) (O)
    C280, EL526, G409, N70, P461, UM660, VU389, W667
"One Bread, One Body" (1 Cor, Comm.)
    C393, EL496, G530, UM620, VU467
        H-3   Chr-156
"Gather Us In" (1 Cor, Luke)
    C284, EL532, G401, S2236, SF2236, W665
"O For a Thousand Tongues to Sing" (Luke) (C)
    B216, C5, E493, EL886, G610, L559, N42, P466, UM57 (PD),
    VU326; G405, WS3001
        H-3   Hbl-79; Chr-142; Desc-17; Org-12
        S-1   #33-38. Various Treatments
"In Christ There Is No East or West" (1 Cor, Luke) (C)
    B385, C687, E529, EL650 (PD), F685, G317/318, L359,
    N394/395, P439/440, UM548, VU606, W659
        H-3   Hbl-71, 104; Chr-111; Desc-95; Org-143
        S-2   #162. Harm.

Additional Hymn Suggestions

"Deep in the Shadows of the Past" (Neh)
    G50, N320, P330, S2246
"For the Beauty of the Earth" (Neh, Pss)
    B44, C56, E416, EL879, F1, G14, L561, P473, N28, UM92
    (PD), VU226, W557
"Great Is Thy Faithfulness" (Neh, Pss)
    B54, C86, EL733, G39, N423, P276, UM140, VU288
"All Things Bright and Beautiful" (Neh, Pss)
    C61, E405, G20, N31, P267, UM147 (PD), VU291
"Blest Be the Tie That Binds" (1 Cor)
    B387, C433, EL656, F560, G306, L370, N393, P438, UM557
    (PD), VU602
"Together We Serve" (1 Cor)
    G767, S2175, SF2175
"They'll Know We Are Christians" (1 Cor)
    C494, G300, S2223, SF2223
"We All Are One in Mission" (1 Cor)
    G733, P435, S2243, SF2243
"Thee We Adore, O Hidden Savior, Thee" (1 Cor)
    EL476 (PD), G495, L199, P519
"Jesus Shall Reign" (1 Cor, Luke)
    B587, C95, E544, EL434, F238, G265, L530, N157, P423,
    UM157 (PD), VU330, W492
"To God Be the Glory" (Luke)
    B4, C72, F363, G634, P485, UM98 (PD)
"There Is a Balm in Gilead" (Luke)
    B269, C501, E676, EL614 (PD), F48, G792, N553, P394,
    UM375, VU612, W608
"Live into Hope" (Luke)
    G772, P332, VU699
"Today We All Are Called to Be Disciples" (Luke)
    G757, P434, VU507
"We Are Called" (Luke)
    EL720, G749, S2172, SF2172

Additional Contemporary Suggestions

"Blessed Be the Name" (Neh)
    M12, S2034, SF2034, UM63
"Holy Is the Lord" (Neh)
    M131, WS3028
"Let My Words Be Few" (Neh)
    M105
"Famous One" (Pss)
    M126

"Indescribable" (Pss)
    M127
"It Is You" (Pss)
    M134
"Sing, Sing, Sing" (Pss)
    M235
"Beautiful Savior" (Pss, Luke)
    M243
"Make Us One" (1 Cor)
    S2224, SF2224, SP137
"We Are One in Christ Jesus" (1 Cor)
    C493, EL643, G322, S2229, SF2229
"We Are the Body of Christ" (1 Cor)
    G768, S2227, SF2227
"Come Now, O Prince of Peace" (1 Cor)
    EL247, G103, S2232, SF2232
"Holy" ("Santo") (Luke)
    EL762, G594, S2019, SF2019
"Holy Spirit, Come to Us" (Luke)
    EL406, G281, S2118, SF2118, W473
"Where the Spirit of the Lord Is" (Luke)
    C264, S2119, SF2119
"Days of Elijah" (Luke)
    M139, WS3186
"Let the River Flow" (Luke)
    M142
"Hear Us from Heaven" (Luke)
    M267

Vocal Solos

"The Heavens Declare His Glory" (Pss)
    V-8   p. 248
"One Bread, One Body" (1 Cor, Comm.)
    V-3 (2)   p. 40
"O For a Thousand Tongues to Sing" (Luke)
    V-1   p. 32
    V-6   p. 28

Anthems

"Come, Ye Sinners" (Luke)
Arr. David Ashley White; AEC-2 p. 38
2-part, keyboard and oboe

"The Spirit of the Lord Is Upon Me" (Luke)
Edward Elgar; Novello 29-0219
SATB with organ

Other Suggestions

Visuals:
    O   Open Bible, scroll, morning, assembly, weeping/joy
    P   Gold, honeycomb, runner, groom
    E   Teamwork, body, health, harmony, gifts
    G   Images of poor/captives/blind/freedom, Jubilee
Call to Worship: WSL68 (1 Cor) or N824 (Pss)
Responsive Invocation: WSL36 (1 Cor)
Prayer: UM594 or UM602 (Neh, Pss)
Prayers: F561, N860, WSL36, F549, N855, C451 (1 Cor)
Prayers: N838, C52 (Luke)
Response: C327. "Write These Words" (Neh, Pss)
Prayer for Illumination: WSL71 (Pss)
Prayer of Thanksgiving: WSL62 (Pss)
Sung Benediction: N161, P299, S2072. "Amen, Amen" (Luke)

Jeremiah 1:4-10

⁴The Lord's word came to me:

⁵"Before I created you in the womb I knew you;
    before you were born I set you apart;
    I made you a prophet to the nations."

⁶"Ah, Lord God," I said, "I don't know how to speak
    because I'm only a child."

⁷The Lord responded,
    "Don't say, 'I'm only a child.'
        Where I send you, you must go;
        what I tell you, you must say.

⁸Don't be afraid of them,
    because I'm with you to rescue you,"
        declares the Lord.

⁹Then the Lord stretched out his hand,
    touched my mouth, and said to me,
    "I'm putting my words in your mouth.

¹⁰This very day I appoint you over nations and empires,
    to dig up and pull down,
    to destroy and demolish,
    to build and plant."

Psalm 71:1-6 (G813, N666, UM794)

I've taken refuge in you, Lord.
    Don't let me ever be put to shame!

²Deliver me and rescue me by your righteousness!
    Bend your ear toward me and save me!

³Be my rock of refuge
    where I can always escape.
You commanded that my life be saved
    because you are my rock and my fortress.

⁴My God, rescue me from the power of the wicked;
    rescue me from the grip of the wrongdoer and the oppressor
    ⁵because you are my hope, Lord.
    You, Lord, are the one I've trusted since childhood.

⁶I've depended on you from birth—
    you cut the cord when I came from my mother's womb.
    My praise is always about you.

1 Corinthians 13:1-13

If I speak in tongues of human beings and of angels but I don't have love, I'm a clanging gong or a clashing cymbal. ²If I have the gift of prophecy and I know all the mysteries and everything else, and if I have such complete faith that I can move mountains but I don't have love, I'm nothing. ³If I give away everything that I have and hand over my own body to feel good about what I've done but I don't have love, I receive no benefit whatsoever.

⁴Love is patient, love is kind, it isn't jealous, it doesn't brag, it isn't arrogant, ⁵it isn't rude, it doesn't seek its own advantage, it isn't irritable, it doesn't keep a record of complaints, ⁶it isn't happy with injustice, but it is happy with the truth. ⁷Love puts up with all things, trusts in all things, hopes for all things, endures all things.

⁸Love never fails. As for prophecies, they will be brought to an end. As for tongues, they will stop. As for knowledge, it will be brought to an end. ⁹We know in part and we prophesy in part; ¹⁰but when the perfect comes, what is partial will be brought to an end. ¹¹When I was a child, I used to speak like a child, reason like a child, think like a child. But now that I have become a man, I've put an end to childish things. ¹²Now we see a reflection in a mirror; then we will see face-to-face. Now I know partially, but then I will know completely in the same way that I have been completely known. ¹³Now faith, hope, and love remain—these three things—and the greatest of these is love.

Luke 4:21-30

²¹He began to explain to them, "Today, this scripture has been fulfilled just as you heard it."

²²Everyone was raving about Jesus, so impressed were they by the gracious words flowing from his lips. They said, "This is Joseph's son, isn't it?"

²³Then Jesus said to them, "Undoubtedly, you will quote this saying to me: 'Doctor, heal yourself. Do here in your hometown what we've heard you did in Capernaum.'" ²⁴He said, "I assure you that no prophet is welcome in the prophet's hometown. ²⁵And I can assure you that there were many widows in Israel during Elijah's time, when it didn't rain for three and a half years and there was a great food shortage in the land. ²⁶Yet Elijah was sent to none of them but only to a widow in the city of Zarephath in the region of Sidon. ²⁷There were also many persons with skin diseases in Israel during the time of the prophet Elisha, but none of them were cleansed. Instead, Naaman the Syrian was cleansed."

²⁸When they heard this, everyone in the synagogue was filled with anger. ²⁹They rose up and ran him out of town. They led him to the crest of the hill on which their town had been built so that they could throw him off the cliff. ³⁰But he passed through the crowd and went on his way.

Primary Hymns and Songs for the Day
"How Firm a Foundation" (Jer) (O)
　　B338, C618, E636/637, EL796, F32, G463, L507, N407, P361,
　　UM529 (PD), VU660, W585
"Take My Life and Let it Be" (Jer)
　　B277/283, C609, E707, EL583/685, G697, L406, P391, N448,
　　UM399 (PD), VU506
"My Life Is in You, Lord" (Pss)
　　S2032, SF2032, SP204
"The Gift of Love" (1 Cor)
　　B423, C526, G693, P335, UM408, VU372
　　　　H-3　Chr-200; Org-45
"Lord, Speak to Me" (Jer, Luke)
　　B568, EL676, G722, N531, P426, UM463 (PD), VU589
"Here I Am, Lord" (Jer, Luke) (C)
　　C452, EL574, G69, P525, UM593, VU509
　　　　H-3　Chr-97; Org-54

Additional Hymn Suggestions
"Lord, When I Came into This Life" (Jer)
　　N354, G691, P522
"Mothering God, You Gave Me Birth" (Jer, 1 Cor)
　　C83, N467, S2050, SF2050, VU320
"I Was There to Hear Your Borning Cry" (Jer, Baptism)
　　C75, EL732, G488, N351, S2051, SF2051, VU644
"A Mighty Fortress Is Our God" (Pss, 1 Cor)
　　B8, C65, E687/688, EL503/504/505, F118, G275, L228/229,
　　N439/440, P259/260, UM110 (PD), VU261/262/263,
　　W575/576
"This Is My Father's World" (1 Cor)
　　B43, C59, E651, EL824 (PD), G370, P293, UM144
"Jesus, the Very Thought of Thee" (1 Cor)
　　B225, C102, E642, EL754, F465, G629, L316, N507, P310,
　　UM175 (PD)
"When Memory Fades" (1 Cor)
　　EL792, G808
"O Love That Wilt Not Let Me Go" (1 Cor)
　　B292, C540, G833, L324, N485, P384, UM480, VU658
"When Love Is Found" (1 Cor, Comm.)
　　C499, N362, UM643, VU489, W745
"Your Love, O God, Has Called Us Here" (1 Cor)
　　B509, E353, N361, UM647
"Healer of Our Every Ill" (1 Cor)
　　C506, EL612, G795, S2213, SF2213, VU619
"Sacred the Body" (1 Cor)
　　G27, S2228, SF2228
"Lord of the Dance" (Luke)
　　G157, P302, UM261, VU352, W636
"Spirit, Spirit of Gentleness" (Luke)
　　C249, EL396, G291, N286, P319, S2120, VU375
"We Are Called" (Luke)
　　EL720, G749, S2172, SF2172
"Gather Us In" (Luke)
　　C284, EL532, G401, S2236, SF2236, W665

Additional Contemporary Suggestions
"I Know the Lord's Laid His Hands on Me" (Jer)
　　S2139, SF2139
"Word of God, Speak" (Jer)
　　M148, WS3184
"Ah, Lord God" (Jer)
　　SP2
"Take My Life" (Jer)
　　M91

"Praise Him" (Jer)
　　WS3041
"Live in Charity" ("*Ubi Caritas*") (1 Cor)
　　C523, EL642, G205, S2179, SF2179, W604
"There's a Song" (1 Cor)
　　S2141, SF2141
"He Came Down" (1 Cor)
　　EL253, G137, S2085, SF2085
"They'll Know We Are Christians" (1 Cor)
　　C494, G300, S2223, SF2223
"Make Us One" (1 Cor)
　　S2224, SF2224, SP137
"Let It Be Said of Us" (1 Cor)
　　M53
"More Love, More Power" (1 Cor)
　　M40
"I Will Rise" (1 Cor)
　　M260
"Days of Elijah" (Luke)
　　M139, WS3186
"Jesus Paid It All" (Luke)
　　M244 (lead sheet and bridge), B134, F273, WS3100
"Marvelous Light" (Luke, Epiphany)
　　M249

Vocal Solos
"Take My Life, and Let It Be Consecrated" (Jer)
　　V-3 (3)　　　p. 17
　　V-8　　　　 p. 262
"Borning Cry" (Jer, Baptism)
　　V-5(1)　　　p. 10
"Steal Away to Heaven" (Pss)
　　V-3 (1)　　　p. 17
"Prayer" (Pss)
　　V-9　　　　 p. 32
"The Gift of Love" (1 Cor)
　　V-8　　　　 p. 120
"Lord of the Dance" (Luke)
　　V-3 (3)　　　p. 34

Anthems
"This Is My Father's World" (1 Cor)
Arr. Elaine Hagenberg; Hinshaw HMC2494
SATB, piano, and violin (bit.ly/HMC2494)

"Love Never Fails" (1 Cor)
J.A.C. Redford; Fred Bock BG2359 (SATB- BG2479)
2-part, cello, keyboard (bit.ly/BG2359)

Other Suggestions
*February is Black History Month, which can be reflected in your choice of
　　music and liturgy.*
This day may include an observance of Boy Scout Sunday.
Visuals:
　　O　　Pregnancy, boy, Jer 1:7b or 9b, hand/mouth, nations
　　P　　Ear, Ps 71:3 or 5a, rock, fortress, rescue, youth
　　E　　Speak, cymbals, remove mts., love, child/adult, mirror
　　G　　Bible, Jesus speaking/walking, widows, famine, leper
Litany: WSL22 (Luke)
Canticle: C525, UM646. "Canticle of Love" (1 Cor)
Prayer of Confession: WSL90 (Jer, Luke)
Blessing: WSL176 (1 Cor)

Isaiah 6:1-8 (9-13)

In the year of King Uzziah's death, I saw the LORD sitting on a high and exalted throne, the edges of his robe filling the temple. ²Winged creatures were stationed around him. Each had six wings: with two they veiled their faces, with two their feet, and with two they flew about. ³They shouted to each other, saying:

"Holy, holy, holy is the LORD of heavenly forces!

All the earth is filled with God's glory!"

⁴The doorframe shook at the sound of their shouting, and the house was filled with smoke.

⁵I said, "Mourn for me; I'm ruined! I'm a man with unclean lips, and I live among a people with unclean lips. Yet I've seen the king, the LORD of heavenly forces!"

⁶Then one of the winged creatures flew to me, holding a glowing coal that he had taken from the altar with tongs. ⁷He touched my mouth and said, "See, this has touched your lips. Your guilt has departed, and your sin is removed."

⁸Then I heard the Lord's voice saying, "Whom should I send, and who will go for us?"

I said, "I'm here; send me."

⁹God said, "Go and say to this people:

Listen intently, but don't understand;

look carefully, but don't comprehend.

¹⁰Make the minds of this people dull.

Make their ears deaf and their eyes blind,

so they can't see with their eyes

or hear with their ears,

or understand with their minds,

and turn, and be healed."

¹¹I said, "How long, LORD?"

And God said, "Until cities lie ruined with no one living in them, until there are houses without people and the land is left devastated." ¹²The LORD will send the people far away, and the land will be completely abandoned. ¹³Even if one-tenth remain there, they will be burned again, like a terebinth or an oak, which when it is cut down leaves a stump. Its stump is a holy seed.

Psalm 138 (G334, N138, P247, UM853)

I give thanks to you with all my heart, LORD.

I sing your praise before all other gods.

²I bow toward your holy temple

and thank your name

for your loyal love and faithfulness

because you have made your name and word

greater than everything else.

³On the day I cried out, you answered me.

You encouraged me with inner strength.

⁴Let all the earth's rulers give thanks to you, LORD,

when they hear what you say.

⁵Let them sing about the LORD's ways

because the LORD's glory is so great!

⁶Even though the LORD is high,

he can still see the lowly,

but God keeps his distance from the arrogant.

⁷Whenever I am in deep trouble,

you make me live again;

you send your power against my enemies' wrath;

you save me with your strong hand.

⁸The LORD will do all this for my sake.

Your faithful love lasts forever, LORD!

Don't let go of what your hands have made.

1 Corinthians 15:1-11

Brothers and sisters, I want to call your attention to the good news that I preached to you, which you also received and in which you stand. ²You are being saved through it if you hold on to the message I preached to you, unless somehow you believed it for nothing. ³I passed on to you as most important what I also received: Christ died for our sins in line with the scriptures, ⁴he was buried, and he rose on the third day in line with the scriptures. ⁵He appeared to Cephas, then to the Twelve, ⁶and then he appeared to more than five hundred brothers and sisters at once—most of them are still alive to this day, though some have died. ⁷Then he appeared to James, then to all the apostles, ⁸and last of all he appeared to me, as if I were born at the wrong time. ⁹I'm the least important of the apostles. I don't deserve to be called an apostle, because I harassed God's church. ¹⁰I am what I am by God's grace, and God's grace hasn't been for nothing. In fact, I have worked harder than all the others—that is, it wasn't me but the grace of God that is with me. ¹¹So then, whether you heard the message from me or them, this is what we preach and this is what you have believed.

Luke 5:1-11

One day Jesus was standing beside Lake Gennesaret when the crowd pressed in around him to hear God's word. ²Jesus saw two boats sitting by the lake. The fishermen had gone ashore and were washing their nets. ³Jesus boarded one of the boats, the one that belonged to Simon, then asked him to row out a little distance from the shore. Jesus sat down and taught the crowds from the boat. ⁴When he finished speaking to the crowds, he said to Simon, "Row out farther, into the deep water, and drop your nets for a catch."

⁵Simon replied, "Master, we've worked hard all night and caught nothing. But because you say so, I'll drop the nets."

⁶So they dropped the nets and their catch was so huge that their nets were splitting. ⁷They signaled for their partners in the other boat to come and help them. They filled both boats so full that they were about to sink. ⁸When Simon Peter saw the catch, he fell at Jesus' knees and said, "Leave me, Lord, for I'm a sinner!" ⁹Peter and those with him were overcome with amazement because of the number of fish they caught. ¹⁰James and John, Zebedee's sons, were Simon's partners and they were amazed too.

Jesus said to Simon, "Don't be afraid. From now on, you will be fishing for people." ¹¹As soon as they brought the boats to the shore, they left everything and followed Jesus.

Primary Hymns and Songs for the Day

"Holy, Holy, Holy! Lord God Almighty" (Isa) (O)
  B2, C4, E362, F323, EL413, G1, L165, N277, P138, UM64/65,
  VU315, W485
          H-3   Hbl-68; Chr-99; Desc-80; Org-97
          S-1   #245-248. Various treatments
"Send Me, Lord" (Isa, Luke, Black History)
  C447, EL809, G746, N360, UM497, VU572
          S-2   #173. Percussion Arr.
"Tú Has Venido a la Orilla" ("Lord, You Have Come to the
Lakeshore") (Luke)
  C342, EL817, G721, N173, P377, UM344, VU563
          H-3   Chr-133; Org-114
"Jesus Calls Us" (Luke) (C)
  B293, C337, EL696, G720, L494, N172, UM398, VU562
          H-3   Chr-115
          S-2   #65. Harm.
  E549/550, N171

Additional Hymn Suggestions

"Immortal, Invisible, God Only Wise" (Isa)
  B6, C66, E423, EL834, F319, G12, L526, N1, P263, UM103
  (PD), VU264, W512
"The God of Abraham Praise" (Isa)
  B34, C24, E401, EL831, F332, G49, L544, N24, P488, UM116
  (PD), VU255, W537
"Dear Lord and Father of Mankind" (Isa)
  B267, C594, E652/563, F422, G169, L506, N502, P345,
  UM358 (PD), VU608
"Gracious Spirit, Heed Our Pleading" (Isa)
  EL401, G287
"Blessing and Honor" (Isa, 1 Cor)
  EL854, G369, L525, P147
"Holy God, We Praise Thy Name" (Isa, 1 Cor)
  E366, F385, EL414 (PD), G4, L535, N276, P460, UM79,
  VU894 (Fr.), W524
"Come Down, O Love Divine" (Isa, Luke)
  C582, E516, EL804, G282, L508, N289, P313, UM475,
  VU367, W472
"Here I Am, Lord" (Isa, Luke)
  C452, EL574, G69, P525, UM593, VU509
"O How I Love Jesus" (1 Cor)
  B217, C99, F634, N52, UM170 (PD)
"We Know That Christ Is Raised" (1 Cor)
  E296, EL449, G485, L189, P495, UM610, VU448, W721
"Amazing Grace" (Luke)
  B330, C546, E671, EL779, F107, G649, L448, N547 and N548,
  P280, UM378 (PD), VU266 (Fr.), W583
"You Satisfy the Hungry Heart" (Luke, Comm)
  C429, EL484, G523, P521, UM629, VU478, W736
"The Summons" (Luke)
  EL798, G726, S2130, SF2130, VU567

Additional Contemporary Suggestions

"Holy, Holy, Holy" (*"Santo, Santo, Santo"*) (Isa)
  C111, EL473, G595, N793, S2007, SF2007
"Holy, Holy" (Isa)
  B254, F149, P140, S2039, SP141
"Jesus, We Are Here" (Isa, Black History)
  EL529, G392, S2273, SF2273
"Open the Eyes of My Heart" (Pss, Matt)
  G452, M57, WS3008
"We Fall Down" (Isa)
  G368, M66, WS3187

"Holy, Holy, Holy" (Isa)
  M95, SP37
"Because We Believe" (Isa)
  M6
"Offering" (Isa)
  M130
"Holy Is the Lord" (Isa)
  M131, WS3028
"It Is You" (Isa)
  M134
"In the Lord I'll Be Ever Thankful" (Pss)
  G654, S2195, SF2195
"Something Beautiful" (1 Cor)
  F656, UM394
"Lord, I Lift Your Name on High" (1 Cor)
  EL857, M2, S2088, SF2088
"Grace Alone" (1 Cor)
  M100, S2162, SF2162
"Amen, Amen" (Luke, Black History)
  N161, P299, S2072
"I Have Decided to Follow Jesus" (Luke)
  B305, C344, S2129, SF2129
"We Walk His Way" (Luke)
  WS3073
"Breathe"
  WS3112, M61
"In Christ Alone" ("My Hope Is Found") (Luke)
  WS3105, M138
"Every Move I Make"
  M122
"Everyday" (Luke)
  M150

Vocal Solos

"Take My Life, and Let It Be Consecrated" (Isa, Luke)
  V-3 (3)   p. 17
  V-8   p. 262
"Here I Am" (Isa, Luke)
  V-11   p. 19

Anthems

"Holy, Holy, Holy!" (Isa)
arr. Robert C. Clatterbuck; Hope C5470
SATB with keyboard (bit.ly/C5470)

"I Will Praise You, O Lord" (Pss)
Mark Patterson; Choristers Guild CGA867
Unison with keyboard (bit.ly/CGA867)

Other Suggestions

Visuals:
      O   burning coals, tongs, stump
      P   thanks, heart, bowing, glory, singing, danger, hand
      E   1 Corinthians 15:1-11, phoenix or peacock,
               resurrection
      G   net, fish, people
Introit: WS3163. "Walking in the Light of God" (Luke,
  Epiphany)
Affirmation of Faith: UM888 (1 Cor)
Response: AH4081, C531, UM84. "Thank You, Lord" (Pss)
Canticle: UM80. "Canticle of the Holy Trinity" (Isa)
Scripture Response: UM212, Response 1 (Isa)
Dismissal: WSL165 (Isa, Luke)

Jeremiah 17:5-10

[5] The LORD proclaims:
Cursed are those who trust in mere humans,
     who depend on human strength
     and turn their hearts from the LORD.
[6] They will be like a desert shrub
     that doesn't know when relief comes.
They will live in the parched places of the wilderness,
     in a barren land where no one survives.
[7] Happy are those who trust in the LORD,
     who rely on the LORD.
[8] They will be like trees planted by the streams,
     whose roots reach down to the water.
They won't fear drought when it comes;
     their leaves will remain green.
They won't be stressed in the time of drought
     or fail to bear fruit.
[9] The most cunning heart—
     it's beyond help.
          Who can figure it out?
[10] I, the LORD, probe the heart
     and discern hidden motives,
          to give everyone what they deserve,
          the consequences of their deeds.

Psalm 1 (G457, N621, P158, UM738)

The truly happy person
     doesn't follow wicked advice,
     doesn't stand on the road of sinners,
     and doesn't sit with the disrespectful.
[2] Instead of doing those things,
     these persons love the LORD's Instruction,
     and they recite God's Instruction day and night!
[3] They are like a tree replanted by streams of water,
     which bears fruit at just the right time
     and whose leaves don't fade.
          Whatever they do succeeds.
[4] That's not true for the wicked!
     They are like dust that the wind blows away.
[5] And that's why the wicked will have no standing in the court of
          justice—
     neither will sinners
     in the assembly of the righteous.
[6] The LORD is intimately acquainted
     with the way of the righteous,
     but the way of the wicked is destroyed.

1 Corinthians 15:12-20

[12] So if the message that is preached says that Christ has been raised from the dead, then how can some of you say, "There's no resurrection of the dead"? [13] If there's no resurrection of the dead, then Christ hasn't been raised either. [14] If Christ hasn't been raised, then our preaching is useless and your faith is useless. [15] We are found to be false witnesses about God, because we testified against God that he raised Christ, when he didn't raise him if it's the case that the dead aren't raised. [16] If the dead aren't raised, then Christ hasn't been raised either. [17] If Christ hasn't been raised, then your faith is worthless; you are still in your sins, [18] and what's more, those who have died in Christ are gone forever. [19] If we have a hope in Christ only in this life, then we deserve to be pitied more than anyone else.

[20] But in fact Christ has been raised from the dead. He's the first crop of the harvest of those who have died.

Luke 6:17-26

[17] Jesus came down from the mountain with them and stood on a large area of level ground. A great company of his disciples and a huge crowd of people from all around Judea and Jerusalem and the area around Tyre and Sidon joined him there. [18] They came to hear him and to be healed from their diseases, and those bothered by unclean spirits were healed. [19] The whole crowd wanted to touch him, because power was going out from him and he was healing everyone.

[20] Jesus raised his eyes to his disciples and said:
     "Happy are you who are poor,
          because God's kingdom is yours.
     [21] Happy are you who hunger now,
          because you will be satisfied.
     Happy are you who weep now,
          because you will laugh.
[22] Happy are you when people hate you, reject you, insult you, and condemn your name as evil because of the Human One. [23] Rejoice when that happens! Leap for joy because you have a great reward in heaven. Their ancestors did the same things to the prophets.
     [24] But how terrible for you who are rich,
          because you have already received your comfort.
     [25] How terrible for you who have plenty now,
          because you will be hungry.
     How terrible for you who laugh now,
          because you will mourn and weep.
     [26] How terrible for you when all speak well of you.
          Their ancestors did the same things to the false prophets.

Primary Hymns and Songs for the Day

"Sing With All the Saints of Glory" (1 Cor) (O)
    EL426, UM702 (PD), W467
        H-3   Hbl-25, 74; Chr-120; Desc-54; Org-58
        S-1   #173-176. Various treatments
"Marching to Zion" (Jer, Luke, Black History) (O)
    B524, C707, EL625, F550, N382, UM733 (PD), VU714
        H-3   Chr-298
"Step by Step" (Jer)
    G743, M51, WS3004
"If Thou But Suffer God to Guide Thee" (Jer, Pss)
    B57, C565, E635, EL769, G816, L453, N410, P282, UM142
    (PD), VU285 (Fr.) and VU286
        H-3   Chr-108; Desc-103; Org-179
"Lord, I Want to Be a Christian" (Luke) (C)
    B489, C589, F421, G729, N454, P372 (PD), UM402

Additional Hymn Suggestions

"Mothering God, You Gave Me Birth" (Jer)
    C83, N467, S2050, SF2050, VU320
"All My Hope Is Firmly Grounded" (Jer, Pss)
    C88, E665, EL757, N408, UM132, VU654 and VU655
"Make Me a Captive, Lord" (Jer, Luke)
    B278, P378, UM421
"Come, We That Love the Lord" (Jer, Luke)
    B525, E392, N379, UM732, VU715, W552
"The Lord of Life, a Vine Is He" (Jer, Luke)
    WS3155
"Let Our Earth Be Peaceful" (Jer, Luke)
    WS3159
"The First Song of Isaiah" (Jer, Pss)
    G71, S2030, SF2030
"The Lone, Wild Bird" (Jer, Pss)
    P320, S2052, SF2052, VU384
"Lead Me, Guide Me" (Jer, Pss)
    C583, EL768, G740, S2214, SF2214
"I'll Praise My Maker While I've Breath" (Pss)
    B35, C20, E429 (PD), G806, P253, UM60, VU867
"O How I Love Jesus" (1 Cor)
    B217, C99, F634, N52, UM170 (PD)
"He Lives" (1 Cor)
    B533, C226, F299, UM310
"Cristo Vive" ("Christ Is Risen") (1 Cor)
    B167, N235, P109, UM313
"We Know That Christ Is Raised" (1 Cor)
    E296, EL449, G485, L189, P495, UM610, VU448, W721
"The Easter Song" (1 Cor)
    WS3090
"Christ Is Risen" (1 Cor, Luke)
    C222, P104, UM307
"Give to the Winds Thy Fears" (Luke)
    G815, N404, P286, UM129 (PD), VU636
"Come, Ye Faithful, Raise the Strain" (Luke)
    C215, E199, EL363, G234, L132, N230, P115, UM315 (PD),
    VU165, W456
"Jesus Calls Us" (Luke)
    B293, C337, E549/550, EL696, F399, G720, L494, N171/172,
    UM398 (PD), VU562
"Rejoice in God's Saints" (Luke)
    C476, EL418, G732, UM708
"I Sing a Song of the Saints of God" (Luke)
    E293, G730, N295, P364, UM712 (PD)
"Holy" ("Santo") (Luke)
    EL762, G594, S2019, SF2019

"Blest Are They" (Luke)
    EL728, G172, S2155, SF2155, VU896
"For All the Saints" (Luke)
    S2283, SF2283
"Because You Live, O Christ" (Luke)
    G249, N231, P105
"O Day of God, Draw Nigh" (Jer, Luke)
    B623, C700, E601, N611, P452, UM730 (PD), VU688/689

Additional Contemporary Suggestions

"My Life Is in You, Lord" (Jer, Pss)
    S2032, SF2032, SP204
"Nothing Can Trouble" ("Nada Te Turbe") (Jer, Pss)
    G820, S2054, SF2054, VU290
"Guide My Feet" (Jer, Pss, Black History)
    G741, N497, P354, S2208
"Praise the Name of Jesus" (Jer, Pss)
    S2066, SF2066, SP87
"Redemption" (Jer, Pss)
    WS3111
"Through It All" (Jer, Pss, Luke)
    C555, F43, UM507
"Alleluia" (1 Cor)
    EL174, G587, S2043, SF2043
"Christ the Lord Is Risen" (1 Cor)
    S2116, SF2116
"Give Thanks" (Luke)
    C528, G647, S2036, SF2036, SP170
"Goodness Is Stronger than Evil" (Luke)
    EL721, G750, S2219, SF2219
"Make Way" (Luke)
    WS3044

Vocal Solos

"Keep A-Inchin' Along" (Jer)
    V-7   p. 32
"A Song of Trust" (Jer, Pss)
    V-4   p. 20
"Then Shall the Righteous Shine Forth" (Luke)
    V-8   p. 274

Anthems

"Sing with All the Saints in Glory" (1 Cor)
William Bradley Roberts; AEC-2 p. 63
Unison/mixed and organ

"The Mystery of Years" (Luke)
Dan Forrest; Lorenz 10/4349L
SATB and piano (bit.ly/10-4349L)

Other Suggestions

Visuals:
    O   tree in desert/ by stream, flowing water
    P   tree, fruit, flowing water
    E   resurrection symbols, risen Christ, butterfly
    G   feeding, comforting, rejoicing, healing, touching
Litany: C157. For All Who Give You a Face (Luke)
Readings: F290, F478, F589 (today's lections)
Affirmation of Faith: WSL83 (Luke)
Prayer: UM392. Prayer for a New Heart (Luke)
Prayer: UM461. For Those Who Mourn (Luke)
Canticle: C185. The Beatitudes (Luke)

Genesis 45:3-11, 15

³Joseph said to his brothers, "I'm Joseph! Is my father really still alive?" His brothers couldn't respond because they were terrified before him.

⁴Joseph said to his brothers, "Come closer to me," and they moved closer. He said, "I'm your brother Joseph! The one you sold to Egypt. ⁵Now, don't be upset and don't be angry with yourselves that you sold me here. Actually, God sent me before you to save lives. ⁶We've already had two years of famine in the land, and there are five years left without planting or harvesting. ⁷God sent me before you to make sure you'd survive and to rescue your lives in this amazing way. ⁸You didn't send me here; it was God who made me a father to Pharaoh, master of his entire household, and ruler of the whole land of Egypt.

⁹"Hurry! Go back to your father. Tell him this is what your son Joseph says: 'God has made me master of all of Egypt. Come down to me. Don't delay.¹⁰You may live in the land of Goshen, so you will be near me, your children, your grandchildren, your flocks, your herds, and everyone with you. ¹¹I will support you there, so you, your household, and everyone with you won't starve, since the famine will still last five years.' . . . ¹⁵He kissed all of his brothers and wept, embracing them. After that, his brothers were finally able to talk to him.

Psalm 37:1-11, 39-40 (G706, UM772)

Don't get upset over evildoers;
    don't be jealous of those who do wrong,
    ²because they will fade fast, like grass;
    they will wither like green vegetables.
³Trust the LORD and do good;
    live in the land, and farm faithfulness.
⁴Enjoy the LORD,
    and he will give what your heart asks.
⁵Commit your way to the LORD!
    Trust him! He will act
    ⁶and will make your righteousness shine like the dawn,
    your justice like high noon.
⁷Be still before the LORD,
    and wait for him.
Don't get upset when someone gets ahead—
    someone who invents evil schemes.
⁸Let go of anger and leave rage behind!
    Don't get upset—it will only lead to evil.
⁹Because evildoers will be eliminated,
    but those who hope in the LORD—
    they will possess the land.
¹⁰In just a little while the wicked won't exist!
    If you go looking around their place,
    they won't be there.
¹¹But the weak will inherit the land;
    they will enjoy a surplus of peace.
. . . .
The salvation of the righteous comes from the LORD;
    he is their refuge in times of trouble.
⁴⁰The LORD will help themand rescue them—
    rescue them from the wicked—and he will save them
    because they have taken refuge in him.

\1 Corinthians 15:35-38, 42-50

³⁵But someone will say, "How are the dead raised? What kind of body will they have when they come back?" ³⁶Look, fool! When you put a seed into the ground, it doesn't come back to life unless it dies. ³⁷What you put in the ground doesn't have the shape that it will have, but it's a bare grain of wheat or some other seed. ³⁸God gives it the sort of shape that he chooses, and he gives each of the seeds its own shape. . . .

⁴²It's the same with the resurrection of the dead: a rotting body is put into the ground, but what is raised won't ever decay. ⁴³It's degraded when it's put into the ground, but it's raised in glory. It's weak when it's put into the ground, but it's raised in power. ⁴⁴It's a physical body when it's put into the ground, but it's raised as a spiritual body.

If there's a physical body, there's also a spiritual body. ⁴⁵So it is also written, *the first human, Adam, became a living person,* and the last Adam became a spirit that gives life. ⁴⁶But the physical body comes first, not the spiritual one—the spiritual body comes afterward. ⁴⁷The first human was from the earth made from dust; the second human is from heaven. ⁴⁸The nature of the person made of dust is shared by people who are made of dust, and the nature of the heavenly person is shared by heavenly people. ⁴⁹We will look like the heavenly person in the same way as we have looked like the person made from dust.

⁵⁰This is what I'm saying, brothers and sisters: Flesh and blood can't inherit God's kingdom. Something that rots can't inherit something that doesn't decay.

Luke 6:27-38

²⁷"But I say to you who are willing to hear: Love your enemies. Do good to those who hate you. ²⁸Bless those who curse you. Pray for those who mistreat you. ²⁹If someone slaps you on the cheek, offer the other one as well. If someone takes your coat, don't withhold your shirt either. ³⁰Give to everyone who asks and don't demand your things back from those who take them. ³¹Treat people in the same way that you want them to treat you.

³²"If you love those who love you, why should you be commended? Even sinners love those who love them. ³³If you do good to those who do good to you, why should you be commended? Even sinners do that. ³⁴If you lend to those from whom you expect repayment, why should you be commended? Even sinners lend to sinners expecting to be paid back in full. ³⁵Instead, love your enemies, do good, and lend expecting nothing in return. If you do, you will have a great reward. You will be acting the way children of the Most High act, for he is kind to ungrateful and wicked people. ³⁶Be compassionate just as your Father is compassionate.

³⁷"Don't judge, and you won't be judged. Don't condemn, and you won't be condemned. Forgive, and you will be forgiven. ³⁸Give, and it will be given to you. A good portion—packed down, firmly shaken, and overflowing—will fall into your lap. The portion you give will determine the portion you receive in return."

Primary Hymns and Songs for the Day

"Where Charity and Love Prevail" (Gen, Luke) (O)
    E581, EL359, G316, L126, N396, UM549
        H-3   Hbl-71, 104; Chr-111; Desc-95; Org-143
        S-2   #162. Harm.
"Now Thank We All Our God" (Gen) (O)
    B638, C715, E396/397, EL839/840, F525, G643, L533 or
    L534, N419, P555, UM102 (PD), VU236 (Fr.), W560
        H-3   Hbl-78; Chr-140; Desc-81; Org-98
        S-1   #252-254. Various treatments
"Give to the Winds Thy Fears" (Gen, Pss)
    G815, N404, P286, UM129 (PD), VU636
"Now the Green Blade Riseth" (1 Cor)
    C230, E204, EL379, G247, L148, N238, UM311, VU186
"For the Healing of the Nations" (Luke) (C)
    C668, G346, N576, UM428, VU678, W643
"Hymn of Promise" (1 Cor) (C)
    C638, G250. N433, UM707, VU703

Additional Hymn Suggestions

"All My Hope Is Firmly Grounded" (Gen)
    C88, E665, EL757, N408, UM132, VU654 and VU655
"Great Is Thy Faithfulness" (Gen)
    B54, C86, EL733, F98, G39, N423, P276, UM140, VU288
"This Is a Day of New Beginnings" (Gen, Comm.)
    B370, C518, N417, UM383, W661
"Draw Us in the Spirit's Tether" (Gen, Comm.)
    C392, EL470, G529, N337, P504, UM632, VU479
"The First Song of Isaiah" (Gen)
    G71, S2030, SF2030
"Forgive Us, Lord" ("*Perdón, Señor*") (Gen)
    G431, S2134, SF2134
"His Eye Is on the Sparrow" (Gen)
    C82, G661, N475, S2146, SF2146
"God Made from One Blood" (Gen)
    C500, N427, S2170, SF2170, VU554
"Come, Share the Lord" (Gen, Comm.)
    C408, G510, S2269, SF2269, VU469
"Nothing Can Trouble" ("*Nada Te Turbe*") (Gen, Pss)
    G820, S2054, SF2054, VU290
"God, How Can We Forgive" (Gen, Luke)
    G445, S2169, SF2169
"Forgive Our Sins as We Forgive" (Gen, Luke)
    E674, EL605, G444, L307, P347, UM390, VU364
"Help Us Accept Each Other" (Gen, Luke)
    C487, G754, N388, P358, UM560, W656
"O For a World" (Gen, Luke)
    C683, G372, N575, P386, VU697
"Blest Be the Tie That Binds" (John)
    B387, C433, EL656, F560, G306, L370, N393, P438, UM557
    (PD), VU602
"You, Lord, Are Both Lamb and Shepherd" (1 Cor)
    G274, SF2102, VU210, WS3043
"Where Cross the Crowded Ways of Life" (Luke)
    C665, E609, EL719, F665, G343, L429, N543, P408, UM427
    (PD), VU681
"O God of Every Nation" (Luke)
    C680, E607, EL713, G756, L416, P289, UM435, VU677
"Healer of Our Every Ill" (Luke)
    C506, EL612, G795, S2213, SF2213, VU619

Additional Contemporary Suggestions

"Mighty to Save" (Gen)
    M246, WS3038

"Through It All" (Gen, Pss)
    C555, F43, UM507
"*Jesu, Jesu*" (Gen, Luke)
    B501, C600, E602, EL708, G203, N498, P367, UM432,
    VU593, W431, S-1 #63. Vocal part
"Bind Us Together" (Gen, Luke)
    S2226, SF2226, SP140
"Love the Lord Your God" (Luke)
    G62, S2168, SF2168
"Make Me a Channel of Your Peace" (Luke)
    G753, S2171, SF2171, VU684
"Live in Charity" ("*Ubi Caritas*") (Luke)
    C523, EL642, G205, S2179, SF2179, W604
"The Family Prayer Song" ("As for Me and My House") (Luke)
    M54, S2188, SF2188
"They'll Know We Are Christians" (Luke)
    AH4074, C494, G300, S2223, SF2223
"Love the Lord" (Luke)
    WS3116, M270
"Welcome" (Luke)
    WS3152
"Let It Be Said of Us" (Luke)
    M53

Vocal Solos

"Then Shall the Righteous Shine Forth" (Gen, Pss)
    V-8   p. 274
"Patiently Have I Waited for the Lord" (Pss)
    V-4   p. 24
"Make Me a Channel of Your Peace" (Gen, Luke)
    V-3 (2)   p. 25
    V-3 (3)   p. 28
    S2171

Anthems

"Kyrie Eleison" (Luke)
David Angerman; Shawnee 35028585
SATB and piano (bit.ly/35028585)

"*Amen Siakudumisa*" (Black History)
Arr. Cameron F. LaBarr; Choristers Guild CGA1285
SATB and opt. percussion (bit.ly/CGA1285)

Other Suggestions

Visuals:
    O   tears, famine, Egyptian motif, embrace
    P   grass, heart, light, prosperity, rescue
    E   wheat, variety of seeds, resurrection, Adam, Christ
    G   cheek, coat, shirt, 6:31, love at work, measure
Introit: WS3153, stanzas 1, 4. "O God, In Whom We Live" (Gen,
    Luke)
Response: AH4098, B420, N416, UM464. "I Will Trust in the
    Lord" (Pss, Black History)
Affirmation of Faith: WSL76 (1 Cor)
Prayer of Confession: WSL84 (Gen, Luke)
Words of Assurance: G445, S2169, SF2169. "God, How Can We
    Forgive," stanza 2 (Gen, Luke)
Sung Benediction: C662, EL725, G762, P407, UM434, VU702,
    stanza 3. "*Cuando El Pobre*" ("When the Poor Ones") (Luke)
Benediction: C30, EL846, G598, N760, S2067, SF2067, VU431.
    "*Amen Siakudumisa*" ("Great Amen") (Black History)

Exodus 34:29-35

²⁹Moses came down from Mount Sinai. As he came down from the mountain with the two covenant tablets in his hand, Moses didn't realize that the skin of his face shone brightly because he had been talking with God. ³⁰When Aaron and all the Israelites saw the skin of Moses' face shining brightly, they were afraid to come near him. ³¹But Moses called them closer. So Aaron and all the leaders of the community came back to him, and Moses spoke with them. ³²After that, all the Israelites came near as well, and Moses commanded them everything that the LORD had spoken with him on Mount Sinai. ³³When Moses finished speaking with them, he put a veil over his face. ³⁴Whenever Moses went into the LORD's presence to speak with him, Moses would take the veil off until he came out again. When Moses came out and told the Israelites what he had been commanded, ³⁵the Israelites would see that the skin of Moses' face was shining brightly. So Moses would put the veil on his face again until the next time he went in to speak with the LORD.

Psalm 99 (G57, N687, UM819)

The LORD rules—
  the nations shake!
  He sits enthroned on the winged heavenly creatures—
  the earth quakes!
²The LORD is great in Zion;
  he is exalted over all the nations.
³Let them thank your great and awesome name.
  He is holy!
⁴Strong king who loves justice,
  you are the one who established what is fair.
  You worked justice and righteousness in Jacob.
⁵Magnify the LORD, our God!
  Bow low at his footstool!
  He is holy!
⁶Moses and Aaron were among his priests,
  Samuel too among those who called on his name.
They cried out to the LORD, and he himself answered them—
  ⁷he spoke to them from a pillar of cloud.
They kept the laws and the rules God gave to them.
⁸LORD our God, you answered them.
  To them you were a God who forgives
  but also the one who avenged their wrong deeds.
⁹Magnify the LORD our God!
  Bow low at his holy mountain
  because the LORD our God is holy!

2 Corinthians 3:12–4:2

¹²So, since we have such a hope, we act with great confidence. ¹³We aren't like Moses, who used to put a veil over his face so that the Israelites couldn't watch the end of what was fading away. ¹⁴But their minds were closed. Right up to the present day the same veil remains when the old covenant is read. The veil is not removed because it is taken away by Christ. ¹⁵Even today, whenever Moses is read, a veil lies over their hearts. ¹⁶But whenever someone turns back to the Lord, the veil is removed. ¹⁷The Lord is the Spirit, and where the Lord's Spirit is, there is freedom. ¹⁸All of us are looking with unveiled faces at the glory of the Lord as if we were looking in a mirror. We are being transformed into that same image from one degree of glory to the next degree of glory. This comes from the Lord, who is the Spirit.

4 This is why we don't get discouraged, given that we received this ministry in the same way that we received God's mercy. ²Instead, we reject secrecy and shameful actions. We don't use deception, and we don't tamper with God's word. Instead, we commend ourselves to everyone's conscience in the sight of God by the public announcement of the truth.

Luke 9:28-36 (37-43a)

²⁸About eight days after Jesus said these things, he took Peter, John, and James, and went up on a mountain to pray. ²⁹As he was praying, the appearance of his face changed and his clothes flashed white like lightning. ³⁰Two men, Moses and Elijah, were talking with him. ³¹They were clothed with heavenly splendor and spoke about Jesus' departure, which he would achieve in Jerusalem. ³²Peter and those with him were almost overcome by sleep, but they managed to stay awake and saw his glory as well as the two men with him.

³³As the two men were about to leave Jesus, Peter said to him, "Master, it's good that we're here. We should construct three shrines: one for you, one for Moses, and one for Elijah"—but he didn't know what he was saying. ³⁴Peter was still speaking when a cloud overshadowed them. As they entered the cloud, they were overcome with awe.

³⁵Then a voice from the cloud said, "This is my Son, my chosen one. Listen to him!" ³⁶Even as the voice spoke, Jesus was found alone. They were speechless and at the time told no one what they had seen.

³⁷The next day, when Jesus, Peter, John, and James had come down from the mountain, a large crowd met Jesus. ³⁸A man from the crowd shouted, "Teacher, I beg you to take a look at my son, my only child. ³⁹Look, a spirit seizes him and, without any warning, he screams. It shakes him and causes him to foam at the mouth. It tortures him and rarely leaves him alone. ⁴⁰I begged your disciples to throw it out, but they couldn't."

⁴¹Jesus answered, "You faithless and crooked generation, how long will I be with you and put up with you? Bring your son here." ⁴²While he was coming, the demon threw him down and shook him violently. Jesus spoke harshly to the unclean spirit, healed the child, and gave him back to his father. ⁴³ᵃEveryone was overwhelmed by God's greatness.

Primary Hymns and Songs for the Day

"When Morning Gilds the Skies" (Exod, Luke) (O)
   B221, C100, E427, EL853 (PD), F322, G667, L546, N86,
   P487, UM185, VU339 (Fr.), W675
      H-3   Hbl-103; Chr-126, 216; Desc-68; Org-76
      S-1   #208. Intro. and interlude
      S-2   #107-109. Harm. and Desc.

"Holy Ground" (Exod, Luke)
   B224, C112, G406, S2272, SF2272, SP86

"Shine, Jesus, Shine" (2 Cor, Transfig.)
   B579, EL671, G192, S2173, SF2173, SP142

"Christ, Whose Glory Fills the Skies" (Luke)
   EL553, F293, G662, L265, P462/463, UM173 (PD), VU336
      H-3   Hbl-51; Chr-206; Desc-89; Org-120
      S-1   #278-279. Harm.

"O Wondrous Sight! O Vision Fair" (Luke)
   E137, UM258 (PD)
      H-3   Hbl-93; Chr-84; Desc-102; Org-175
      S-2   #191. Harm.
      S-2   #191. Harm.
   EL316 (PD), G189, L80, N184, P75

"Jesus, Take Us to the Mountain" (Luke)
   G193, N183

"Be Thou My Vision" (Luke) (C)
   B60, C595, E488, EL793, F468, G450, N451, P339, UM451,
   VU642
      H-3   Hbl-15, 48; Chr-36; Org-153
      S-1   #319. Arr. for organ and voices in canon

Additional Hymn Suggestions

"Immortal, Invisible, God Only Wise" (Exod)
   B6, C66, E423, EL834, F319, G12, L526, N1, P263, UM103
   (PD), VU264, W512

"Every Time I Feel the Spirit" (Exod)
   C592, G66, N282, P315, UM404

"My Hope Is Built" (2 Cor, Transfig.)
   B406, C537, EL596, G353, N368, P379, UM368

"Spirit of the Living God" (2 Cor)
   B244, C259, G288, N283, P322, SP131, UM393, VU376

"Come, Holy Ghost, Our Souls Inspire" (2 Cor)
   E503/504, L472/473, N268, G278, P125, UM651, VU201

"O Splendor of God's Glory Bright" (2 Cor)
   E5, G666, N87, P474, UM679, VU413

"Thee We Adore, O Hidden Savior, Thee" (2 Cor)
   EL476 (PD), G495, L199, P519

"Sing of God Made Manifest" (Luke)
   C176, G156

"Here, O My Lord, I See Thee" (Luke, Comm.)
   C416, E318, G517, L211, N336, P520, UM623, VU459

"God Is Here Today" ("Dios Está Aquí") (Luke)
   G411, S2049, SF2049

"Swiftly Pass the Clouds of Glory" (Luke)
   G190, P73, S2102

"We Have Come at Christ's Own Bidding" (Luke) (O)
   G191, N182, S2103, SF2103, VU104

"You, Lord, Are Both Lamb and Shepherd" (Transfig.)
   G274, SF2102, VU210, WS3043

Additional Contemporary Suggestions

"Arise, Shine" (Exod, Luke, Transfig.)
   S2005, SF2005

"You Have Saved Us" (Exod, Luke)
   M266

"Come, All You People" ("Uyai Mose") (Pss)
   EL819, G388, S2274, SF2274

"Where the Spirit of the Lord Is" (2 Cor)
   C264, S2119, SF2119

"Shine on Us" (2 Cor, Transfig.)
   M19

"Let It Rise" (2 Cor)
   M4

"In Christ Alone" ("My Hope Is Found") (2 Cor, Transfig.)
   M138, WS3105

"Turn Your Eyes upon Jesus" (Luke)
   B320, F621, SP218, UM349

"Awesome in This Place" (Luke)
   M36

"We Declare Your Majesty" (Luke)
   M43

"He Is Exalted" (Luke)
   S2070, SF2070, SP66

"Honor and Praise" (Luke)
   S2018, SF2018

"All Hail King Jesus" (Luke, Transfig.)
   S2069, SF2069, SP63

"How Great Is Our God" (Luke, Transfig.)
   WS3003, M117

"Jesus, the Light of the World" (Luke)
   AH4038, G127, N160 (See also WS3056)

"Lord Jesus Christ, Your Light Shines" (Luke)
   WS3137

"Beautiful Savior" (Transfig.)
   M243

"Great and Mighty Is He" (Transfig.)
   SP4, M11

Vocal Solos

"Be Thou My Vision" (Exod, Luke)
Inclusive Text UM451
      V-6   p. 13
"Shine, Jesus, Shine" (Luke, Transfig.)
      V-3 (2)   p. 48
"I Saw the Lord, and All Beside Was Darkness" (Transfig.)
      V-8   p. 268

Anthems

"Come, All You People" ("Uyai Mose") (Pss)
Arr. Kevin Holland; Choristers Guild CGA1373
SATB with percussion (bit.ly/CGA1373)

"Be Thou My Vision" (Luke)
Arr. Marie Pooler; AEC-1 p. 9
Unison and keyboard, opt. descant

Other Suggestions

Visuals:
      O   Mountain, tablets, veil
      P   Throne, earthquake, footstool, cloud, mountain
      E   Veil, glory, mirror, transformer, Bible, 2 Cor 3:17b
      G   Mountain, prayer, dazzling light, 3 booths, cloud
Introit: EL529, G392, S2273, SF2273. "Jesus, We Are Here"
   ("Yesu Tawa Pano") (Luke, Black History)
Prayers: C332, N826, UM259, WSL13 (Transfig.)
Scripture Response: E440, EL520, G395, N74, P454, UM596
   (PD), VU500, stanza 3. "Blessed Jesus, at Thy Word" (2 Cor)

Joel 2:1-2, 12-17

Blow the horn in Zion;
  give a shout on my holy mountain!
Let all the people of the land tremble,
  for the day of the LORD is coming.
It is near—
  ²a day of darkness and no light,
  a day of clouds and thick darkness!
Like blackness spread out upon the mountains,
  a great and powerful army comes,
    unlike any that has ever come before them,
    or will come after them in centuries ahead.
. . . .
¹²Yet even now, says the LORD,
  return to me with all your hearts,
    with fasting, with weeping, and with sorrow;
¹³tear your hearts
  and not your clothing.
  Return to the LORD your God,
    for he is merciful and compassionate,
    very patient, full of faithful love,
    and ready to forgive.
¹⁴Who knows whether he will have a change of heart
  and leave a blessing behind him,
  a grain offering and a drink offering
    for the LORD your God?
¹⁵Blow the horn in Zion;
  demand a fast;
  request a special assembly.
¹⁶Gather the people;
  prepare a holy meeting;
  assemble the elders;
  gather the children,
    even nursing infants.
Let the groom leave his room
  and the bride her chamber.
¹⁷Between the porch and the altar
  let the priests, the LORD's ministers, weep.
  Let them say, "Have mercy, LORD, on your people,
  and don't make your inheritance a disgrace,
  an example of failure among the nations.
  Why should they say among the peoples,
    'Where is their God?'"

Psalm 51:1-17 (G421-423, N657, P195/196, UM785)

Have mercy on me, God, according to your faithful love!
  Wipe away my wrongdoings according to your great
    compassion!
²Wash me completely clean of my guilt;
  purify me from my sin!
³Because I know my wrongdoings,
  my sin is always right in front of me.
⁴I've sinned against you—you alone.
  I've committed evil in your sight.
That's why you are justified when you render your verdict,
  completely correct when you issue your judgment.
⁵Yes, I was born in guilt, in sin,
  from the moment my mother conceived me.
⁶And yes, you want truth in the most hidden places;
  you teach me wisdom in the most secret space.
⁷Purify me with hyssop and I will be clean;
  wash me and I will be whiter than snow.
⁸Let me hear joy and celebration again;
  let the bones you crushed rejoice once more.
⁹Hide your face from my sins;
  wipe away all my guilty deeds!
¹⁰Create a clean heart for me, God;
  put a new, faithful spirit deep inside me!
¹¹Please don't throw me out of your presence;

please don't take your holy spirit away from me.
¹²Return the joy of your salvation to me
  and sustain me with a willing spirit.
¹³Then I will teach wrongdoers your ways,
  and sinners will come back to you.
¹⁴Deliver me from violence, God, God of my salvation,
  so that my tongue can sing of your righteousness.
¹⁵Lord, open my lips,
  and my mouth will proclaim your praise.
¹⁶You don't want sacrifices.
  If I gave an entirely burned offering,
  you wouldn't be pleased.
¹⁷A broken spirit is my sacrifice, God.
  You won't despise a heart, God, that is broken and crushed.

2 Corinthians 5:20b–6:10

²⁰ᵇWe beg you as Christ's representatives, "Be reconciled to God!" ²¹God caused the one who didn't know sin to be sin for our sake so that through him we could become the righteousness of God.

6 Since we work together with him, we are also begging you not to receive the grace of God in vain. ²He says, *I listened to you at the right time, and I helped you on the day of salvation.* Look, now is the right time! Look, now is the day of salvation!

³We don't give anyone any reason to be offended about anything so that our ministry won't be criticized. ⁴Instead, we commend ourselves as ministers of God in every way. We did this with our great endurance through problems, disasters, and stressful situations. ⁵We went through beatings, imprisonments, and riots. We experienced hard work, sleepless nights, and hunger. ⁶We displayed purity, knowledge, patience, and generosity. We served with the Holy Spirit, genuine love,⁷telling the truth, and God's power. We carried the weapons of righteousness in our right hand and our left hand. ⁸We were treated with honor and dishonor and with verbal abuse and good evaluation. We were seen as both fake and real, ⁹as unknown and well known, as dying—and look, we are alive! We were seen as punished but not killed, ¹⁰as going through pain but always happy, as poor but making many rich, and as having nothing but owning everything.

Matthew 6:1-6, 16-21

"Be careful that you don't practice your religion in front of people to draw their attention. If you do, you will have no reward from your Father who is in heaven.

²"Whenever you give to the poor, don't blow your trumpet as the hypocrites do in the synagogues and in the streets so that they may get praise from people. I assure you, that's the only reward they'll get. ³But when you give to the poor, don't let your left hand know what your right hand is doing ⁴so that you may give to the poor in secret. Your Father who sees what you do in secret will reward you.

⁵"When you pray, don't be like hypocrites. They love to pray standing in the synagogues and on the street corners so that people will see them. I assure you, that's the only reward they'll get. ⁶But when you pray, go to your room, shut the door, and pray to your Father who is present in that secret place. Your Father who sees what you do in secret will reward you. . . .

¹⁶"And when you fast, don't put on a sad face like the hypocrites. They distort their faces so people will know they are fasting. I assure you that they have their reward. ¹⁷When you fast, brush your hair and wash your face. ¹⁸Then you won't look like you are fasting to people, but only to your Father who is present in that secret place. Your Father who sees in secret will reward you.

¹⁹"Stop collecting treasures for your own benefit on earth, where moth and rust eat them and where thieves break in and steal them. ²⁰Instead, collect treasures for yourselves in heaven, where moth and rust don't eat them and where thieves don't break in and steal them. ²¹Where your treasure is, there your heart will be also."

Primary Hymns and Songs for the Day

"Lord, Who Throughout These Forty Days" (Lent) (O)
    C180, E142, EL319, G166, N211, P81, UM269, W417
        H-3   Chr-106; Desc-65; Org-72
        S-2   #105. Flute/violin Desc.
              #106. Harm.
"More Love to Thee, O Christ" (Matt)
    B473, C527, F476, G828, N456, P359, UM453 (PD)
        H-3   Org-94
"Come and Find the Quiet Center" (Matt)
    C575, S2128, SF2128, VU374
"Sunday's Palms Are Wednesday's Ashes" (Pss)
    S2138, SF2138, VU107
        H-3   Hbl-14, 64; Chr-132, 203
        S-2   #22. Descant
"Lord, I Want to Be a Christian" (Joel, Matt) (C)
    B489, C589, F421, G729, N454, P372 (PD), UM402
        H-3   Chr-130

Additional Hymn Suggestions

"O Master, Let Me Walk with Thee" (Joel)
    B279, C602, E659/660, EL818, F442, G738, L492, N503,
    P357, UM430 (PD), VU560
"Jesus, the Very Thought of Thee" (2 Cor)
    B225, C102, E642, EL754, F465, G629, L316, N507, P310,
    UM175 (PD)
"Alas! and Did My Savior Bleed" (2 Cor)
    B145, EL337, F274, G212, L98, N200, P78, UM294 (PD)
    B139, C204, N199, UM359 (PD) (alternate tune)
"What Wondrous Love Is This" (2 Cor)
    B143 (PD), C200, E439, EL666, F283, G215, L385, N223,
    P85, UM292, VU147 (Fr.), W600
"We Walk by Faith" (2 Cor, Matt)
    E209, EL635, G817, N256, P399, S2196, SF2196, W572
"Amazing Grace" (Matt)
    B330, C546, E671, EL779, F107, G649, L448, N547 and N548,
    P280, UM378 (PD), VU266 (Fr.), W583
"The Lord's Prayer" (Matt)
    B462, C307-C310, F440, G464, P589, S2278, SF2278. UM271,
    WS3068-WS3071
"Be Thou My Vision" (Matt)
    B60, C595, E488, EL793, F468, G450, N451, P339, UM451,
    VU642
"Near to the Heart of God" (Matt)
    B295, C581, F35, G824, P527, UM472 (PD)
"The Glory of These Forty Days" (Matt)
    E143, EL320, G165, P87, W422
"Forty Days and Forty Nights" (Matt)
    C179, E150, G167, N205, P77, VU114, W419

Additional Contemporary Suggestions

"Shout to the North" (Joel, Pss)
    G319, M99, WS3042
"Because of Your Love" (Joel, Pss, Lent)
    M224
"Purify My Heart" (Pss)
    M90, WS3103
"Give Us Clean Hands" (Pss, Ash Wednesday, Comm.)
    M153
"Grace Like Rain" (Pss, Lent)
    M251
"Hosanna" (Pss, Lent)
    WS3188, M268
"How Great Is the Love" (Pss, Lent)
    M277

"Give Me a Clean Heart" (Pss)
    C515, N188, S2133, SF2133
"Come and Fill Our Hearts" (Pss)
    EL538, G466, S2157, SF2157, W561
"Change My Heart, O God" (Pss)
    EL801, G695, SP195, S2152, SF2152
"You Are My Hiding Place" (Pss, Matt)
    C554, S2055, SF2055
"Open Our Eyes, Lord" (Pss, Matt)
    B499, S2086, SF2086, SP199
"The Power of Your Love" (Pss, Matt)
    M26
"Open the Eyes of My Heart" (Pss, Matt)
    G452, M57, WS3008
"I Will Boast" (2 Cor)
    M227
"Jesus, We Are Here" (Matt, Black History)
    EL529, G392, S2273, SF2273
"In the Secret" ("I Want to Know You") (Matt)
    M38
"When It's All Been Said and Done" (Matt)
    M115
"Be the Centre" (Matt)
    M156
"As It Is in Heaven" (Matt)
    M241
"You Are My All in All" (Matt, Lent)
    G519, SP220, WS3040

Vocal Solos

"If With All Your Hearts" (Joel)
    V-8   p. 277
"A Contrite Heart" (Pss)
    V-4   p. 10
"Turn My Heart to You" (Pss)
    V-5(2)   p. 14
"The Gospel of Grace" (Matt)
    V-3 (1)   p.44

Anthems

"A Right Spirit" (Pss)
Stephan Casurella; AEC-3 p. 5
Treble voices and organ, opt. descant

"Out of the Depths I Cry to Thee" (Ash Wednesday)
Arr. K. Lee Scott; AEC-1 p.47
2-part mixed and keyboard

Other Suggestions

Visuals:
    O   Trumpet, alarm, dark, cloud, weeping, heart
    P   Blot, wash, heart, hyssop, snow, Ps 51:10, joy, sing
    E   Christ, cross, clock, suffer, serve, weep/joy
    G   Hands, prayer, closed door, oil/basin, moth/rust,
           treasure/heart, treasure box
Call to Prayer: EL752, S2207, SF2207. "Lord, Listen to Your
    Children" (Matt)
Prayers: WSL14, WSL15, WSL123, C456, C574 (Ash Wed.)
Confession and Assurance: N846 and N840 (Joel)
Sung Confession: G431, S2134, SF2134. "Forgive Us, Lord" (Pss,
    Matt)

Deuteronomy 26:1-11

Once you have entered the land the LORD your God is giving you as an inheritance, and you take possession of it and are settled there, ²take some of the early produce of the fertile ground that you have harvested from the land the LORD your God is giving you, and put it in a basket. Then go to the location the LORD your God selects for his name to reside. ³Go to the priest who is in office at that time and say to him: "I am declaring right now before the LORD my God that I have indeed arrived in the land the LORD swore to our ancestors to give us."

⁴The priest will then take the basket from you and place it before the LORD your God's altar. ⁵Then you should solemnly state before the LORD your God:

"My father was a starving Aramean. He went down to Egypt, living as an immigrant there with few family members, but that is where he became a great nation, mighty and numerous. ⁶The Egyptians treated us terribly, oppressing us and forcing hard labor on us. ⁷So we cried out for help to the LORD, our ancestors' God. The LORD heard our call. God saw our misery, our trouble, and our oppression. ⁸The LORD brought us out of Egypt with a strong hand and an outstretched arm, with awesome power, and with signs and wonders. ⁹He brought us to this place and gave us this land—a land full of milk and honey. ¹⁰So now I am bringing the early produce of the fertile ground that you, LORD, have given me."

Set the produce before the LORD your God, bowing down before the LORD your God. ¹¹Then celebrate all the good things the LORD your God has done for you and your family—each one of you along with the Levites and the immigrants who are among you.

Psalm 91:1-2, 9-16 (G43/168, N681, P212, UM810)

Living in the Most High's shelter,
  camping in the Almighty's shade,
²I say to the LORD, "You are my refuge, my stronghold!
  You are my God—the one I trust!"
. . . .
Because you've made the LORD my refuge,
  the Most High, your place of residence—
    ¹⁰no evil will happen to you;
    no disease will come close to your tent.
¹¹Because he will order his messengers to help you,
  to protect you wherever you go.
¹²They will carry you with their own hands
  so you don't bruise your foot on a stone.
¹³You'll march on top of lions and vipers;
  you'll trample young lions and serpents underfoot.
¹⁴God says, "Because you are devoted to me,
  I'll rescue you.
  I'll protect you because you know my name.
¹⁵Whenever you cry out to me, I'll answer.
  I'll be with you in troubling times.
  I'll save you and glorify you.
¹⁶I'll fill you full with old age.
  I'll show you my salvation."

Romans 10:8b-13

⁸ᵇ*The word is near you, in your mouth and in your heart* (that is, the message of faith that we preach).⁹Because if you confess with your mouth "Jesus is Lord" and in your heart you have faith that God raised him from the dead, you will be saved. ¹⁰Trusting with the heart leads to righteousness, and confessing with the mouth leads to salvation. ¹¹The scripture says, *All who have faith in him won't be put to shame.* ¹²There is no distinction between Jew and Greek, because the same Lord is Lord of all, who gives richly to all who call on him. ¹³*All who call on the Lord's name will be saved.*

Luke 4:1-13

Jesus returned from the Jordan River full of the Holy Spirit, and was led by the Spirit into the wilderness. ²There he was tempted for forty days by the devil. He ate nothing during those days and afterward Jesus was starving. ³The devil said to him, "Since you are God's Son, command this stone to become a loaf of bread."

⁴Jesus replied, "It's written, *People won't live only by bread.*"

⁵Next the devil led him to a high place and showed him in a single instant all the kingdoms of the world. ⁶The devil said, "I will give you this whole domain and the glory of all these kingdoms. It's been entrusted to me and I can give it to anyone I want. ⁷Therefore, if you will worship me, it will all be yours."

⁸Jesus answered, "It's written, *You will worship the Lord your God and serve only him.*"

⁹The devil brought him into Jerusalem and stood him at the highest point of the temple. He said to him, "Since you are God's Son, throw yourself down from here; ¹⁰for it's written: *He will command his angels concerning you, to protect you* ¹¹*and they will take you up in their hands so that you won't hit your foot on a stone.*"

¹²Jesus answered, "It's been said, *Don't test the Lord your God.*" ¹³After finishing every temptation, the devil departed from him until the next opportunity.

Primary Hymns and Songs for the Day

"Lord, Who Throughout These Forty Days" (Luke) (O)
    C180, E142, EL319, G166, N211, P81, UM269, W417

"The God of Abraham Praise" (Deut) (O)
    B34, C24, E401, EL831, F332, G49, L544, N24, P488, UM116
    (PD), VU255, W537
        H-3   Hbl-62, 95; Chr-59; Org-77
        S-1   #211. Harm.

"Praise, My Soul, the King of Heaven" (Deut) (O)
    B32, C23, E410, EL864/865, F339, G619/620, L549,
    P478/479, UM66 (PD), VU240, W530
        H-3   Hbl-88; Chr-162; Desc-67; Org-75
        S-1   #205. Harm.
                    #206. Descant

"As Those of Old Their First Fruits Brought" (Deut)
    B639, E705, G712, P414, VU518

"The Glory of These Forty Days" (Luke)
    E143, EL320, G165, P87, W422

"Forty Days and Forty Nights" (Luke)
    C179, E150, G167, N205, P77, VU114, W419

"Jesus Walked This Lonesome Valley" (Luke, Lent) (C)
    C211, F217, P80, S2112, W427

Additional Hymn Suggestions

"For the Fruits of This Creation" (Deut)
    B643, C714, E424, EL679, G36, L563, N425, P553, UM97,
    VU227, W562

"In the Midst of New Dimensions" (Deut)
    G315, N391, S2238, SF2238

"Praise God for This Holy Ground" (Deut, Luke)
    G405, WS3009

"O Holy Spirit, Root of Life" (Pss, Lent)
    C251, EL399, N57, S2121, SF2121, VU379

"I Love to Tell the Story" (Rom)
    B572, C480, EL661, G462, L390, N522, UM156, VU343

"In Christ There Is No East or West" (Rom)
    B385, C687, E529, EL650 (PD), F685, G317/318, L359,
    N394/395, P439/440, UM548, VU606, W659

"Come, Share the Lord" ("We Gather Here") (Rom)
    C408, G510, S2269, SF2269, VU469

"A Place at the Table" (Rom, Comm.)
    G769, WS3149

"We Walk by Faith" (Rom, Luke)
    E209, EL635, G817, N256, P399, S2196, SF2196, W572

"Hope of the World" (Luke)
    C538, E472, G734, L493, N46, P360, UM178, VU215

"We Meet You, O Christ" (Luke)
    P311, UM257, VU183

"Loving Spirit" (Luke)
    C244, EL397, G293, P323, S2123, SF2123, VU387

Additional Contemporary Suggestions

"Nothing Can Trouble" ("*Nada Te Turbe*") (Pss)
    G820, S2054, SF2054, VU290

"Holy Spirit, Come to Us" (Pss)
    EL406, G281, S2118, SF2118, W473

"Everlasting God" (Pss)
    M182, WS3021

"Still" (Pss, Lent)
    M216, WS3134

"The Power of Your Love" (Pss, Lent)
    M26

"Who Can Satisfy My Soul Like You?" (Pss)
    M28

"Better Is One Day" (Pss)
    M60

"I Stand Amazed" (Pss, Lent)
    M79

"Eagle's Wings" (Pss)
    M158

"Came to My Rescue" (Pss)
    M257

"Made Me Glad" (Pss, Luke)
    M123

"I Will Call upon the Lord" (Rom)
    G621, S2002, SF2002, SP224

"Please Enter My Heart, Hosanna" (Rom)
    S2154, SF2154

"God Is So Good" (Rom)
    B23, G658, S2056, SF2056

"God Is Good, All the Time" (Rom)
    AH4010, M45, WS3026

"Come, Now Is the Time to Worship" (Rom)
    M56, WS3176

"He Is Lord" (Rom)
    B178, C117, F234, SP122, UM177

"At the Cross" (Rom, Lent)
    M225

"That's Why We Praise Him" (Luke, Lent)
    M94

"How Great Is the Love" (Lent)
    M277

Vocal Solos

"On Eagle's Wings" (Pss)
    V-3 (2)   p. 2
    V-3 (3)   p. 4

"It Is Well with My Soul" (Pss)
    V-5(2)   p. 35

"Prayer" (Pss)
    V-9   p. 32

"Grace Greater Than Our Sin" (Rom)
    V-8   p. 180

Anthems

"Praise, My Soul, the King of Heaven" (Deut)
Arr. Howard Helvey; Hinshaw HMC2464
SATB and organ, opt. brass (bit.ly/HMC2464)

"Not What These Hands Have Done" (Luke)
Jonathan Kohrs; Augsburg 978-1-4514-9255-2
SATB a cappella (bit.ly/9255-2)

Other Suggestions

This day may include an observance of Girl Scout Sunday.
Visuals:
    O   Basket with food/produce, hand, arm, wrapped gift
    P   Angels, stone, lion, snake, "deliverance"
    E   Faces, professing, multiracial, all ages, Christ
    G   Loaf bread, stone (also arranged as a wall), angels
Introit: S2138, SF2138, VU107. "Sunday's Palms Are Wednesday's
    Ashes," stanza 1 (Lent)
Call to Prayer or Response to Psalm: S2053, SF2053. "If It Had
    Not Been for the Lord" (Pss)
Prayers: WSL14, WSL16, UM268, C178, F218 (Luke, Lent)

Genesis 15:1-12, 17-18

After these events, the LORD's word came to Abram in a vision, "Don't be afraid, Abram. I am your protector. Your reward will be very great."

²But Abram said, "LORD God, what can you possibly give me, since I still have no children? The head of my household is Eliezer, a man from Damascus." ³He continued, "Since you haven't given me any children, the head of my household will be my heir."

⁴The LORD's word came immediately to him, "This man will not be your heir. Your heir will definitely be your very own biological child." ⁵Then he brought Abram outside and said, "Look up at the sky and count the stars if you think you can count them." He continued, "This is how many children you will have." ⁶Abram trusted the LORD, and the LORD recognized Abram's high moral character.

⁷He said to Abram, "I am the LORD, who brought you out of Ur of the Chaldeans to give you this land as your possession."

⁸But Abram said, "LORD God, how do I know that I will actually possess it?"

⁹He said, "Bring me a three-year-old female calf, a three-year-old female goat, a three-year-old ram, a dove, and a young pigeon." ¹⁰He took all of these animals, split them in half, and laid the halves facing each other, but he didn't split the birds.¹¹When vultures swooped down on the carcasses, Abram waved them off. ¹²After the sun set, Abram slept deeply. A terrifying and deep darkness settled over him. . . .

¹⁷After the sun had set and darkness had deepened, a smoking vessel with a fiery flame passed between the split-open animals.¹⁸That day the LORD cut a covenant with Abram: "To your descendants I give this land, from Egypt's river to the great Euphrates."

Psalm 27 (G90, G841/842, N637, P179, UM758)

The LORD is my light and my salvation.
    Should I fear anyone?
  The LORD is a fortress protecting my life.
    Should I be frightened of anything?
²When evildoers come at me trying to eat me up—
  it's they, my foes and my enemies,
  who stumble and fall!
³If an army camps against me,
  my heart won't be afraid.
  If war comes up against me,
  I will continue to trust in this:
⁴I have asked one thing from the LORD—
  it's all I seek:
    to live in the LORD's house all the days of my life,
    seeing the LORD's beauty
    and constantly adoring his temple.
⁵Because he will shelter me in his own dwelling
  during troubling times;
  he will hide me in a secret place in his own tent;
  he will set me up high, safe on a rock.
⁶Now my head is higher than the enemies surrounding me,
  and I will offer sacrifices in God's tent—
    sacrifices with shouts of joy!
  I will sing and praise the LORD.
⁷LORD, listen to my voice when I cry out—
  have mercy on me and answer me!
⁸Come, my heart says, seek God's face.
  LORD, I do seek your face!
⁹Please don't hide it from me!
  Don't push your servant aside angrily—
    you have been my help!

God who saves me,
    don't neglect me!
    Don't leave me all alone!
¹⁰Even if my father and mother left me all alone,
  the LORD would take me in.
¹¹LORD, teach me your way;
  because of my opponents, lead me on a good path.
¹²Don't give me over to the desires of my enemies,
  because false witnesses and violent accusers
  have taken their stand against me.
¹³But I have sure faith
  that I will experience the LORD's goodness
  in the land of the living!
¹⁴Hope in the LORD!
  Be strong! Let your heart take courage!
    Hope in the LORD!

Philippians 3:17–4:1

¹⁷Brothers and sisters, become imitators of me and watch those who live this way—you can use us as models. ¹⁸As I have told you many times and now say with deep sadness, many people live as enemies of the cross. ¹⁹Their lives end with destruction. Their god is their stomach, and they take pride in their disgrace because their thoughts focus on earthly things.²⁰Our citizenship is in heaven. We look forward to a savior that comes from there—the LORD Jesus Christ. ²¹He will transform our humble bodies so that they are like his glorious body, by the power that also makes him able to subject all things to himself.

4 Therefore, my brothers and sisters whom I love and miss, who are my joy and crown, stand firm in the Lord.

Luke 13:31-35

³¹At that time, some Pharisees approached Jesus and said, "Go! Get away from here, because Herod wants to kill you."

³²Jesus said to them, "Go, tell that fox, 'Look, I'm throwing out demons and healing people today and tomorrow, and on the third day I will complete my work. ³³However, it's necessary for me to travel today, tomorrow, and the next day because it's impossible for a prophet to be killed outside of Jerusalem.'

³⁴"Jerusalem, Jerusalem, you who kill the prophets and stone those who were sent to you! How often I have wanted to gather your people just as a hen gathers her chicks under her wings. But you didn't want that. ³⁵ Look, your house is abandoned. I tell you, you won't see me until the time comes when you say, *Blessings on the one who comes in the Lord's name.*"

Primary Hymns and Songs for the Day

"The God of Abraham Praise" (Gen) (O)
B34, C24, E401, EL831, F332, G49, L544, N24, P488, UM116
(PD), VU255, W537
>> H-3   Hbl-62, 95; Chr-59; Org-77
>> S-1   #211. Harm.

"In the Cross of Christ I Glory" (Phil) (C)
B554, C207, E441, EL324, F251, G213, L104, N193, P84,
UM295
>> H-3   Hbl-72; Chr-113; Desc-89; Org-119
>> S-1   #276-277. Desc. and Harm.

"O Jesus, I Have Promised" (Phil) (C)
B276, C612, E655, EL810, F402, G724/725, L503, N493,
P388/389, UM396 (PD), VU120
>> S-2   #9. Descant

"We Sing to You, O God" (Luke) (C)
EL791, N9, S2001, SF2001
>> H-3   Hbl-8, 53, 90; Chr-37; Desc-27; Org-24
>> S-1   #78-80. Various treatments

Additional Hymn Suggestions

"Great Is Thy Faithfulness" (Gen) (O)
B54, C86, EL733, G39, N423, P276, UM140, VU288

"If Thou But Suffer God to Guide Thee" (Gen)
B57, C565, E635, EL769, G816, L453, N410, P282, UM142
(PD), VU285 (Fr.) and VU286

"A Hymn of Glory Let Us Sing" (Gen)
E218, G258, L157, N259, P141, W469

"Jesus, Lover of My Soul" (Pss)
B180 (PD), C542, E699, F222, G440, N546, P303, UM479
(PD), VU669

"Lead On, O King Eternal" (Pss, Phil)
B621, C632, E555, EL805, F595, G269, L495, N573, P447/
P448, UM580

"Immortal, Invisible, God Only Wise" (Phil)
B6, C66, E423, EL834, F319, G12, L526, N1, P263, UM103
(PD), VU264, W512

"O Sacred Head, Now Wounded" (Phil)
B137, C202, E168/169, EL351/352, F284, G221, L116/117,
N226, P98, UM286, VU145 (Fr.), W434

"I Am Thine, O Lord" (Phil)
B290, C601, F455, N455, UM419 (PD)

"Fight the Good Fight" (Phil)
E552, F613, G846, L461, P307 (PD), VU674

"By Gracious Powers" (Phil, Luke)
E695/696, G818, N413, P342, UM517, W577

"Praise to the Lord, the Almighty" (Luke)
B14, C25, E390, EL858 (PD) and 859, F337, G35, L543, N22,
P482, UM139, VU220 (Fr.) and VU221, W547

"O Love, How Deep" (Luke, Comm.)
E448/449, EL322, G618, N209, P83, UM267, VU348

"When Jesus Wept" (Luke)
C199, E715, G194, P312, S2106, SF2106, VU146

"Loving Spirit" (Luke)
C244, EL397, G293, P323, S2123, SF2123, VU387

"Gather Us In" (Luke)
C284, EL532, G401, S2236, SF2236, W665

Additional Contemporary Suggestions

"El Shaddai" (Gen)
UM123

"Saranam, Saranam" ("Refuge") (Pss)
G789, UM523

"I Will Call upon the Lord" (Pss)
G621, S2002, SF2002, SP224

"Nothing Can Trouble" ("Nada Te Turbe") (Pss)
G820, S2054, SF2054, VU290

"Someone Asked the Question" (Pss)
N523, S2144

"Lord, Listen to Your Children" (Pss)
EL752, S2207, SF2207

"We Are Marching" ("Siyahamba") (Pss)
C442, EL866, G853, N526, S2235, SF2235, VU646

"Everlasting God" (Pss)
M182, WS3021

"Gentle Shepherd" (Pss, Lent)
WS3096

"The Lord Is My Light" (Pss)
SP209

"No Higher Calling" (Pss, Phil)
M70

"Just Let Me Say" (Pss, Phil)
M83

"Step by Step" (Pss, Phil, Luke)
G743, M51, WS3004

"In Christ Alone" (Pss, Phil, Luke)
M138, WS3105

"You Never Let Go" (Pss, Luke)
M258

"On Eagle's Wings" (Luke)
B71, C77, EL787, G43, N775, UM143, VU807/808, S-2 #143.
Stanzas for soloist

"Lord of the Dance" (Luke)
G157, P302, UM261, VU352, W636

"The Power of Your Love" (Luke)
M26

Vocal Solos

"Be Thou My Vision" (Gen)
>> V-6   p. 13

"The Lord Is My Light" (Pss)
>> V-8   p. 57

"Lord of the Dance" (Luke)
>> V-3 (3)   p. 34

Anthems

"Be Thou My Vision" (Gen)
Arr. Vicente Chavarria; Augsburg 978-1-5064-2196-4
SATB and organ (bit.ly/2196-4)

"When Jesus Wept" (Luke)
Arr. Gwyneth Walker; E.C. Schirmer 7034
SATB and piano, opt. percussion (bit.ly/7034-Wept)

Other Suggestions

Visuals:
>> **O**   Shield, stars, heifer, goat, ram, pigeon, fire, torch
>> **P**   Light, army/war, sanctuary, tent, rock, singing, path
>> **E**   Cross, "citizens," Christ, love, crown, Phil 4:1c
>> **G**   Jerusalem, hen/chicks, Luke 13:35c

Call to Prayer: EL751, G471, S2200, SF2200. "O Lord, Hear My
Prayer" (Pss)

Prayers: UM691, C103, C11, WSL165, N873 (Gen, Pss, Luke)

Call to Communion: C418. Behold These Emblems (Luke)

Sung Benediction: G80, S2279, SF2279, SP128, VU884. "The
Trees of the Field" (Pss)

Isaiah 55:1-9

All of you who are thirsty, come to the water!
Whoever has no money, come, buy food and eat!
Without money, at no cost, buy wine and milk!
²Why spend money for what isn't food,
    and your earnings for what doesn't satisfy?
Listen carefully to me and eat what is good;
    enjoy the richest of feasts.
³Listen and come to me;
    listen, and you will live.
I will make an everlasting covenant with you,
    my faithful loyalty to David.
⁴Look, I made him a witness to the peoples,
    a prince and commander of peoples.
⁵Look, you will call a nation you don't know,
    a nation you don't know will run to you
    because of the Lᴏʀᴅ your God,
    the holy one of Israel, who has glorified you.
⁶Seek the Lᴏʀᴅ when he can still be found;
    call him while he is yet near.
⁷Let the wicked abandon their ways
    and the sinful their schemes.
Let them return to the Lᴏʀᴅ so that he may have mercy on
    them,
    to our God, because he is generous with forgiveness.
⁸My plans aren't your plans,
nor are your ways my ways, says the Lᴏʀᴅ.
⁹Just as the heavens are higher than the earth,
    so are my ways higher than your ways,
    and my plans than your plans.

Psalm 63:1-8 (G696, N660, P198/199, UM788)

God! My God! It's you—
    I search for you!
    My whole being thirsts for you!
    My body desires you
        in a dry and tired land,
        no water anywhere.
²Yes, I've seen you in the sanctuary;
    I've seen your power and glory.
³My lips praise you
    because your faithful love
    is better than life itself!
⁴So I will bless you as long as I'm alive;
    I will lift up my hands in your name.
⁵I'm fully satisfied—
    as with a rich dinner.
My mouth speaks praise with joy on my lips—
    ⁶whenever I ponder you on my bed,
    whenever I meditate on you
        in the middle of the night—
    ⁷because you've been a help to me and I shout for joy in the
        protection of your wings.
⁸My whole being clings to you;
    your strong hand upholds me.

1 Corinthians 10:1-13

Brothers and sisters, I want you to be sure of the fact that our ancestors were all under the cloud and they all went through the sea. ²All were baptized into Moses in the cloud and in the sea. ³All ate the same spiritual food, ⁴and all drank the same spiritual drink. They drank from a spiritual rock that followed them, and the rock was Christ. ⁵However, God was unhappy with most of them, and they were struck down in the wilderness. ⁶These things were examples for us, so we won't crave evil things like they did. ⁷Don't worship false gods like some of them did, as it is written, *The people sat down to eat and drink and they got up to play.* ⁸Let's not practice sexual immorality, like some of them did, and twenty-three thousand died in one day. ⁹Let's not test Christ, like some of them did, and were killed by the snakes. ¹⁰Let's not grumble, like some of them did, and were killed by the destroyer. ¹¹These things happened to them as an example and were written as a warning for us to whom the end of time has come. ¹²So those who think they are standing need to watch out or else they may fall. ¹³No temptation has seized you that isn't common for people. But God is faithful. He won't allow you to be tempted beyond your abilities. Instead, with the temptation, God will also supply a way out so that you will be able to endure it.

Luke 13:1-9

Some who were present on that occasion told Jesus about the Galileans whom Pilate had killed while they were offering sacrifices. ²He replied, "Do you think the suffering of these Galileans proves that they were more sinful than all the other Galileans? ³No, I tell you, but unless you change your hearts and lives, you will die just as they did. ⁴ What about those eighteen people who were killed when the tower of Siloam fell on them? Do you think that they were more guilty of wrongdoing than everyone else who lives in Jerusalem? ⁵ No, I tell you, but unless you change your hearts and lives, you will die just as they did."

⁶Jesus told this parable: "A man owned a fig tree planted in his vineyard. He came looking for fruit on it and found none. ⁷ He said to his gardener, 'Look, I've come looking for fruit on this fig tree for the past three years, and I've never found any. Cut it down! Why should it continue depleting the soil's nutrients?' ⁸The gardener responded, 'Lord, give it one more year, and I will dig around it and give it fertilizer. ⁹ Maybe it will produce fruit next year; if not, then you can cut it down.'"

Primary Hymns and Songs for the Day

"There's a Wideness in God's Mercy" (Isa) (O)
　　B25, C73, E470, EL587/88F115, G435, L290, N23, P298,
　　UM121, VU271, W595
　　　　　H-3　　Chr-195; Desc-102; Org-179
"We Walk by Faith" (Isa)
　　E209, EL635, G817, N256, P399, S2196, SF2196, W572
　　　　　H-3　　Chr-21
"O Jesus, I Have Promised" (1 Cor)
　　B276, C612, E655, EL810, F402, G724/725, L503, N493,
　　P388/389, UM396 (PD), VU120
　　　　　S-2　　#9. Descant
"Guide Me, O Thou Great Jehovah" (Isa, 1 Cor) (C)
　　B56, C622, E690, EL618, F608, G65, L343, N18/19, P281,
　　UM127 (PD), VU651 (Fr.)
　　　　　H-3　　Hbl-25, 51, 58; Chr-89; Desc-26; Org-23
　　　　　S-1　　#76-77. Desc. and Harm.

Additional Hymn Suggestions

"Light Dawns on a Weary World" (Isa)
　　EL726, G79
"Come, Ye Sinners, Poor and Needy" (Isa)
　　B323 (PD), G415, UM340, W756
"Come Back Quickly to the Lord" (Isa)
　　G416, P381, UM343
"There Is a Balm in Gilead" (Isa)
　　B269, C501, E676, EL614 (PD), F48, G792, N553, P394,
　　UM375, VU612, W608
"Come, Ye Disconsolate" (Isa)
　　B67, C502, EL607, SF2132, UM510 (PD)
"You Satisfy the Hungry Heart" (Isa)
　　C429, EL484, G523, P521, UM629, VU478, W736
"I'll Fly Away" (Isa)
　　N595, S2282, SF2282
"O for a Closer Walk with God" (Isa)
　　E684, G739, N450, P396
"Feed Us, Lord" (Isa, Pss, Comm.)
　　G501, WS3167
"We Sing to You, O God" (Pss, 1 Cor)
　　EL791, N9, S2001, SF2001
"Rock of Ages" (1 Cor)
　　B342, C214, E685, EL623, F108, G438, L327, N596, UM361
"Lift Every Voice and Sing" (1 Cor, Luke)
　　B627, C631, E599, EL841, G339, L562, N593, P563, UM519
"Just as I Am, Without One Plea" (Luke)
　　B303/307, C339, E693, EL592, F417, G442, L296, N207,
　　P370, UM357 (PD), VU508
"Amazing Grace" (Luke)
　　B330, C546, E671, EL779, F107, G649, L448, N547 and N548,
　　P280, UM378 (PD), VU266 (Fr.), W583
"Forth in Thy Name, O Lord" (Luke)
　　L505, UM438 (PD), VU416
"God of Grace and God of Glory" (Luke)
　　B395, C464, E594/595, EL705, F528, G307, L415, N436,
　　P420, UM577, VU686
"As a Chalice Cast of Gold" (Luke)
　　C287, G429, P336, VU505
"God the Sculptor of the Mountains" (Luke)
　　EL736, G5, S2060, SF2060

Additional Contemporary Suggestions

"All Who Are Thirsty" (Isa)
　　M159
"Holy and Anointed One" (Isa, Lent)
　　M32

"Step by Step" (Isa, Pss, Lent)
　　G743, M51, WS3004
"Fill My Cup, Lord" (Isa)
　　C351, F481, UM641, WS3093
"Falling on My Knees" ("Hungry") (Isa, Pss, Lent)
　　M155, WS3099
"Your Love, Oh Lord" (Isa, Pss)
　　M189
"On Eagle's Wings" (Pss)
　　B71, C77, EL787, G43, N775, UM143, VU807/808
"As the Deer" (Pss)
　　G626, S2025, SF2025, SP200, VU766
"Someone Asked the Question" (Pss)
　　N523, S2144
"Jesus, Draw Me Close" (Pss)
　　M48, S2159, SF2159
"Draw Me Close" (Pss)
　　M29
"Eagle's Wings" (Pss)
　　M158
"Desert Song" (Pss)
　　M262
"Praise the Name of Jesus" (1 Cor)
　　S2066, SF2066, SP87

Vocal Solos

"There Is a Balm in Gilead" (Isa)
　　V-3 (1)　　p. 29
"Maybe the Rain" (Isa, Lent)
　　V-5 (2)　　p. 27
"Just a Closer Walk with Thee" (Isa, Lent)
　　V-5 (2)　　p. 31
　　V-8　　　　p. 323
"My Heart Is Steadfast" (Pss)
　　V-5 (2)　　p. 40
"Wondrous Love" (Lent)
　　V-6　　　　p. 47

Anthems

"I'm Going on a Journey" (1 Cor, Baptism)
Arr. Mark Hayes; AEC-1 p. 27
Unison or 2-part and piano, opt. flute (bit.ly/AEC-1-27)

"That Priceless Grace" (Luke)
Arr. John Helgen; AEC-1 p. 64
Unison with piano, opt. descant (bit.ly/AEC-1-64)

Other Suggestions

Visuals:
　　O　　Water, wine/milk/honey, money, listen, Isa 55:6a
　　P　　Desert, lifted hands, food, bed, Ps 63:7b, wings
　　E　　Water/food, larger rock, bread/wine, baptism
　　G　　Fig branch or tree, figs, axe, cross
Introit: S2132, SP219. "You Who Are Thirsty" (Isa)
Opening Prayer: WSL17 (Isa, Pss, 1 Cor)
Canticle: N734 or UM125 (Isa)
Call to Confession: S2138, SF2138, VU107. "Sunday's Palms Are
　　Wednesday's Ashes," stanza 3 (Lent)
Sung Confession: G431, S2134, SF2134. "Forgive Us, Lord"
　　("*Perdón, Señor*") (Pss, Lent)
Prayers: C524, N855, UM423 (Pss); UM268 (1 Cor)

Joshua 5:9-12

[9]Then the LORD said to Joshua, "Today I have rolled away from you the disgrace of Egypt." So the place was called Gilgal, as it is today.

[10]The Israelites camped in Gilgal. They celebrated Passover on the evening of the fourteenth day of the month on the plains of Jericho. [11]On the very next day after Passover, they ate food produced in the land: unleavened bread and roasted grain.[12]The manna stopped on that next day, when they ate food produced in the land. There was no longer any manna for the Israelites. So that year they ate the crops of the land of Canaan.

Psalm 32 (G446, N642, P1814, UM766)

The one whose wrongdoing is forgiven,
    whose sin is covered over, is truly happy!
[2]The one the LORD doesn't consider guilty—
    in whose spirit there is no dishonesty—
    that one is truly happy!
[3]When I kept quiet, my bones wore out;
    I was groaning all day long—
    every day, every night!—
[4]because your hand was heavy upon me.
    My energy was sapped as if in a summer drought.   *[Selah]*
[5]So I admitted my sin to you;
    I didn't conceal my guilt.
    "I'll confess my sins to the LORD, " is what I said.
    Then you removed the guilt of my sin.   *[Selah]*
[6]That's why all the faithful should pray to you during troubled times,
    so that a great flood of water won't reach them.
[7]You are my secret hideout!
    You protect me from trouble.
    You surround me with songs of rescue!   *[Selah]*
[8]I will instruct you and teach you
    about the direction you should go.
    I'll advise you and keep my eye on you.
[9]Don't be like some senseless horse or mule,
    whose movement must be controlled
    with a bit and a bridle.
        Don't be anything like that!
[10]The pain of the wicked is severe,
    but faithful love surrounds the one who trusts the LORD.
[11]You who are righteous, rejoice in the LORD and be glad!
    All you whose hearts are right, sing out in joy!

2 Corinthians 5:16-21

[16]So then, from this point on we won't recognize people by human standards. Even though we used to know Christ by human standards, that isn't how we know him now. [17]So then, if anyone is in Christ, that person is part of the new creation. The old things have gone away, and look, new things have arrived!

[18]All of these new things are from God, who reconciled us to himself through Christ and who gave us the ministry of reconciliation. [19]In other words, God was reconciling the world to himself through Christ, by not counting people's sins against them. He has trusted us with this message of reconciliation.

[20]So we are ambassadors who represent Christ. God is negotiating with you through us. We beg you as Christ's representatives, "Be reconciled to God!" [21]God caused the one who didn't know sin to be sin for our sake so that through him we could become the righteousness of God.

Luke 15:1-3, 11b-32

All the tax collectors and sinners were gathering around Jesus to listen to him. [2]The Pharisees and legal experts were grumbling, saying, "This man welcomes sinners and eats with them." [3]Jesus told them this parable: . . .

[11b] "A certain man had two sons. [12]The younger son said to his father, 'Father, give me my share of the inheritance.' Then the father divided his estate between them. [13]Soon afterward, the younger son gathered everything together and took a trip to a land far away. There, he wasted his wealth through extravagant living.

[14]"When he had used up his resources, a severe food shortage arose in that country and he began to be in need. [15]He hired himself out to one of the citizens of that country, who sent him into his fields to feed pigs. [16]He longed to eat his fill from what the pigs ate, but no one gave him anything. [17]When he came to his senses, he said, 'How many of my father's hired hands have more than enough food, but I'm starving to death![18]I will get up and go to my father, and say to him, "Father, I have sinned against heaven and against you. [19] I no longer deserve to be called your son. Take me on as one of your hired hands." ' [20]So he got up and went to his father.

"While he was still a long way off, his father saw him and was moved with compassion. His father ran to him, hugged him, and kissed him. [21]Then his son said, 'Father, I have sinned against heaven and against you. I no longer deserve to be called your son.' [22]But the father said to his servants, 'Quickly, bring out the best robe and put it on him! Put a ring on his finger and sandals on his feet! [23]Fetch the fattened calf and slaughter it. We must celebrate with feasting [24]because this son of mine was dead and has come back to life! He was lost and is found!' And they began to celebrate.

[25]"Now his older son was in the field. Coming in from the field, he approached the house and heard music and dancing. [26]He called one of the servants and asked what was going on. [27]The servant replied, 'Your brother has arrived, and your father has slaughtered the fattened calf because he received his son back safe and sound.' [28] Then the older son was furious and didn't want to enter in, but his father came out and begged him. [29]He answered his father, 'Look, I've served you all these years, and I never disobeyed your instruction. Yet you've never given me as much as a young goat so I could celebrate with my friends. [30] But when this son of yours returned, after gobbling up your estate on prostitutes, you slaughtered the fattened calf for him.' [31] Then his father said, 'Son, you are always with me, and everything I have is yours. [32] But we had to celebrate and be glad because this brother of yours was dead and is alive. He was lost and is found.'"

Primary Hymns and Songs for the Day
"All My Hope Is Firmly Grounded" (Josh) (O)
    C88, E665, EL757, N408, UM132, VU654 and VU655
        H-3   Chr-23, 78
"Lord God, Your Love Has Called Us Here" (2 Cor) (O)
    EL358, P353, UM579
        S-1   #57-61. Various treatments
"My Song Is Love Unknown" (2 Cor)
    E458, EL343, G209, N222, P76, S2083, SF2083, VU143
        H-3   Chr-139, 158; Desc-90; Org-126
        S-1   #284-285. Desc. and Harm.
"Great Is Thy Faithfulness" (Luke)
    B54, C86, EL733, G39, N423, P276, UM140, VU288
        H-3   Chr-87; Desc-39; Org-39
        S-2   #59. Piano Arr.
"This Is a Day of New Beginnings" (2 Cor, Luke) (C)
    B370, C518, N417, UM383, W661
        H-3   Chr-196
"Love Divine, All Loves Excelling" (2 Cor, Luke) (C)
    B208, C517, E657, EL631, F21, G366, N43, P376, UM384
    (PD), VU333, W588
        H-3   Chr-134; Desc-18; Org-13
        S-1   #41-42. Desc. and Harm.

Additional Hymn Suggestions
"Now Thank We All Our God" (Josh)
    B638, C715, E396/397, EL839/840, F525, G643, L533 or
    L534, N419, P555, UM102 (PD), VU236 (Fr.), W560
"All Who Hunger" (Josh, Comm.)
    C419, EL461, G509, S2126, SF2126, VU460
"Come Back Quickly to the Lord" (Josh, Luke)
    G416, P381, UM343
"What Wondrous Love Is This" (2 Cor)
    B143 (PD), C200, E439, EL666, F283, G215, L385, N223,
    P85, UM292, VU147 (Fr.), W600
"Womb of Life" (2 Cor)
    C14, G3, N274, S2046, SF2046
"My Life Flows On" ("How Can I Keep from Singing") (2 Cor)
    C619, EL763, G821, N476, S2212, SF2212, VU716
"To God Be the Glory" (2 Cor)
    B4, C72, F363, G634, P485, UM98 (PD)
"Mothering God, You Gave Me Birth" (2 Cor, Luke)
    C83, N467, S2050, SF2050, VU320
"How Like a Gentle Spirit" (Luke)
    C69, N443, UM115
"Come, Ye Sinners, Poor and Needy" (Luke)
    B323 (PD), G415, UM340, W756
"Softly and Tenderly Jesus Is Calling" (Luke)
    B312, C340, EL608 (PD), F432, G418, N449, UM348
"*Cuando El Pobre*" ("When the Poor Ones") (Luke)
    C662, EL725, G762, P407, UM434, VU702
"Bring Many Names" (Luke)
    C10, G760, N11, S2047, SF2047, VU268
"Lord of All Hopefulness" (Luke)
    E482, EL765, G683, L469, S2197, SF2197, W568
"Lead Me, Guide Me" (Luke)
    C583, EL768, G740, S2214, SF2214
"O God, How We Have Wandered" (Luke)
    EL606, N202, VU112
"Heaven Is Singing for Joy" ("*El cielo canta alegría*") (Luke)
    G382, EL664, VU230

Additional Contemporary Suggestions
"Holy Ground" (Josh)
    B224, C112, G406, S2272, SF2272, SP86

"Awesome in This Place" (Josh)
    M36
"My Life Is in You, Lord" (Pss)
    S2032, SF2032, SP204
"Shout to the Lord" (Pss)
    EL821, S2074, SF2074, M16; V-3 (2) p. 32 Vocal Solo
"Through It All" (Pss, Luke)
    C555, F43, UM507
"Hallelujah" ("Your Love Is Amazing") (Pss, Luke)
    M118, WS3027
"My Redeemer Lives" (Pss, Lent)
    M73
"You Have Saved Us" (2 Cor)
    M266
"Refresh My Heart" (2 Cor)
    M49
"That's Why We Praise Him" (2 Cor, Luke)
    M94
"He Knows My Name" (Luke)
    M109
"I'm So Glad Jesus Lifted Me" (Luke)
    C529, EL860 (PD), N474, S2151, SF2151
"Because of Your Love" (Luke)
    M224
"Mighty to Save" (Luke)
    M246, WS3038
"Forever Reign" (Luke)
    M256
"Falling on My Knees" ("Hungry") (Luke)
    M155, WS3099
"You Are My King" ("Amazing Love") (Luke)
    M82, WS3102

Vocal Solos
"Brighter than the Sun" (2 Cor, Baptism)
    V-5(1)   p. 57
"Softly and Tenderly" (Luke)
    V-5(3)   p. 52
"So Art Thou with Me" (Luke, Lent)
    V-9   p. 34

Anthems
"How Can I Keep from Singing" (2 Cor)
Robert A. Hobby; MorningStar MSM-50-7105
SATB and organ, opt. handbells (bit.ly/50-7105)

"Our Father, We Have Wandered" (Luke)
Ralph M. Johnson; Augsburg 978-1-4514-9257-6
SATB and piano, oboe or clarinet (bit.ly/9257-6)

Other Suggestions
Visuals:
    O   Fruit, vegetable, grain, unleavened bread
    P   Praying hands, embracing arms, bridle/bit
    E   Butterfly/chrysalis, flowering bulbs, Spring flowers
    G   Rembrandt "Return of the Prodigal," embrace, lost/
            found, robe, ring, sandals, goat, calf
Call to Prayer: EL751, G471, S2200, SF2200. "O Lord, Hear My
    Prayer" (Luke, Lent)
Prayers: C653, UM639 or C660, UM446, UM639 (Luke)
Offertory Prayer: WSL111 (2 Cor)

Isaiah 43:16-21

[16]The LORD says—who makes a way in the sea
and a path in the mighty waters,
[17]who brings out chariot and horse,
army and battalion;
they will lie down together and will not rise;
they will be extinguished, extinguished like a wick.
[18]Don't remember the prior things;
don't ponder ancient history.
[19]Look! I'm doing a new thing;
now it sprouts up; don't you recognize it?
I'm making a way in the desert,
paths in the wilderness.
[20]The beasts of the field,
the jackals and ostriches, will honor me,
because I have put water in the desert
and streams in the wilderness
to give water to my people,
my chosen ones,
[21]this people whom I formed for myself,
who will recount my praise.

Psalm 126 (G73/74, N707, P237, UM847)

When the LORD changed Zion's circumstances for the better,
it was like we had been dreaming.
[2]Our mouths were suddenly filled with laughter;
our tongues were filled with joyful shouts.
It was even said, at that time, among the nations,
"The LORD has done great things for them!"
[3]Yes, the LORD has done great things for us,
and we are overjoyed.
[4]LORD, change our circumstances for the better,
like dry streams in the desert waste!
[5]Let those who plant with tears
reap the harvest with joyful shouts.
[6]Let those who go out,
crying and carrying their seed,
come home with joyful shouts,
carrying bales of grain!

Philippians 3:4b-14

[4b]If anyone else has reason to put their confidence in physical advantages, I have even more:
[5]I was circumcised on the eighth day.
I am from the people of Israel and the tribe of Benjamin.
I am a Hebrew of the Hebrews.
With respect to observing the Law, I'm a Pharisee.
[6]With respect to devotion to the faith, I harassed the church.
With respect to righteousness under the Law, I'm blameless.

[7]These things were my assets, but I wrote them off as a loss for the sake of Christ. [8]But even beyond that, I consider everything a loss in comparison with the superior value of knowing Christ Jesus my Lord. I have lost everything for him, but what I lost I think of as sewer trash, so that I might gain Christ [9]and be found in him. In Christ I have a righteousness that is not my own and that does not come from the Law but rather from the faithfulness of Christ. It is the righteousness of God that is based on faith. [10]The righteousness that I have comes from knowing Christ, the power of his resurrection, and the participation in his sufferings. It includes being conformed to his death [11]so that I may perhaps reach the goal of the resurrection of the dead.

[12]It's not that I have already reached this goal or have already been perfected, but I pursue it, so that I may grab hold of it because Christ grabbed hold of me for just this purpose. [13]Brothers and sisters, I myself don't think I've reached it, but I do this one thing: I forget about the things behind me and reach out for the things ahead of me. [14]The goal I pursue is the prize of God's upward call in Christ Jesus.

John 12:1-8

Six days before Passover, Jesus came to Bethany, home of Lazarus, whom Jesus had raised from the dead. [2]Lazarus and his sisters hosted a dinner for him. Martha served and Lazarus was among those who joined him at the table. [3]Then Mary took an extraordinary amount, almost three-quarters of a pound, of very expensive perfume made of pure nard. She anointed Jesus' feet with it, then wiped his feet dry with her hair. The house was filled with the aroma of the perfume. [4]Judas Iscariot, one of his disciples (the one who was about to betray him), complained, [5]"This perfume was worth a year's wages! Why wasn't it sold and the money given to the poor?" ([6]He said this not because he cared about the poor but because he was a thief. He carried the money bag and would take what was in it.)

[7]Then Jesus said, "Leave her alone. This perfume was to be used in preparation for my burial, and this is how she has used it. [8]You will always have the poor among you, but you won't always have me."

Primary Hymns and Songs for the Day

"Sing Praise to God Who Reigns Above" (Isa) (O)
    B20, C6, E408, EL871, F343, G645, N6, P483, UM126 (PD),
    VU216, W528
        H-3   Hbl-92; Chr-173; Desc-76; Org-91
        S-1   #237. Descant
"When God Restored Our Common Life" (Pss)
    G74, S2182, SF2182
        H-3   Chr-139; Desc-90; Org-123
"When I Survey the Wondrous Cross" (Phil)
    B144, C195, EL803, F258, G223, N224, P101, UM298
        H-3   Hbl-6, 102; Chr-213; Desc-49; Org-49
        S-1   #155. Descant
    E474, L482, G224, P100, UM299 (PD), VU149 (Fr.)
        H-3   Hbl-47; Chr-214; Desc-90; Org-127
        S-1   #288. Transposition to E-flat major
"More Love to Thee, O Christ" (John) (C)
    B473, C527, F476, G828, N456, P359, UM453 (PD)
        H-3   Org-94

Additional Hymn Suggestions

"*Cantemos al Señor*" ("Let's Sing unto the Lord") (Isa, Pss)
    B38, C60, EL555, G669, N39, UM149
"This Is a Day of New Beginnings" (Isa, Phil)
    B370, C518, N417, UM383, W661
"Go Down, Moses" (Isa, Phil)
    C663, E648, G52, N572, P334, UM448, W508
"Jesus, Savior, Pilot Me" (Isa)
    EL755, L334, N441, UM509 (PD), VU637
"How Firm a Foundation" (Isa) (O)
    B338, C618, E636/637, EL796, F32, G463, L507, N407, P361,
    UM529 (PD), VU660, W585
"O For a Thousand Tongues to Sing" (Pss, John)
    B216, C5, E493, EL886, F349, G610, L559, N42, P466, UM57
    (PD), VU326
"O For a Thousand Tongues to Sing" (Ps, John)
    G405, WS3001
"Beneath the Cross of Jesus" (Phil)
    B291, C197, E498, EL338, F253, G216, L107, N190, P92,
    UM297 (PD), VU135
"Guide My Feet" (Phil)
    G741, N497, P354, S2208
"Healer of Our Every Ill" (Phil)
    C506, EL612, G795, S2213, SF2213, VU619
"To God Be the Glory" (Phil)
    B4, C72, F363, G634, P485, UM98 (PD)
"Fight the Good Fight" (Phil)
    E552, F613, G846, L461, P307 (PD), VU674
"O How I Love Jesus" (John)
    B217, C99, F634, N52, UM170 (PD)
"Jesus, the Very Thought of Thee" (John)
    B225, C102, E642, EL754, F465, G629, L316, N507, P310,
    UM175 (PD)
"Fairest Lord Jesus" (John)
    B176, C97, E383, EL838, F240, G630, L518, N44, P306,
    UM189 (PD), VU341
"Woman in the Night" (John)
    C188, G161, UM274
"Jesus, Priceless Treasure" (John)
    E701, EL775, F277, G830, L457, N480 P365, UM532 (PD),
    VU667 and VU668 (Fr.)
"Said Judas to Mary" (John)
    N210, VU129, W644
"A Woman Came Who Did Not Count the Cost" (John)
    N206

Additional Contemporary Suggestions

"Refresh My Heart" (Isa)
    M49
"You Have Saved Us" (Isa)
    M266
"Trading My Sorrows" (Pss)
    M75, WS3108
"There Is a Higher Throne" (Pss)
    WS3189
"From the Inside Out" (Pss)
    M263
"Something Beautiful" (Phil)
    F656, UM394
"Sanctuary" (Phil)
    G701, M52, S2164, SF2164
"He Who Began a Good Work in You" (Phil)
    S2163, SF2163, SP180
"The Power of the Cross" (Phil)
    M222, WS3085
"Purify My Heart" (Phil)
    M90, WS3103
"The Jesus in Me" (Phil)
    AH4109, WS3151
"In the Secret" ("I Want to Know You") (Phil)
    M38
"Knowing You" ("All I Once Held Dear") (Phil)
    M30
"Holy and Anointed One" (John)
    M32
"Cry of My Heart" (John)
    M39, S2165, SF2165

Vocal Solos

"God Will Make a Way" (with "He Leadeth Me") (Isa)
    V-3 (2)   p. 9
"O For a Thousand Tongues to Sing" (Pss, John)
    V-6   p. 28
    V-1   p. 32
"Jesus Revealed in Me" (Phil)
    V-8   p. 347
"And Can It Be that I Should Gain" (Phil)
    V-1   p. 29

Anthems

"Come Away to the Skies" (Isa, Pss, Phil)
Arr. David Sims; Augsburg 978-1-5064-2200-8
Unison and organ (bit.ly/2200-8)

"Sanctuary" (Phil)
Arr. Lloyd Larson; Hope C-5892
SAB and piano (bit.ly/C-5892)

Other Suggestions

Visuals:
    O   Sand, water, horse/chariot, wick, river, animals
    P   Laughter, joy, sheaves of wheat, water, baptism
    E   Trash can with "things," baptism, cross /black drape
    G   Perfume bottle, leather bag, anointing, baptism
Call and Confession: N833 and N834 (Lent)
Response: EL336, G518, S2113, SF2113. "Lamb of God" (Lent)
Prayers: N847, N871 (Luke) and WSL19 (Isa)

Palm Readings
Luke 19:28-40

[28]After Jesus said this, he continued on ahead, going up to Jerusalem.

[29]As Jesus came to Bethphage and Bethany on the Mount of Olives, he gave two disciples a task. [30]He said, "Go into the village over there. When you enter it, you will find tied up there a colt that no one has ever ridden. Untie it and bring it here. [31]If someone asks, 'Why are you untying it?' just say, 'Its master needs it.'" [32]Those who had been sent found it exactly as he had said.

[33]As they were untying the colt, its owners said to them, "Why are you untying the colt?"

[34]They replied, "Its master needs it." [35]They brought it to Jesus, threw their clothes on the colt, and lifted Jesus onto it. [36]As Jesus rode along, they spread their clothes on the road.

[37]As Jesus approached the road leading down from the Mount of Olives, the whole throng of his disciples began rejoicing. They praised God with a loud voice because of all the mighty things they had seen. [38]They said,

"Blessings on the king who comes in the name of the Lord.
Peace in heaven and glory in the highest heavens."

[39]Some of the Pharisees from the crowd said to Jesus, "Teacher, scold your disciples! Tell them to stop!"

[40]He answered, "I tell you, if they were silent, the stones would shout."

Psalm 118:1-2, 19-29 (G391/681, N700, P230-232, UM839)

Give thanks to the Lord because he is good,
    because his faithful love lasts forever.
[2]Let Israel say it:
    "God's faithful love lasts forever!"

. . . .

[19]Open the gates of righteousness for me
    so I can come in and give thanks to the Lord!
[20]This is the Lord's gate;
    those who are righteous enter through it.
[21]I thank you because you answered me,
    because you were my saving help.
[22]The stone rejected by the builders
    is now the main foundation stone!
[23]This has happened because of the Lord;
    it is astounding in our sight!
[24]This is the day the Lord acted;
    we will rejoice and celebrate in it!
[25]Lord, please save us!
    Lord, please let us succeed!
[26]The one who enters in the Lord's name is blessed;
    we bless all of you from the Lord's house.
[27]The Lord is God!
    He has shined a light on us!
So lead the festival offering with ropes
    all the way to the horns of the altar.
[28]You are my God—I will give thanks to you!
    You are my God—I will lift you up high!
[29]Give thanks to the Lord because he is good,
    because his faithful love lasts forever.

Passion Readings
Isaiah 50:4-9a

[4]The Lord God gave me an educated tongue
    to know how to respond to the weary
    with a word that will awaken them in the morning.
    God awakens my ear in the morning to listen,
    as educated people do.
[5]The Lord God opened my ear;
    I didn't rebel; I didn't turn my back.
[6]Instead, I gave my body to attackers,
    and my cheeks to beard pluckers.
I didn't hide my face
    from insults and spitting.
[7]The Lord God will help me;
    therefore, I haven't been insulted.
Therefore, I set my face like flint,
    and knew I wouldn't be ashamed.
[8]The one who will declare me innocent is near.
    Who will argue with me?
Let's stand up together.
    Who will bring judgment against me?
    Let him approach me.
[9a]Look! The Lord God will help me.

Psalm 31:9-16 (G214/811, N640/641, P182/183, UM764)

[9]Have mercy on me, Lord, because I'm depressed.
    My vision fails because of my grief,
    as do my spirit and my body.
[10]My life is consumed with sadness;
    my years are consumed with groaning.
Strength fails me because of my suffering;
    my bones dry up.
[11]I'm a joke to all my enemies,
    still worse to my neighbors.
    I scare my friends,
    and whoever sees me in the street runs away!
[12]I am forgotten, like I'm dead,
    completely out of mind;
    I am like a piece of pottery, destroyed.
[13]Yes, I've heard all the gossiping,
    terror all around;
    so many gang up together against me,
        they plan to take my life!
[14]But me? I trust you, Lord!
    I affirm, "You are my God."
[15]My future is in your hands.
    Don't hand me over to my enemies,
    to all who are out to get me!
[16]Shine your face on your servant;
    save me by your faithful love!

Philippians 2:5-11

[5]Adopt the attitude that was in Christ Jesus:
    [6]Though he was in the form of God,
        he did not consider being equal with God something to
            exploit.
    [7]But he emptied himself
        by taking the form of a slave
        and by becoming like human beings.
    When he found himself in the form of a human,
        [8]he humbled himself by becoming obedient to the point
            of death,
        even death on a cross.
    [9]Therefore, God highly honored him
        and gave him a name above all names,
    [10]so that at the name of Jesus everyone
        in heaven, on earth, and under the earth might bow
        [11]and every tongue confess that
            Jesus Christ is Lord, to the glory of God the Father.

Luke 22:14–23:56 or Luke 23:1-49

[14]When the time came, Jesus took his place at the table, and the apostles joined him. [15]He said to them, "I have earnestly desired to eat this Passover with you before I suffer. [16] I tell you, I won't eat it until it is fulfilled in God's kingdom." [17]After taking a cup and giving thanks, he said, "Take this and share it among yourselves. [18] I tell you that from now on I won't drink from the fruit of the vine until God's kingdom has come."[19]After taking the bread and giving thanks, he broke it and gave it to them, saying, "This is my body, which is given for you. Do this in remembrance of me." [20]In the same way, he took the cup after the meal and said, "This cup is the new covenant by my blood, which is poured out for you.

[21]"But look! My betrayer is with me; his hand is on this table.[22] The Human One goes just as it has been determined. But how terrible it is for that person who betrays him." [23]They began to argue among themselves about which of them it could possibly be who would do this.

[24]An argument broke out among the disciples over which one of them should be regarded as the greatest.

[25]But Jesus said to them, "The kings of the Gentiles rule over their subjects, and those in authority over them are called 'friends of the people.' [26]But that's not the way it will be with you. Instead, the greatest among you must become like a person of lower status and the leader like a servant. [27]So which one is greater, the one who is seated at the table or the one who serves at the table? Isn't it the one who is seated at the table? But I am among you as one who serves.

[28]"You are the ones who have continued with me in my trials.[29]And I confer royal power on you just as my Father granted royal power to me. [30]Thus you will eat and drink at my table in my kingdom, and you will sit on thrones overseeing the twelve tribes of Israel.

[31]"Simon, Simon, look! Satan has asserted the right to sift you all like wheat. [32] However, I have prayed for you that your faith won't fail. When you have returned, strengthen your brothers and sisters."

[33]Peter responded, "Lord, I'm ready to go with you, both to prison and to death!"

[34]Jesus replied, "I tell you, Peter, the rooster won't crow today before you have denied three times that you know me."

[35]Jesus said to them, "When I sent you out without a wallet, bag, or sandals, you didn't lack anything, did you?"

They said, "Nothing."

[36]Then he said to them, "But now, whoever has a wallet must take it, and likewise a bag. And those who don't own a sword must sell their clothes and buy one. [37] I tell you that this scripture must be fulfilled in relation to me: *And he was counted among criminals.* Indeed, what's written about me is nearing completion."

[38]They said to him, "Lord, look, here are two swords."

He replied, "Enough of that!"

[39]Jesus left and made his way to the Mount of Olives, as was his custom, and the disciples followed him. [40]When he arrived, he said to them, "Pray that you won't give in to temptation." [41]He withdrew from them about a stone's throw, knelt down, and prayed. [42]He said, "Father, if it's your will, take this cup of suffering away from me. However, not my will but your will must be done." [43]Then a heavenly angel appeared to him and strengthened him. [44]He was in anguish and prayed even more earnestly. His sweat became like drops of blood falling on the ground. [45]When he got up from praying, he went to the disciples. He found them asleep, overcome by grief. [46]He said to them, "Why are you sleeping? Get up and pray so that you won't give in to temptation."

[47]While Jesus was still speaking, a crowd appeared, and the one called Judas, one of the Twelve, was leading them. He approached Jesus to kiss him.

[48]Jesus said to him, "Judas, would you betray the Human One with a kiss?"

[49]When those around him recognized what was about to happen, they said, "Lord, should we fight with our swords?"[50]One of them struck the high priest's servant, cutting off his right ear.

[51]Jesus responded, "Stop! No more of this!" He touched the slave's ear and healed him.

[52]Then Jesus said to the chief priests, the officers of the temple guard, and the elders who had come to get him, "Have you come with swords and clubs to arrest me, as though I were a thief? [53] Day after day I was with you in the temple, but you didn't arrest me. But this is your time, when darkness rules."

[54]After they arrested Jesus, they led him away and brought him to the high priest's house. Peter followed from a distance.[55]When they lit a fire in the middle of the courtyard and sat down together, Peter sat among them.

[56]Then a servant woman saw him sitting in the firelight. She stared at him and said, "This man was with him too."

[57]But Peter denied it, saying, "Woman, I don't know him!"

[58]A little while later, someone else saw him and said, "You are one of them too."

But Peter said, "Man, I'm not!"

[59]An hour or so later, someone else insisted, "This man must have been with him, because he is a Galilean too."

[60]Peter responded, "Man, I don't know what you are talking about!" At that very moment, while he was still speaking, a rooster crowed. [61]The Lord turned and looked straight at Peter, and Peter remembered the Lord's words: "Before a rooster crows today, you will deny me three times." [62]And Peter went out and cried uncontrollably.

[63]The men who were holding Jesus in custody taunted him while they beat him. [64]They blindfolded him and asked him repeatedly, "Prophesy! Who hit you?" [65]Insulting him, they said many other horrible things against him.

[66]As morning came, the elders of the people, both chief priests and legal experts, came together, and Jesus was brought before their council.

[67]They said, "If you are the Christ, tell us!"

He answered, "If I tell you, you won't believe. [68] And if I ask you a question, you won't answer. [69] But from now on, *the Human One will be seated on the right side of the power of God.*"

[70]They all said, "Are you God's Son, then?"

He replied, "You say that I am."

[71]Then they said, "Why do we need further testimony? We've heard it from his own lips."

23 The whole assembly got up and led Jesus to Pilate and [2]began to accuse him. They said, "We have found this man misleading our people, opposing the payment of taxes to Caesar, and claiming that he is the Christ, a king."

[3]Pilate asked him, "Are you the king of the Jews?"

Jesus replied, "That's what you say."

[4]Then Pilate said to the chief priests and the crowds, "I find no legal basis for action against this man."

[5]But they objected strenuously, saying, "He agitates the people with his teaching throughout Judea—starting from Galilee all the way here."

[6]Hearing this, Pilate asked if the man was a Galilean. [7]When he learned that Jesus was from Herod's district, Pilate sent him to Herod, who was also in Jerusalem at that time. [8]Herod was very glad to see Jesus, for he had heard about Jesus and had wanted to see him for quite some time. He was hoping to see Jesus perform some sign. [9]Herod questioned Jesus at length, but

Jesus didn't respond to him. [10]The chief priests and the legal experts were there, fiercely accusing Jesus. [11]Herod and his soldiers treated Jesus with contempt. Herod mocked him by dressing Jesus in elegant clothes and sent him back to Pilate.[12]Pilate and Herod became friends with each other that day. Before this, they had been enemies.

[13]Then Pilate called together the chief priests, the rulers, and the people. [14]He said to them, "You brought this man before me as one who was misleading the people. I have questioned him in your presence and found nothing in this man's conduct that provides a legal basis for the charges you have brought against him. [15]Neither did Herod, because Herod returned him to us. He's done nothing that deserves death. [16]Therefore, I'll have him whipped, then let him go."

[18]But with one voice they shouted, "Away with this man! Release Barabbas to us." ([19]Barabbas had been thrown into prison because of a riot that had occurred in the city, and for murder.)

[20]Pilate addressed them again because he wanted to release Jesus.

[21]They kept shouting out, "Crucify him! Crucify him!"

[22]For the third time, Pilate said to them, "Why? What wrong has he done? I've found no legal basis for the death penalty in his case. Therefore, I will have him whipped, then let him go."

[23]But they were adamant, shouting their demand that Jesus be crucified. Their voices won out. [24]Pilate issued his decision to grant their request. [25]He released the one they asked for, who had been thrown into prison because of a riot and murder. But he handed Jesus over to their will.

[26]As they led Jesus away, they grabbed Simon, a man from Cyrene, who was coming in from the countryside. They put the cross on his back and made him carry it behind Jesus. [27]A huge crowd of people followed Jesus, including women, who were mourning and wailing for him. [28]Jesus turned to the women and said, "Daughters of Jerusalem, don't cry for me. Rather, cry for yourselves and your children. [29] The time will come when they will say, 'Happy are those who are unable to become pregnant, the wombs that never gave birth, and the breasts that never nursed a child.' [30] Then *they will say to the mountains, 'Fall on us,' and to the hills, 'Cover us.'* [31] If they do these things when the tree is green, what will happen when it is dry?"

[32]They also led two other criminals to be executed with Jesus.[33]When they arrived at the place called The Skull, they crucified him, along with the criminals, one on his right and the other on his left. [34]Jesus said, "Father, forgive them, for they don't know what they're doing." They drew lots as a way of dividing up his clothing.

[35]The people were standing around watching, but the leaders sneered at him, saying, "He saved others. Let him save himself if he really is the Christ sent from God, the chosen one."

[36]The soldiers also mocked him. They came up to him, offering him sour wine [37]and saying, "If you really are the king of the Jews, save yourself." [38]Above his head was a notice of the formal charge against him. It read "This is the king of the Jews."

[39]One of the criminals hanging next to Jesus insulted him: "Aren't you the Christ? Save yourself and us!"

[40]Responding, the other criminal spoke harshly to him, "Don't you fear God, seeing that you've also been sentenced to die? [41]We are rightly condemned, for we are receiving the appropriate sentence for what we did. But this man has done nothing wrong." [42]Then he said, "Jesus, remember me when you come into your kingdom."

[43]Jesus replied, "I assure you that today you will be with me in paradise."

[44]It was now about noon, and darkness covered the whole earth until about three o'clock, [45]while the sun stopped shining. Then the curtain in the sanctuary tore down the middle. [46]Crying out in a loud voice, Jesus said, "Father, *into your hands I entrust my life.*" After he said this, he breathed for the last time.

[47]When the centurion saw what happened, he praised God, saying, "It's really true: this man was righteous." [48]All the crowds who had come together to see this event returned to their homes beating their chests after seeing what had happened. [49]And everyone who knew him, including the women who had followed him from Galilee, stood at a distance observing these things.

[50]Now there was a man named Joseph who was a member of the council. He was a good and righteous man. [51]He hadn't agreed with the plan and actions of the council. He was from the Jewish city of Arimathea and eagerly anticipated God's kingdom. [52]This man went to Pilate and asked for Jesus' body.[53]Taking it down, he wrapped it in a linen cloth and laid it in a tomb carved out of the rock, in which no one had ever been buried. [54]It was the Preparation Day for the Sabbath, and the Sabbath was quickly approaching. [55]The women who had come with Jesus from Galilee followed Joseph. They saw the tomb and how Jesus' body was laid in it, [56]then they went away and prepared fragrant spices and perfumed oils. They rested on the Sabbath, in keeping with the commandment.

Primary Hymns and Songs for the Day

"Hosanna, Loud Hosanna" (Palms Gospel) (O)
    B130, F248, G197, N213, P89, UM278 (PD), VU123
        H-3   Hbl-16, 22, 68; Chr-101; Desc-37
        S-1   #115. Harm.
"Ride On! Ride On in Majesty!"
    C191, EL346, G198, N215, P90/91, VU127 (Palms Gospel)
"He Never Said a Mumbalin' Word" (Isa)
    C208, EL350, G219, P95 (PD), UM291, VU141
"O Sacred Head, Now Wounded" (Passion, Comm.)
    B137, C202, E168/169, EL351/352, F284, G221, L116/117,
    N226, P98, UM286, VU145 (Fr.), W434
        H-3   Hbl-82; Chr-148; Desc-86; Org-111
"My Song Is Love Unknown" (Palms/Passion) (C)
    E458, EL343, G209, L94, N222, P76, S2083, SF2083, VU143,
    W439
        H-3   Chr-139, 158; Desc-90; Org-126
"All Glory, Laud, and Honor" (Palms Gospel) (C)
    B126, C192, E154/ E155, EL344, F249, G196, L108,
    N216/217, P88, UM280 (PD), VU122, W428
        H-3   Hbl-45; Chr-22; Desc-96; Org-144
        S-1   #309-310. Desc. and Harm.
        S-1   #284-285. Desc. and Harm.

Additional Hymn Suggestions

"Tell Me the Stories of Jesus" (Palms)
    B129, C190, F212, UM277 (PD), VU357
"*Mantos y Palmas*" ("Filled with Excitement") (Palms)
    G199, N214, UM279
"This Is the Day the Lord Hath Made" (Ps 118)
    B358, G681, P230, UM658
"At the Name of Jesus" (Phil)
    B198, E435, EL416, F351, G264, L179, P148, UM168, VU335,
    W499
"What Wondrous Love Is This" (Passion)
    B143 (PD), C200, E439, EL666, F283, G215, L385, N223,
    P85, UM292, VU147 (Fr.), W600
"Alas! and Did My Savior Bleed" (Passion)
    B145, EL337, F274, G212, L98, N200, P78, UM294 (PD)
    B139, C204, N199, UM359 (PD) (alternate tune)
"Lord, Whose Love Through Humble Service" (Passion)
    C461, E610, EL712, L423, P427, UM581, W630
"For the Bread Which You Have Broken" (Passion)
    C411, E340/341, EL494, G516, L200, P508/509,
    UM614/615, VU470
"The Bread of Life for All Is Broken" (Passion)
    E342, N333, UM633
"When Jesus Wept" (Passion Gospel)
    C199, E715, G194, P312, S2106, SF2106, VU146
"Why Has God Forsaken Me?" (Passion Gospel)
    G809, P406, S2110, VU154
"Sunday's Palms Are Wednesday's Ashes" (Palms/Passion)
    S2138, SF2138, VU107
"How Long, O Lord" (Passion Gospel)
    G777, S2209, SF2209
"In Remembrance of Me" (Passion Gospel, Comm.)
    B365, C403, G521, S2254

Additional Contemporary Suggestions

"Forever" (Ps 118)
    M68, WS3023
"Make Way" (Ps 118, Palms Gospel)
    WS3044
"Hosanna" (Palms, Passion Gospels)
    WS3079 or S2109, SF2109 (different tunes and texts)

"I Will Enter His Gates" (Ps 118)
    S2270, SF2270, SP168
"All Hail King Jesus" (Palms Gospel)
    S2069, SF2069, SP63
"King of Kings" (Palms Gospel)
    B234, S2075, SF2075, SP94, VU167
"The King of Glory Comes" (Palms Gospel)
    B127, S2091, SF2091, W501
"Open the Eyes of My Heart" (Isa)
    G452, M57, WS3008
"Step by Step" (Ps 31)
    G743, M51, WS3004
"How Majestic Is Your Name" (Phil)
    C63, G613, S2023, SF2023, SP14
"He Is Exalted" (Phil)
    S2070, SF2070, SP66
"Jesus, Name above All Names" (Phil)
    S2071, SF2071, SP76
"Come, Now Is the Time to Worship" (Phil)
    M56, WS3176
"Jesus Messiah" (Phil, Passion Gospel, Comm.)
    M253
"At the Cross" (Phil, Passion Gospel)
    M225
"Lamb of God" (Passion Gospel)
    EL336, G518, S2113, SF2113
"Eat This Bread" (Passion Gospel, Comm.)
    C414, EL472, G527, N788, UM628, VU466, W734
"Above All" (Passion Gospel)
    M77; V-3 (2) p. 17 Vocal Solo
"The Power of the Cross" (Passion, Holy Week)
    M222, WS3085

Vocal Solos

"Ride On, Jesus" (Palms Gospel)
    V-7   p. 8
"The Shepherd Became a Lamb" (Palms, Passion)
    V-10   p. 48

Anthems

"This Is the Day" (Ps 118)
Harold Silvester; Augsburg 978-1-5064-2217-6
SATB and organ, opt. brass/percussion (bit.ly/2217-6)

"Jesus Christ Is Lord" (Phil)
Philip Stopford; MorningStar MSM-50-3061
SATB divisi, a cappella (bit.ly/50-3061)

Other Suggestions

Visuals:
    Palms Gospel   Palms, cloaks, colt, crowd, Jesus, stones
    Ps 118   Gates, cornerstone, joy, light
    O   Teacher, morning, cheek/beard, spitting,
    Ps 31   Grief, starvation, broken jar, whispering
    E   Jesus, manacles, Crucifixion, knees bent
    Passion Gospel   Rooster, two swords, pray, kiss, robe
Call to Worship: WSL21 (Palms Gospel) or N821 (Pss)
Litanies: WSL76, C96, UM167 (Phil, Passion Gospel)
Prayers: WSL26, F286, UM283 or UM403 (Passion Gospel)
Response: C569, EL616, G227, P599, UM488, VU148, W423.
    "Jesus Remember Me" (Passion Gospel)

Exodus 12:1-4 (5-10) 11-14

The LORD said to Moses and Aaron in the land of Egypt,[2]"This month will be the first month; it will be the first month of the year for you. [3]Tell the whole Israelite community: On the tenth day of this month they must take a lamb for each household, a lamb per house. [4]If a household is too small for a lamb, it should share one with a neighbor nearby. You should divide the lamb in proportion to the number of people who will be eating it. [5]Your lamb should be a flawless year-old male. You may take it from the sheep or from the goats. [6]You should keep close watch over it until the fourteenth day of this month. At twilight on that day, the whole assembled Israelite community should slaughter their lambs. [7]They should take some of the blood and smear it on the two doorposts and on the beam over the door of the houses in which they are eating. [8]That same night they should eat the meat roasted over the fire. They should eat it along with unleavened bread and bitter herbs. [9]Don't eat any of it raw or boiled in water, but roasted over fire with its head, legs, and internal organs. [10]Don't let any of it remain until morning, and burn any of it left over in the morning. [11]This is how you should eat it. You should be dressed, with your sandals on your feet and your walking stick in your hand. You should eat the meal in a hurry. It is the Passover of the LORD. [12]I'll pass through the land of Egypt that night, and I'll strike down every oldest child in the land of Egypt, both humans and animals. I'll impose judgments on all the gods of Egypt. I am the LORD. [13]The blood will be your sign on the houses where you live. Whenever I see the blood, I'll pass over you. No plague will destroy you when I strike the land of Egypt.

[14]"This day will be a day of remembering for you. You will observe it as a festival to the LORD. You will observe it in every generation as a regulation for all time."

Psalm 116:1-4, 12-19 (G655/799, N699, P228, UM116)

I love the LORD because he hears
    my requests for mercy.
[2]I'll call out to him as long as I live,
    because he listens closely to me.
[3]Death's ropes bound me;
    the distress of the grave found me—
    I came face-to-face with trouble and grief.
[4]So I called on the LORD's name:
    "LORD, please save me!"
. . . .
What can I give back to the LORD
    for all the good things he has done for me?
[13]I'll lift up the cup of salvation.
    I'll call on the LORD's name.
[14]I'll keep the promises I made to the LORD
    in the presence of all God's people.
[15]The death of the LORD's faithful
    is a costly loss in his eyes.
[16]Oh yes, LORD, I am definitely your servant!
    I am your servant and the son of your female servant—
    you've freed me from my chains.
[17]So I'll offer a sacrifice of thanksgiving to you,
    and I'll call on the LORD's name.
[18]I'll keep the promises I made to the LORD
    in the presence of all God's people,
    [19]in the courtyards of the LORD's house,
      which is in the center of Jerusalem.
Praise the LORD!

1 Corinthians 11:23-26

[23]I received a tradition from the Lord, which I also handed on to you: on the night on which he was betrayed, the Lord Jesus took bread. [24]After giving thanks, he broke it and said, "This is my body, which is for you; do this to remember me." [25]He did the same thing with the cup, after they had eaten, saying, "This cup is the new covenant in my blood. Every time you drink it, do this to remember me." [26]Every time you eat this bread and drink this cup, you broadcast the death of the Lord until he comes.

John 13:1-17, 31b-35

Before the Festival of Passover, Jesus knew that his time had come to leave this world and go to the Father. Having loved his own who were in the world, he loved them fully. [2]Jesus and his disciples were sharing the evening meal. The devil had already provoked Judas, Simon Iscariot's son, to betray Jesus. [3]Jesus knew the Father had given everything into his hands and that he had come from God and was returning to God. [4]So he got up from the table and took off his robes. Picking up a linen towel, he tied it around his waist. [5]Then he poured water into a washbasin and began to wash the disciples' feet, drying them with the towel he was wearing. [6]When Jesus came to Simon Peter, Peter said to him, "Lord, are you going to wash my feet?"

[7]Jesus replied, "You don't understand what I'm doing now, but you will understand later."

[8]"No!" Peter said. "You will never wash my feet!"

Jesus replied, "Unless I wash you, you won't have a place with me."

[9]Simon Peter said, "Lord, not only my feet but also my hands and my head!"

[10]Jesus responded, "Those who have bathed need only to have their feet washed, because they are completely clean. You disciples are clean, but not every one of you." [11]He knew who would betray him. That's why he said, "Not every one of you is clean."

[12]After he washed the disciples' feet, he put on his robes and returned to his place at the table. He said to them, "Do you know what I've done for you? [13]You call me 'Teacher' and 'Lord,' and you speak correctly, because I am. [14]If I, your Lord and teacher, have washed your feet, you too must wash each other's feet. [15]I have given you an example: Just as I have done, you also must do. [16]I assure you, servants aren't greater than their master, nor are those who are sent greater than the one who sent them. [17]Since you know these things, you will be happy if you do them.
. . .

[31b] "Now the Human One has been glorified, and God has been glorified in him. [32]If God has been glorified in him, God will also glorify the Human One in himself and will glorify him immediately. [33]Little children, I'm with you for a little while longer. You will look for me—but, just as I told the Jewish leaders, I also tell you now—'Where I'm going, you can't come.'

[34]"I give you a new commandment: Love each other. Just as I have loved you, so you also must love each other. [35]This is how everyone will know that you are my disciples, when you love each other."

Primary Hymns and Songs for the Day

"Here, O My Lord, I See Thee" (Exod, Comm.) (O)
    C416, E318, F567, G517, L211, N336, P520, UM623, VU459
        S-1   #265. Descant
"*Jesu, Jesu*" (John, Footwashing)
    B501, C600, E602, EL708, G203, N498, P367, UM432,
    VU593, W431
        H-3   Chr-114; Org-19
        S-1   #63. Vocal part
"I Love the Lord" (Pss)
    G799, P362, N511, VU617, WS3142
"In Remembrance of Me" (1 Cor, Comm.)
    B365, C403, G521, S2254
"Ah, Holy Jesus" (John) (C)
    C210, E158, EL349, G218, N218, P93, UM289, VU138
        H-3   Chr-20; Desc-51
        S-2   #81-85. Harm.
                #86. Instrumental descant
"What Wondrous Love Is This" (John) (C)
    B143 (PD), C200, E439, EL666, F283, G215, L385, N223,
    P85, UM292, VU147 (Fr.), W600
        H-3   Hbl-102; Chr-212; Org-185
        S-1   #347. Harm.

Additional Hymn Suggestions

"Deep in the Shadows of the Past" (Exod)
    G50, N320, P330, S2246
"God the Sculptor of the Mountains" (Exod)
    EL736, G5, S2060, SF2060
"For the Bread Which You Have Broken" (1 Cor, Comm.)
    C411, E340/341, EL494, G516, L200, P508/509,
    UM614/615, VU470
"Let Us Break Bread Together" (1 Cor, Comm.)
    B366, C425, EL471 (PD), F564, G525, L212, N330, P513,
    UM618, VU480, W727
"Draw Us in the Spirit's Tether" (1 Cor, Comm.)
    C392, EL470, G529, N337, P504, UM632, VU479, W731
"The Bread of Life for All Is Broken" (1 Cor, Comm.)
    E342, N333, UM633
"Mothering God, You Gave Me Birth" (1 Cor, Comm.)
    C83, N467, S2050, SF2050, VU320
"Healer of Our Every Ill" (John)
    C506, EL612, G795, S2213, SF2213, VU619
"In the Singing" (1 Cor, Comm.)
    EL466, G533, S2255, SF2255
"Come, Share the Lord" (1 Cor, Comm.)
    C408, G510, S2269, SF2269, VU469
"By Gracious Powers" (John)
    E695/696, G818, N413, P342, UM517, W577
"Now It Is Evening" (John, Comm.)
    C471, EL572, S2187, SF2187
"As We Gather at Your Table" (John, Comm.)
    EL522, N332, S2268, SF2268, VU457

Additional Contemporary Suggestions

"We Bring the Sacrifice of Praise" (Pss)
    S2031, SF2031, SP1
"I Will Call upon the Lord" (Pss)
    G621, S2002, SF2002, SP224
"I Love You, Lord" (Pss)
    B212, G627, S2068, SF2068, SP72
"Because of Your Love" (Pss)
    M224
"Beautiful Savior" (Pss, Holy Week)
    M243

"I Stand Amazed" (Pss)
    M79
"Fill My Cup, Lord" (Pss, Comm.)
    C351, F481, UM641, WS3093
"Eat This Bread" (1 Cor, Comm.)
    C414, EL472, G527, N788, UM628, VU466, W734
"Take Our Bread" (1 Cor, Comm.)
    C413, UM640
"Here Is Bread, Here Is Wine" (1 Cor, Comm.)
    EL483, S2266, SF2266
"Make Me a Servant" (John)
    S2176, SF2176, SP193
"Make Us One" (John)
    S2224, SF2224, SP137
"They'll Know We Are Christians" (John)
    C494, G300, S2223, SF2223
"Live in Charity" ("*Ubi Caritas*") (John)
    C523, EL642, G205, S2179, SF2179, W604
"Bind Us Together" (John)
    S2226, SF2226, SP140
"An Upper Room Did Our Lord Prepare" (John)
    C385, G202, P94, VU130

Vocal Solos

"King of Glory, King of Peace" (Pss, Lent)
    V-9   p. 24
"In Remembrance" (John, Comm.)
    V-5(2)   p. 7
"He Breaks the Bread, He Pours the Wine" (John, Comm.)
    V-10   p. 43

Anthems

"When Twilight Come" (John)
Arr. Robert Buckley Farlee; AEC-1 p. 82
2-part mixed and piano (bit.ly/AEC-1-82)

"Ah, Holy Jesus" (John)
Donald McCullough; MorningStar MSM-50-3480
SATB and organ (bit.ly/50-3480)

Other Suggestions

Visuals:
    O   Lamb/blood/doorpost, sandals, staff, Exod 12:14
    P   Ear, snare, cup, open shackles, Ps 116:4b, 12, 13, or 15
    E   Broken loaf, cup, 1 Cor 11:24b or 25b
    G   Robe, towel/basin, footwashing, disciples, love
Opening Prayer: N827 (John)
Readings: C189, F562, F566 (2 Cor, John, Lent)
Call to Prayer: EL348, G204, S2198, SF2198. "Stay with Me"
    ("*Noho Pū*") (Holy Thursday)
Prayer: UM283 (Holy Thursday, 2 Cor)
Prayer: C332. God of Wondrous Darkness (Exod)
Response: EL152, S2275, SF2275, WS3133. "*Kyrie*" (Lent,
    Comm.)
Offertory Prayer: WSL154 (John)
Closing Prayer: WSL27 (John)

Isaiah 52:13–53:12

¹³Look, my servant will succeed.
    He will be exalted and lifted very high.
¹⁴Just as many were appalled by you,
    he too appeared disfigured, inhuman,
    his appearance unlike that of mortals.
¹⁵But he will astonish many nations.
    Kings will be silenced because of him,
    because they will see what they haven't seen before;
    what they haven't heard before, they will ponder.
53 Who can believe what we have heard,
    and for whose sake has the Lord's arm been revealed?
²He grew up like a young plant before us,
    like a root from dry ground.
He possessed no splendid form for us to see,
    no desirable appearance.
³He was despised and avoided by others;
    a man who suffered, who knew sickness well.
Like someone from whom people hid their faces,
    he was despised, and we didn't think about him.
⁴It was certainly our sickness that he carried,
    and our sufferings that he bore,
    but we thought him afflicted,
    struck down by God and tormented.
⁵He was pierced because of our rebellions
    and crushed because of our crimes.
    He bore the punishment that made us whole;
    by his wounds we are healed.
⁶Like sheep we had all wandered away,
    each going its own way,
    but the Lord let fall on him all our crimes.
⁷He was oppressed and tormented,
    but didn't open his mouth.
Like a lamb being brought to slaughter,
    like a ewe silent before her shearers,
    he didn't open his mouth.
⁸Due to an unjust ruling he was taken away,
    and his fate—who will think about it?
He was eliminated from the land of the living,
    struck dead because of my people's rebellion.
⁹His grave was among the wicked,
    his tomb with evildoers,
    though he had done no violence,
    and had spoken nothing false.
¹⁰But the Lord wanted to crush him
    and to make him suffer.
If his life is offered as restitution,
    he will see his offspring; he will enjoy long life.
    The Lord's plans will come to fruition through him.
¹¹After his deep anguish he will see light, and he will be satisfied.
Through his knowledge, the righteous one, my servant,
    will make many righteous,
    and will bear their guilt.
¹²Therefore, I will give him a share with the great,
    and he will divide the spoil with the strong,
    in return for exposing his life to death
    and being numbered with rebels,
    though he carried the sin of many
    and pleaded on behalf of those who rebelled.

Psalm 22 (G631, N632, P168, UM752)

My God! My God,
    why have you left me all alone?
    Why are you so far from saving me—
        so far from my anguished groans?
²My God, I cry out during the day,
    but you don't answer;
    even at nighttime I don't stop.
³You are the holy one, enthroned.
You are Israel's praise.
⁴Our ancestors trusted you—
    they trusted you and you rescued them;
    ⁵they cried out to you and they were saved;
    they trusted you and they weren't ashamed.
⁶But I'm just a worm, less than human;
    insulted by one person, despised by another.
⁷All who see me make fun of me—
    they gape, shaking their heads:
    ⁸"He committed himself to the Lord,
        so let God rescue him;
        let God deliver him
        because God likes him so much."
⁹But you are the one who pulled me from the womb,
    placing me safely at my mother's breasts.
¹⁰I was thrown on you from birth;
    you've been my God
    since I was in my mother's womb.
¹¹Please don't be far from me,
    because trouble is near
    and there's no one to help.
¹²Many bulls surround me;
    mighty bulls from Bashan encircle me.
¹³They open their mouths at me
    like a lion ripping and roaring!
¹⁴I'm poured out like water.
    All my bones have fallen apart.
        My heart is like wax;
        it melts inside me.
¹⁵My strength is dried up
    like a piece of broken pottery.
My tongue sticks to the roof of my mouth;
    you've set me down in the dirt of death.
¹⁶Dogs surround me;
    a pack of evil people circle me like a lion—
    oh, my poor hands and feet!
¹⁷I can count all my bones!
    Meanwhile, they just stare at me, watching me.
¹⁸They divvy up my garments among themselves;
    they cast lots for my clothes.
¹⁹But you, Lord! Don't be far away!
    You are my strength!
    Come quick and help me!
²⁰Deliver me from the sword.
    Deliver my life from the power of the dog.
²¹ Save me from the mouth of the lion.
    From the horns of the wild oxen
    you have answered me!
²²I will declare your name to my brothers and sisters;
    I will praise you in the very center of the congregation!
²³All of you who revere the Lord—praise him!
    All of you who are Jacob's descendants—honor him!
    All of you who are all Israel's offspring—
        stand in awe of him!
²⁴Because he didn't despise or detest
    the suffering of the one who suffered—
    he didn't hide his face from me.
    No, he listened when I cried out to him for help.
²⁵I offer praise in the great congregation
    because of you;
    I will fulfill my promises
    in the presence of those who honor God.
²⁶Let all those who are suffering eat and be full!

Let all who seek the LORD praise him!
    I pray your hearts live forever!
27Every part of the earth
    will remember and come back to the LORD;
    every family among all the nations will worship you.
28Because the right to rule belongs to the LORD,
    he rules all nations.
29Indeed, all the earth's powerful
    will worship him;
    all who are descending to the dust
    will kneel before him;
    my being also lives for him.
30Future descendants will serve him;
    generations to come will be told about my LORD.
31They will proclaim God's righteousness
    to those not yet born,
    telling them what God has done.

Hebrews 10:16-25

16*This is the covenant that I will make with them.*
    After these days, says the LORD,
      I will place my laws in their hearts
      and write them on their minds.
    17*And I won't remember their sins*
      and their lawless behavior anymore.

18When there is forgiveness for these things, there is no longer an offering for sin.

19Brothers and sisters, we have confidence that we can enter the holy of holies by means of Jesus' blood, 20through a new and living way that he opened up for us through the curtain, which is his body, 21and we have a great high priest over God's house. 22Therefore, let's draw near with a genuine heart with the certainty that our faith gives us, since our hearts are sprinkled clean from an evil conscience and our bodies are washed with pure water. 23Let's hold on to the confession of our hope without wavering, because the one who made the promises is reliable. 24And let us consider each other carefully for the purpose of sparking love and good deeds. 25Don't stop meeting together with other believers, which some people have gotten into the habit of doing. Instead, encourage each other, especially as you see the day drawing near.

John 18:1–19:42

After he said these things, Jesus went out with his disciples and crossed over to the other side of the Kidron Valley. He and his disciples entered a garden there. 2Judas, his betrayer, also knew the place because Jesus often gathered there with his disciples. 3Judas brought a company of soldiers and some guards from the chief priests and Pharisees. They came there carrying lanterns, torches, and weapons. 4Jesus knew everything that was to happen to him, so he went out and asked, "Who are you looking for?"

5They answered, "Jesus the Nazarene."

He said to them, "I Am." (Judas, his betrayer, was standing with them.) 6When he said, "I Am," they shrank back and fell to the ground. 7He asked them again, "Who are you looking for?"

They said, "Jesus the Nazarene."

8Jesus answered, "I told you, 'I Am.' If you are looking for me, then let these people go." 9This was so that the word he had spoken might be fulfilled: "I didn't lose anyone of those whom you gave me."

10Then Simon Peter, who had a sword, drew it and struck the high priest's servant, cutting off his right ear. (The servant's name was Malchus.) 11Jesus told Peter, "Put your sword away!

Am I not to drink the cup the Father has given me?" 12Then the company of soldiers, the commander, and the guards from the Jewish leaders took Jesus into custody. They bound him 13and led him first to Annas. He was the father-in-law of Caiaphas, the high priest that year. (14Caiaphas was the one who had advised the Jewish leaders that it was better for one person to die for the people.)

15Simon Peter and another disciple followed Jesus. Because this other disciple was known to the high priest, he went with Jesus into the high priest's courtyard. 16However, Peter stood outside near the gate. Then the other disciple (the one known to the high priest) came out and spoke to the woman stationed at the gate, and she brought Peter in. 17The servant woman stationed at the gate asked Peter, "Aren't you one of this man's disciples?"

"I'm not," he replied. 18The servants and the guards had made a fire because it was cold. They were standing around it, warming themselves. Peter joined them there, standing by the fire and warming himself.

19Meanwhile, the chief priest questioned Jesus about his disciples and his teaching. 20Jesus answered, "I've spoken openly to the world. I've always taught in synagogues and in the temple, where all the Jews gather. I've said nothing in private. 21Why ask me? Ask those who heard what I told them. They know what I said."

22After Jesus spoke, one of the guards standing there slapped Jesus in the face. "Is that how you would answer the high priest?" he asked.

23Jesus replied, "If I speak wrongly, testify about what was wrong. But if I speak correctly, why do you strike me?" 24Then Annas sent him, bound, to Caiaphas the high priest.

25Meanwhile, Simon Peter was still standing with the guards, warming himself. They asked, "Aren't you one of his disciples?"

Peter denied it, saying, "I'm not."

26A servant of the high priest, a relative of the one whose ear Peter had cut off, said to him, "Didn't I see you in the garden with him?" 27Peter denied it again, and immediately a rooster crowed.

28The Jewish leaders led Jesus from Caiaphas to the Roman governor's palace. It was early in the morning. So that they could eat the Passover, the Jewish leaders wouldn't enter the palace; entering the palace would have made them ritually impure.

29So Pilate went out to them and asked, "What charge do you bring against this man?"

30They answered, "If he had done nothing wrong, we wouldn't have handed him over to you."

31Pilate responded, "Take him yourselves and judge him according to your Law."

The Jewish leaders replied, "The Law doesn't allow us to kill anyone." (32This was so that Jesus' word might be fulfilled when he indicated how he was going to die.)

33Pilate went back into the palace. He summoned Jesus and asked, "Are you the king of the Jews?"

34Jesus answered, "Do you say this on your own or have others spoken to you about me?"

35Pilate responded, "I'm not a Jew, am I? Your nation and its chief priests handed you over to me. What have you done?"

36Jesus replied, "My kingdom doesn't originate from this world. If it did, my guards would fight so that I wouldn't have been arrested by the Jewish leaders. My kingdom isn't from here."

37"So you are a king?" Pilate said.

Jesus answered, "You say that I am a king. I was born and came into the world for this reason: to testify to the truth. Whoever accepts the truth listens to my voice."

[38]"What is truth?" Pilate asked.

After Pilate said this, he returned to the Jewish leaders and said, "I find no grounds for any charge against him. [39]You have a custom that I release one prisoner for you at Passover. Do you want me to release for you the king of the Jews?"

[40]They shouted, "Not this man! Give us Barabbas!" (Barabbas was an outlaw.)

19 Then Pilate had Jesus taken and whipped. [2]The soldiers twisted together a crown of thorns and put it on his head, and dressed him in a purple robe. [3]Over and over they went up to him and said, "Greetings, king of the Jews!" And they slapped him in the face.

[4]Pilate came out of the palace again and said to the Jewish leaders, "Look! I'm bringing him out to you to let you know that I find no grounds for a charge against him." [5]When Jesus came out, wearing the crown of thorns and the purple robe, Pilate said to them, "Here's the man."

[6]When the chief priests and their deputies saw him, they shouted out, "Crucify, crucify!"

Pilate told them, "You take him and crucify him. I don't find any grounds for a charge against him."

[7]The Jewish leaders replied, "We have a Law, and according to this Law he ought to die because he made himself out to be God's Son."

[8]When Pilate heard this word, he was even more afraid. [9]He went back into the residence and spoke to Jesus, "Where are you from?" Jesus didn't answer. [10]So Pilate said, "You won't speak to me? Don't you know that I have authority to release you and also to crucify you?"

[11]Jesus replied, "You would have no authority over me if it had not been given to you from above. That's why the one who handed me over to you has the greater sin." [12]From that moment on, Pilate wanted to release Jesus.

However, the Jewish leaders cried out, saying, "If you release this man, you aren't a friend of the emperor! Anyone who makes himself out to be a king opposes the emperor!"

[13]When Pilate heard these words, he led Jesus out and seated him on the judge's bench at the place called Stone Pavement (in Aramaic, *Gabbatha*). [14]It was about noon on the Preparation Day for the Passover. Pilate said to the Jewish leaders, "Here's your king."

[15]The Jewish leaders cried out, "Take him away! Take him away! Crucify him!"

Pilate responded, "What? Do you want me to crucify your king?"

"We have no king except the emperor," the chief priests answered. [16]Then Pilate handed Jesus over to be crucified.

The soldiers took Jesus prisoner. [17]Carrying his cross by himself, he went out to a place called Skull Place (in Aramaic, *Golgotha*). [18]That's where they crucified him—and two others with him, one on each side and Jesus in the middle. [19]Pilate had a public notice written and posted on the cross. It read "Jesus the Nazarene, the king of the Jews." [20]Many of the Jews read this sign, for the place where Jesus was crucified was near the city and it was written in Aramaic, Latin, and Greek. [21]Therefore, the Jewish chief priests complained to Pilate, "Don't write, 'The king of the Jews' but 'This man said, "I am the king of the Jews."'"

[22]Pilate answered, "What I've written, I've written."

[23]When the soldiers crucified Jesus, they took his clothes and his sandals, and divided them into four shares, one for each soldier. His shirt was seamless, woven as one piece from the top to the bottom. [24]They said to each other, "Let's not tear it. Let's cast lots to see who will get it." This was to fulfill the scripture,

They divided my clothes among themselves,
 and they cast lots for my clothing.
That's what the soldiers did.

[25]Jesus' mother and his mother's sister, Mary the wife of Clopas, and Mary Magdalene stood near the cross. [26]When Jesus saw his mother and the disciple whom he loved standing nearby, he said to his mother, "Woman, here is your son." [27]Then he said to the disciple, "Here is your mother." And from that time on, this disciple took her into his home.

[28]After this, knowing that everything was already completed, in order to fulfill the scripture, Jesus said, "I am thirsty." [29]A jar full of sour wine was nearby, so the soldiers soaked a sponge in it, placed it on a hyssop branch, and held it up to his lips. [30]When he had received the sour wine, Jesus said, "It is completed." Bowing his head, he gave up his life.

[31]It was the Preparation Day and the Jewish leaders didn't want the bodies to remain on the cross on the Sabbath, especially since that Sabbath was an important day. So they asked Pilate to have the legs of those crucified broken and the bodies taken down. [32]Therefore, the soldiers came and broke the legs of the two men who were crucified with Jesus. [33]When they came to Jesus, they saw that he was already dead so they didn't break his legs. [34]However, one of the soldiers pierced his side with a spear, and immediately blood and water came out. [35]The one who saw this has testified, and his testimony is true. He knows that he speaks the truth, and he has testified so that you also can believe. [36]These things happened to fulfill the scripture, *They won't break any of his bones.* [37]And another scripture says, *They will look at him whom they have pierced.*

[38]After this Joseph of Arimathea asked Pilate if he could take away the body of Jesus. Joseph was a disciple of Jesus, but a secret one because he feared the Jewish authorities. Pilate gave him permission, so he came and took the body away. [39]Nicodemus, the one who at first had come to Jesus at night, was there too. He brought a mixture of myrrh and aloe, nearly seventy-five pounds in all. [40]Following Jewish burial customs, they took Jesus' body and wrapped it, with the spices, in linen cloths. [41]There was a garden in the place where Jesus was crucified, and in the garden was a new tomb in which no one had ever been laid. [42]Because it was the Jewish Preparation Day and the tomb was nearby, they laid Jesus in it.

Primary Hymns and Songs for the Day

"Ah, Holy Jesus" (John) (O)
　　C210, E158, EL349, G218, N218, P93, UM289, VU138
　　　　H-3　　Chr-20; Desc-51
　　　　S-2　　#81-85. Harm.
　　　　　　　　#86. Instrumental descant
"Go to Dark Gethsemane" (John) (O)
　　C196, E171, EL347, F281, G220, L109, N219, P97, UM290
　　(PD), VU133
　　　　H-3　　Hbl-18; Chr-74; Desc-89; Org-121
　　　　S-2　　#150. Harm.
"Alas! and Did My Savior Bleed" (Isa, John)
　　B145, EL337, F274, G212, L98, N200, P78, UM294 (PD)
　　B139, C204, N199, UM359 (PD) (alternate tune)
"Why Stand So Far Away, My God?" (Pss)
　　C671, G786, S2180, SF2180
　　　　H-3　　Chr-139, 145; Desc-77
　　　　S-1　　#241-242. Orff Arr. and descant
"Were You There" (John) (C)
　　B156, C198, E172, EL353, F287, G228, L92, N230, P102,
　　UM288, VU144, W436

Additional Hymn Suggestions

"You, Lord, Are Both Lamb and Shepherd" (Isa)
　　G274, SF2102, WS3043, VU210
"He Never Said a Mumbalin' Word" (Isa)
　　C208, EL350, G219, P95 (PD), UM291, VU141
"O God, My God" (Pss)
　　N515
"How Long, O Lord" (Pss, Good Friday)
　　G777, S2209, SF2209
"Taste and See" (Pss, Comm.)
　　EL493, G520, S2267, SF2267
"I Am Thine, O Lord" (Heb)
　　B290, C601, F455, N455, UM419 (PD)
"Near to the Heart of God" (Heb)
　　B295, C581, F35, G824, P527, UM472 (PD)
"O Love, How Deep" (John)
　　E448/449, EL322, G618, N209, P83, UM267, VU348
"O Sacred Head, Now Wounded" (John)
　　B137, C202, E168/169, EL351/352, F284, G221, L116/117,
　　N226, P98, UM286, VU145 (Fr.), W434
"In the Cross of Christ I Glory" (John)
　　B554, C207, E441, EL324, F251, G213, L104, N193, P84,
　　UM295
"When I Survey the Wondrous Cross" (John)
　　B144, C195, EL803, F258, G223, N224, P101, UM298
　　E474, L482, G224, P100, UM299 (PD), VU149 (Fr.)
"The Bread of Life for All Is Broken" (John, Comm.)
　　E342, N333, UM633
"My Song Is Love Unknown" (Good Friday)
　　E458, EL343, G209, L94, N222, P76, S2083, SF2083, VU143,
　　W439
"When Jesus Wept" (John)
　　C199, E715, G194, P312, S2106, SF2106, VU146
"Why Has God Forsaken Me?" (Good Friday)
　　G809, P406, S2110, VU154

Additional Contemporary Suggestions

"Now Behold the Lamb" (Isa, Good Friday)
　　EL341, WS3081
"The Power of the Cross" (Isa, John, Good Friday)
　　M222, WS3085
"In Christ Alone" ("My Hope Is Found") (Good Friday)
　　M138, WS3105

"At the Cross" (Isa, Good Friday)
　　M225
"Our God Reigns" (Isa)
　　SP64
"Because of Your Love" (Heb)
　　M224
"Jesus, Remember Me" (John)
　　C569, EL616, G227, P599, UM488, VU148, W423
"Jesus, We Crown You with Praise" (John, Good Friday)
　　M24
"Above All" (John, Good Friday)
　　M77;　V-3 (2) p. 17 Vocal Solo
"The Wonderful Cross" (John, Good Friday)
　　M76
"Stay with Me" ("*Noho Pū*") (Good Friday)
　　EL348, G204, S2198, SF2198
"There Is a Redeemer" (Good Friday)
　　G443, SP111
"Amazing Love" (Good Friday)
　　M81
"Revelation Song" (Good Friday)
　　M274
"How Great Is the Love" (Good Friday)
　　M277
"Jesus Died My Soul to Save" (John, Good Friday)
　　M278

Vocal Solos

"Steal Away to Heaven" (Pss, Good Friday)
　　V-3 (1)　　p. 17
"Lamb of God" (John, Good Friday)
　　V-5(2)　　p. 5
"Were You There?" (John, Good Friday)
　　V-7　　　p. 60
"O Love Divine, What hast Thou Done!" (John)
　　V-1　　　p. 17
"Ah, Holy Jesus" (John)
　　V-6　　　p. 24

Anthems

"Cross of Jesus" (John)
Robert Benson; AEC-2 p. 46
Unison and keyboard

"Into Your Hands I Surrender My Soul" (John)
Michael John Trotta; MorningStar MSM-50-3979
SATB a cappella (bit.ly/50-3979)

Other Suggestions

Visuals: Cross draped in black, altar stripped
　　O　　Crucifixion, root, Isa 53:3, lamb, shears, grave, light
　　P　　Worm, mock, nursing child, spilled water, melted wax,
　　　　　　dice
　　E　　Open Bible, heart, Crucifixion, water, Heb 10:23a
　　G　　Torch, sword, fire, cock crowing, robe, INRI, wine,
　　　　　　branch, spear, linen cloth, tomb
Introit: EL341, WS3081. "Now Behold the Lamb" (Isa, Lent)
Readings: C201, F245, F272, F286, F356, UM293 (Isa, John)
Sung Prayer: EL152, S2275, SF2275, WS3133. "Kyrie" (Lent)
Prayers: WSL24, WSL155, C332, N834, F257, UM284 (John)
Response: EL336, G518, S2113, SF2113. "Lamb of God" (Lent)

Acts 10:34-43

³⁴Peter said, "I really am learning that God doesn't show partiality to one group of people over another. ³⁵Rather, in every nation, whoever worships him and does what is right is acceptable to him. ³⁶This is the message of peace he sent to the Israelites by proclaiming the good news through Jesus Christ: He is Lord of all! ³⁷You know what happened throughout Judea, beginning in Galilee after the baptism John preached. ³⁸You know about Jesus of Nazareth, whom God anointed with the Holy Spirit and endowed with power. Jesus traveled around doing good and healing everyone oppressed by the devil because God was with him. ³⁹We are witnesses of everything he did, both in Judea and in Jerusalem. They killed him by hanging him on a tree, ⁴⁰but God raised him up on the third day and allowed him to be seen,⁴¹not by everyone but by us. We are witnesses whom God chose beforehand, who ate and drank with him after God raised him from the dead. ⁴²He commanded us to preach to the people and to testify that he is the one whom God appointed as judge of the living and the dead. ⁴³All the prophets testify about him that everyone who believes in him receives forgiveness of sins through his name."

Psalm 118:1-2, 14-24 (G391/681, N700, P230-232, UM839)

Give thanks to the LORD because he is good,
　because his faithful love lasts forever.
²Let Israel say it:
　"God's faithful love lasts forever!"
. . . .
¹⁴The LORD was my strength and protection;
　he was my saving help!
¹⁵The sounds of joyful songs and deliverance
　are heard in the tents of the righteous:
　"The LORD's strong hand is victorious!
¹⁶The LORD's strong hand is ready to strike!
　　The LORD's strong hand is victorious!"
¹⁷I won't die—no, I will live
　and declare what the LORD has done.
¹⁸Yes, the LORD definitely disciplined me,
　but he didn't hand me over to death.
¹⁹Open the gates of righteousness for me
　so I can come in and give thanks to the LORD!
²⁰This is the LORD's gate;
　those who are righteous enter through it.
²¹I thank you because you answered me,
　because you were my saving help.
²²The stone rejected by the builders
　is now the main foundation stone!
²³This has happened because of the LORD;
　it is astounding in our sight!
²⁴This is the day the LORD acted;
　we will rejoice and celebrate in it!

1 Corinthians 15:19-26

¹⁹If we have a hope in Christ only in this life, then we deserve to be pitied more than anyone else.

²⁰But in fact Christ has been raised from the dead. He's the first crop of the harvest of those who have died. ²¹Since death came through a human being, the resurrection of the dead came through one too. ²²In the same way that everyone dies in Adam, so also everyone will be given life in Christ. ²³Each event will happen in the right order: Christ, the first crop of the harvest, then those who belong to Christ at his coming, ²⁴and then the end, when Christ hands over the kingdom to God the Father, when he brings every form of rule, every authority and power to an end. ²⁵It is necessary for him to rule until *he puts all enemies under his feet.* ²⁶Death is the last enemy to be brought to an end.

John 20:1-18 (or Luke 24:1-12)

Early in the morning of the first day of the week, while it was still dark, Mary Magdalene came to the tomb and saw that the stone had been taken away from the tomb. ²She ran to Simon Peter and the other disciple, the one whom Jesus loved, and said, "They have taken the Lord from the tomb, and we don't know where they've put him." ³Peter and the other disciple left to go to the tomb. ⁴They were running together, but the other disciple ran faster than Peter and was the first to arrive at the tomb. ⁵Bending down to take a look, he saw the linen cloths lying there, but he didn't go in. ⁶Following him, Simon Peter entered the tomb and saw the linen cloths lying there. ⁷He also saw the face cloth that had been on Jesus' head. It wasn't with the other clothes but was folded up in its own place. ⁸Then the other disciple, the one who arrived at the tomb first, also went inside. He saw and believed. ⁹They didn't yet understand the scripture that Jesus must rise from the dead.¹⁰Then the disciples returned to the place where they were staying.

¹¹Mary stood outside near the tomb, crying. As she cried, she bent down to look into the tomb. ¹²She saw two angels dressed in white, seated where the body of Jesus had been, one at the head and one at the foot. ¹³The angels asked her, "Woman, why are you crying?"

She replied, "They have taken away my Lord, and I don't know where they've put him." ¹⁴As soon as she had said this, she turned around and saw Jesus standing there, but she didn't know it was Jesus.

¹⁵Jesus said to her, "Woman, why are you crying? Who are you looking for?"

Thinking he was the gardener, she replied, "Sir, if you have carried him away, tell me where you have put him and I will get him."

¹⁶Jesus said to her, "Mary."

She turned and said to him in Aramaic, "Rabbouni" (which means *Teacher*).

¹⁷Jesus said to her, "Don't hold on to me, for I haven't yet gone up to my Father. Go to my brothers and sisters and tell them, 'I'm going up to my Father and your Father, to my God and your God.'"

¹⁸Mary Magdalene left and announced to the disciples, "I've seen the Lord." Then she told them what he said to her.

[Luke 24:1-12] Very early in the morning on the first day of the week, the women went to the tomb, bringing the fragrant spices they had prepared. ²They found the stone rolled away from the tomb, ³but when they went in, they didn't find the body of the LORD Jesus. ⁴They didn't know what to make of this. Suddenly, two men were standing beside them in gleaming bright clothing.⁵The women were frightened and bowed their faces toward the ground, but the men said to them, "Why do you look for the living among the dead? ⁶He isn't here, but has been raised. Remember what he told you while he was still in Galilee, ⁷that the Human One must be handed over to sinners, be crucified, and on the third day rise again." ⁸Then they remembered his words. ⁹When they returned from the tomb, they reported all these things to the eleven and all the others. ¹⁰It was Mary Magdalene, Joanna, Mary the mother of James, and the other women with them who told these things to the apostles.¹¹Their words struck the apostles as nonsense, and they didn't believe the women. ¹²But Peter ran to the tomb. When he bent over to look inside, he saw only the linen cloth. Then he returned home, wondering what had happened.

Primary Hymns and Songs for the Day
"Christ the Lord Is Risen Today" (John, Luke) (O)
   B159, C216, F289, N233, UM302 (PD), VU155 and VU157
      H-3   Hbl-8, 51; Chr-49; Desc-31; Org-32
      S-1   #104-108. Various treatments
   G245, P113, W463
      H-3   Hbl-72; Chr-50; Desc-69; Org-78
      S-1   #213. Desc.
   EL373, L130
"Jesus Christ Is Risen Today" (John, Luke)
   B159, E207, EL365 (PD), F297, G232, L151, N240, P123, UM302, W442
      H-3   Hbl-8, 51; Chr-49; Desc-31; Org-32
      S-1   #104-108. Various treatments
"Hail the Day That Sees Him Rise" (1 Cor, John)
   E214, UM312, W471 (PD)
      H-3   Hbl-72; Chr-50; Desc-69; Org-78
      S-1   #213. Desc.
   B165, N260, VU189
"The Day of Resurrection" (John, Luke) (C)
   B164, C228, E210, EL361, G233, L141, N245, P118, UM303 (PD), VU164
      H-3   Hbl-74; Chr-123; Desc-64; Org-71
      S-1   #9-197. Various treatments

Additional Hymn Suggestions
"We Meet You, O Christ" (Acts)
   C183, P311, UM257, VU183
"Christ Jesus Lay in Death's Strong Bands" (Acts, John)
   E186, EL370, G237, L134, P110, UM319 (PD)
"Thine Be the Glory" (1 Cor, John)
   B163, C218, EL376, F291, G238, L145, N253, P122, UM308, VU173 (Fr.)
"Now the Green Blade Riseth" (John, Luke)
   C230, E204, EL379, G247, L148, N238, UM311, VU186
"In the Garden" (John, Luke)
   B187, C227, F588, N237, UM314
"Come, Ye Faithful, Raise the Strain" (John, Luke)
   C215, E199, EL363, G234, L132, N230, P115, UM315 (PD), VU165, W456
"This Joyful Eastertide" (John, Luke)
   E192, EL391, G244, L149, N232, VU177, W449
"O Sons and Daughters, Let Us Sing" (John, Luke)
   C220, E203, EL386/387, G235, L139, N244, P116 (PD), UM317, VU170, W447
"Christ Is Alive" (John, Luke)
   B173, E182, EL389, G246, L363, P108, UM318, VU158
"Up from the Grave He Arose" (John, Luke)
   B160, C224, UM322 (PD)
"Hail Thee, Festival Day" (John, Luke)
   E175, EL394, L142, N262, UM324, VU163, W444
"Because You Live, O Christ" (John, Luke)
   G249, N231, P105

Additional Contemporary Suggestions
"Alleluia" (Pss, 1 Cor, Easter)
   EL174, G587, S2043, SF2043
"I Will Enter His Gates" (Pss)
   S2270, SF2270, SP168
"Forever" (Pss)
   M68, WS3023
"Hallelujah" ("Your Love Is Amazing") (Pss)
   M118, WS3027
"You Are My All in All" (Pss, Easter)
   G519, SP220, WS3040

"Lord, I Lift Your Name on High" (1 Cor, Easter)
   EL857, M2, S2088, SF2088
"Christ the Lord Is Risen" (1 Cor, Easter)
   S2116, SF2116
"Alleluia" (John, Luke)
   B223, C106, F361, N765, SP108, UM186, S-2 #3-4. Desc. and Harm.
"Jesus, You Are the New Day" (John, Luke)
   WS3143
"Above All" (John)
   M77; V-3 (2) p. 17 Vocal Solo
"Christ Rose Up from the Dead" (John, Luke, Easter)
   N239, UM316
"In Christ Alone" ("My Hope Is Found") (Easter)
   M138, WS3105
"Holy, Holy" (Easter)
   B254, F149, P140, S2039, SP141
"Sing Alleluia to the Lord" (Easter, Comm.)
   B214, C32, S2258, SF2258, SP93

Vocal Solos
"Jesus Christ Is Risen Today" (Easter)
   V-1   p. 50
"Crown Him, the Risen King" (Easter)
   V-10   p. 55
"I Know That My Redeemer Liveth" (1 Cor)
   V-2
   V-5(2)   p. 22

Anthems
"The Day of Resurrection" (John, Luke) (SAB available)
Robert Buckley Farlee; Augsburg 978-1-4514-9260-6
SATB and organ, brass quintet (bit.ly/9260-6)

"The Chief Cornerstone" (Easter)
Bradley Ellingboe; AEC-1 p. 69
2-part mixed with keyboard, opt. trumpet (bit.ly/AEC-1-69)

Other Suggestions
Visuals: Flowers, butterfly, peacock
  Acts Risen Christ, cross draped in white, all nations
  P   Right hand, gates, cornerstone, Ps 118:1a, b, 17 or 24
  E   Resurrection, fruit, empty tomb
  G   Stone, running feet, shroud, rolled napkin, weep/joy
Greetings: N821 or N822 (Pss); WSL29 (Luke, John, Easter)
Introit: B359, C286, N84, SP236, UM657/658, VU412. "This Is the Day" (Pss)
Canticle: C217. The Easter Affirmations (1 Cor)
Prayers: F294, UM320, or UM360 (1 Cor, Easter)
Offertory Prayer: WSL119 (Easter)
Sung Benediction: S2237, SF2237, VU578. "As a Fire Is Meant for Burning," stanza 3 (Easter)
Blessing: N872 (John, Easter)

Acts 5:27-32

[27]The apostles were brought before the council where the high priest confronted them: [28]"In no uncertain terms, we demanded that you not teach in this name. And look at you! You have filled Jerusalem with your teaching. And you are determined to hold us responsible for this man's death."

[29]Peter and the apostles replied, "We must obey God rather than humans! [30]The God of our ancestors raised Jesus from the dead—whom you killed by hanging him on a tree. [31]God has exalted Jesus to his right side as leader and savior so that he could enable Israel to change its heart and life and to find forgiveness for sins. [32]We are witnesses of such things, as is the Holy Spirit, whom God has given to those who obey him."

Psalm 150 (G33/389/617/633, N723, P258, UM862)

Praise the LORD!
Praise God in his sanctuary!
　　Praise God in his fortress, the sky!
[2]Praise God in his mighty acts!
　　Praise God as suits his incredible greatness!
[3]Praise God with the blast of the ram's horn!
　　Praise God with lute and lyre!
[4]Praise God with drum and dance!
　　Praise God with strings and pipe!
[5]Praise God with loud cymbals!
　　Praise God with clashing cymbals!
[6]Let every living thing praise the LORD!
Praise the LORD!

Revelation 1:4-8

[4]John, to the seven churches that are in Asia:
Grace and peace to you from the one who is and was and is coming, and from the seven spirits that are before God's throne,[5]and from Jesus Christ—the faithful witness, the firstborn from among the dead, and the ruler of the kings of the earth.

To the one who loves us and freed us from our sins by his blood, [6]who made us a kingdom, priests to his God and Father—to him be glory and power forever and always. Amen.

[7]Look, he is coming with the clouds! Every eye will see him, including those who pierced him, and all the tribes of the earth will mourn because of him. This is so. Amen. [8]"I am the Alpha and the Omega," says the Lord God, "the one who is and was and is coming, the Almighty."

John 20:19-31

[19]It was still the first day of the week. That evening, while the disciples were behind closed doors because they were afraid of the Jewish authorities, Jesus came and stood among them. He said, "Peace be with you." [20]After he said this, he showed them his hands and his side. When the disciples saw the Lord, they were filled with joy. [21]Jesus said to them again, "Peace be with you. As the Father sent me, so I am sending you." [22]Then he breathed on them and said, "Receive the Holy Spirit. [23]If you forgive anyone's sins, they are forgiven; if you don't forgive them, they aren't forgiven."

[24]Thomas, the one called Didymus, one of the Twelve, wasn't with the disciples when Jesus came. [25]The other disciples told him, "We've seen the Lord!"

But he replied, "Unless I see the nail marks in his hands, put my finger in the wounds left by the nails, and put my hand into his side, I won't believe."

[26]After eight days his disciples were again in a house and Thomas was with them. Even though the doors were locked, Jesus entered and stood among them. He said, "Peace be with you." [27]Then he said to Thomas, "Put your finger here. Look at my hands. Put your hand into my side. No more disbelief. Believe!"

[28]Thomas responded to Jesus, "My Lord and my God!"

[29]Jesus replied, "Do you believe because you see me? Happy are those who don't see and yet believe."

[30]Then Jesus did many other miraculous signs in his disciples' presence, signs that aren't recorded in this scroll. [31]But these things are written so that you will believe that Jesus is the Christ, God's Son, and that believing, you will have life in his name.

Primary Hymns and Songs for the Day

"Ye Servants of God" (Rev) (O)
    B589, C110, E535, EL825 (PD), F360, G299, N305, P477,
    UM181 (PD), VU342
        H-3   Hbl-90, 105; Chr-221; Desc-49; Org-51
        S-2   #71-74. Intro. and Harm.
"Praise to the Lord, the Almighty" (Pss) (O)
    B14, C25, E390, EL858 (PD) and 859, F337, G35, L543, N22,
    P482, UM139, VU220 (Fr.) and VU221, W547
        H-3   Hbl-89; Chr-163; Desc-69; Org-79
        S-1   #218-222. Various treatments
"Come, Ye Faithful, Raise the Strain" (Acts, John)
    C215, E199, EL363, G234, L132, N230, P115, UM315 (PD),
    VU165, W456
        H-3   Hbl-53; Chr-57; Desc-94; Org-141
        S-2   #161. Descant
"The Head That Once Was Crowned" (Acts)
    E483, EL432, L173, P149, UM326 (PD), VU190, W464
        H-3   Chr-187, 207; Desc-95; Org-142
        S-1   #305. Descant
"Praise Ye the Lord" (Pss)
    EL872, G633. P258, S2010
"Lo, He Comes with Clouds Descending" (Rev)
    B199, E57/58, EL435, F306, G348, L27, P6, UM718, VU25
        H-3   Hbl-93; Chr-129; Desc-50; Org-53
        S-1   #157. Descant
"We Walk by Faith" (John) (C)
    E209, EL635, G817, N256, P399, S2196, SF2196, W572
        H-3   Chr-21

Additional Hymn Suggestions

"Of the Father's Love Begotten" (Rev)
    B251, C104, E82, EL295, F172 (PD), G108, L42, N118, P309,
    UM184, VU61, W398
"Deck Thyself, My Soul, with Gladness" (Rev)
    E339, EL488/489, G514, P506, UM612 (PD), VU463
"Alleluia! Sing to Jesus!" (Rev)
    C233, E460/461, EL392, G260, N257, P144, W737
"Come, O Spirit, Dwell Among Us" (Rev)
    G280, N267, P129, VU198
"Thine Be the Glory" (John)
    B163, C218, EL376, F291, G238, L145, N253, P122, UM308,
    VU173 (Fr.)
"O Sons and Daughters, Let Us Sing" (John, Easter)
    C220, E203, EL386/387, G235/255, L139, N244, P116 (PD),
    UM317, VU170, W447
Dona Nobis Pacem (John)
    C297, E712, EL753, G752, UM376 (PD)
"Breathe on Me, Breath of God" (John)
    B241, C254, E508, F161, G286, L488, N292, P316, UM420
    (PD), VU382 (Fr.), W725
"Holy Spirit, Truth Divine" (John)
    C241, EL398, L257, N63, P321, UM465 (PD), VU368
"Spirit of God, Descend upon My Heart" (John)
    B245, C265, EL800, F147, G688, L486, N290, P326, UM500
    (PD), VU378
"That Easter Day with Joy Was Bright" (John)
    C229, E193, EL384 (PD), G254, P121, W457
"Peace I Leave with You, My Friends" (John)
    N249
"These Things Did Thomas Count" (John)
    G256, N254
"The Risen Christ" (John)
    EL390, G257, VU168

"Here, O My Lord, I See Thee" (John, Comm.)
    C416, E318, G517, L211, N336, P520, UM623, VU459
"We Live by Faith and Not by Sight" (John)
    E209, EL635, G817, N256, P399, S2196, SF2196, W572
"In the Singing" (John, Comm.)
    EL466, G533, S2255, SF2255

Additional Contemporary Suggestions

"He Is Exalted" (Acts)
    S2070, SF2070, SP66
"Jesus, Draw Me Close" (Acts)
    M48, S2159, SF2159
"Let Everything That Has Breath" (Pss)
    M59
"Turn Your Eyes upon Jesus" (Rev, John)
    B320, F621, SP218, UM349
"We Will Glorify" (Rev)
    B213, S2087, SF2087, SP68
"Soon and Very Soon" (Rev)
    B192, EL439, G384, UM706, S-2 #187. Piano Arr.
"Surely the Presence of the Lord" (Rev)
    C263, SP243, UM328; S-2 #200. Stanzas for soloist
"Let It Breathe on Me" (John)
    C260, N288, UM503
"Open Our Eyes, Lord" (John)
    B499, S2086, SF2086, SP199
"Where the Spirit of the Lord Is" (John)
    C264, S2119, SF2119
"Here Is Bread, Here Is Wine" (John, Comm.)
    EL483, S2266, SF2266
"Trading My Sorrows" (John)
    M75, WS3108
"The Power of Your Love" (John)
    M26

Vocal Solos

"Come, O Thou Traveler Unknown" (John)
    V-1   p. 21
"I Know That My Redeemer Lives" (John, Easter)
    V-5(2)   p. 22

Anthems

"Psalm 150" (Pss)
Nathan Jensen; AEC-3 p. 41
Unison and keyboard, opt. congregation

"We Walk by Faith" (John)
Anne Krentz Organ; Augsburg 978-1-4514-9263-7
2-part mixed and piano (http://bit.ly/9263-7)

Other Suggestions

Visuals:
    Acts   Cross draped in white
    P   Musical instruments, dancing
    E   Alpha/Omega, clouds, art–Christ descending, 7 flames
    G   Risen Christ, Holy Spirit, nails, kneel, closed door
Introit: WS3012. "When Words Alone Cannot Express" (Pss)
Sung Prayer: C250, UM543, VU202, WS3146, stanzas 2-3. "O
    Breath of Life" (John)
Prayers: F146, N831, UM335, WSL34, WSL73 (Rev, John)
Blessing: N872 or N876 (John, Easter)

Acts 9:1-6 (7-20)

Meanwhile, Saul was still spewing out murderous threats against the Lord's disciples. He went to the high priest, [2]seeking letters to the synagogues in Damascus. If he found persons who belonged to the Way, whether men or women, these letters would authorize him to take them as prisoners to Jerusalem. [3]During the journey, as he approached Damascus, suddenly a light from heaven encircled him. [4]He fell to the ground and heard a voice asking him, "Saul, Saul, why are you harassing me?"

[5]Saul asked, "Who are you, Lord?"

"I am Jesus, whom you are harassing," came the reply. [6]"Now get up and enter the city. You will be told what you must do."

[7]Those traveling with him stood there speechless; they heard the voice but saw no one. [8]After they picked Saul up from the ground, he opened his eyes but he couldn't see. So they led him by the hand into Damascus. [9]For three days he was blind and neither ate nor drank anything.

[10]In Damascus there was a certain disciple named Ananias. The Lord spoke to him in a vision, "Ananias!"

He answered, "Yes, Lord."

[11]The Lord instructed him, "Go to Judas' house on Straight Street and ask for a man from Tarsus named Saul. He is praying. [12]In a vision he has seen a man named Ananias enter and put his hands on him to restore his sight."

[13]Ananias countered, "Lord, I have heard many reports about this man. People say he has done horrible things to your holy people in Jerusalem. [14]He's here with authority from the chief priests to arrest everyone who calls on your name."

[15]The Lord replied, "Go! This man is the agent I have chosen to carry my name before Gentiles, kings, and Israelites. [16]I will show him how much he must suffer for the sake of my name."

[17]Ananias went to the house. He placed his hands on Saul and said, "Brother Saul, the Lord sent me—Jesus, who appeared to you on the way as you were coming here. He sent me so that you could see again and be filled with the Holy Spirit." [18]Instantly, flakes fell from Saul's eyes and he could see again. He got up and was baptized. [19]After eating, he regained his strength.

He stayed with the disciples in Damascus for several days.[20]Right away, he began to preach about Jesus in the synagogues. "He is God's Son," he declared.

Psalm 30 (G798/805, N639, P181, UM762)

I exalt you, LORD, because you pulled me up;

I exalt you, LORD, because you pulled me up; / you didn't let my enemies celebrate over me. / [2]LORD, my God, I cried out to you for help, / and you healed me. / [3]LORD, you brought me up from the grave, / brought me back to life from among those going down to the pit.

[4]You who are faithful to the LORD, / sing praises to him; / give thanks to his holy name! / [5]His anger lasts for only a second, / but his favor lasts a lifetime. / Weeping may stay all night, / but by morning, joy!

[6]When I was comfortable, I said, / "I will never stumble." / [7]Because it pleased you, LORD, / you made me a strong mountain. / But then you hid your presence. / I was terrified. / [8]I cried out to you, LORD. / I begged my Lord for mercy: / [9]"What is to be gained by my spilled blood, / by my going down into the pit? / Does dust thank you? / Does it proclaim your faithfulness? / [10]LORD, listen and have mercy on me! / LORD, be my helper!"

[11]You changed my mourning into dancing. / You took off my funeral clothes / and dressed me up in joy / [12]so that my whole being / might sing praises to you and never stop. / LORD, my God, I will give thanks to you forever.r.

Revelation 5:11-14

[11]Then I looked, and I heard the sound of many angels surrounding the throne, the living creatures, and the elders. They numbered in the millions—thousands upon thousands. [12]They said in a loud voice,

"Worthy is the slaughtered Lamb
    to receive power, wealth, wisdom, and might,
    and honor, glory, and blessing."

[13]And I heard every creature in heaven and on earth and under the earth and in the sea—I heard everything everywhere say,

"Blessing, honor, glory, and power belong
to the one seated on the throne
    and to the Lamb
        forever and always."

[14]Then the four living creatures said, "Amen," and the elders fell down and worshipped.

John 21:1-19

Later, Jesus himself appeared again to his disciples at the Sea of Tiberias. This is how it happened: [2]Simon Peter, Thomas (called Didymus), Nathanael from Cana in Galilee, Zebedee's sons, and two other disciples were together. [3]Simon Peter told them, "I'm going fishing."

They said, "We'll go with you." They set out in a boat, but throughout the night they caught nothing. [4]Early in the morning, Jesus stood on the shore, but the disciples didn't realize it was Jesus.

[5]Jesus called to them, "Children, have you caught anything to eat?"

They answered him, "No."

[6]He said, "Cast your net on the right side of the boat and you will find some."

So they did, and there were so many fish that they couldn't haul in the net. [7]Then the disciple whom Jesus loved said to Peter, "It's the Lord!" When Simon Peter heard it was the Lord, he wrapped his coat around himself (for he was naked) and jumped into the water. [8]The other disciples followed in the boat, dragging the net full of fish, for they weren't far from shore, only about one hundred yards.

[9]When they landed, they saw a fire there, with fish on it, and some bread. [10]Jesus said to them, "Bring some of the fish that you've just caught." [11]Simon Peter got up and pulled the net to shore. It was full of large fish, one hundred fifty-three of them. Yet the net hadn't torn, even with so many fish. [12]Jesus said to them, "Come and have breakfast." None of the disciples could bring themselves to ask him, "Who are you?" They knew it was the LORD. [13]Jesus came, took the bread, and gave it to them. He did the same with the fish. [14]This was now the third time Jesus appeared to his disciples after he was raised from the dead.

[15]When they finished eating, Jesus asked Simon Peter, "Simon son of John, do you love me more than these?"

Simon replied, "Yes, Lord, you know I love you."

Jesus said to him, "Feed my lambs." [16]Jesus asked a second time, "Simon son of John, do you love me?"

Simon replied, "Yes, Lord, you know I love you."

Jesus said to him, "Take care of my sheep." [17]He asked a third time, "Simon son of John, do you love me?"

Peter was sad that Jesus asked him a third time, "Do you love me?" He replied, "Lord, you know everything; you know I love you."

Jesus said to him, "Feed my sheep. [18]I assure you that when you were younger you tied your own belt and walked around wherever you wanted. When you grow old, you will stretch out your hands and another will tie your belt and lead you where you don't want to go." [19]He said this to show the kind of death by which Peter would glorify God. After saying this, Jesus said to Peter, "Follow me."

Primary Hymns and Songs for the Day
"Christ, Whose Glory Fills the Skies" (Acts, John) (O)
    EL553, F293, G662, L265, P462/463, UM173 (PD), VU336
        H-3   Hbl-51; Chr-206; Desc-89; Org-120
        S-1   #278-279. Harm.
"Amazing Grace" (Acts, Pss)
    B330, C546, E671, EL779, F107, G649, L448, N547 and N548,
    P280, UM378 (PD), VU266 (Fr.), W583
        H-3   Hbl-14, 46; Chr-27; Desc-14; Org-4
        S-2   #5-7. Various treatments
"Amazing Grace" ("My Chains Are Gone") (Acts, Pss)
    M205, WS3104
"Joy Comes with the Dawn" (Pss, John)
    S2210, SF2210, VU166
"More Love to Thee, O Christ" (John) (C)
    B473, C527, F476, G828, N456, P359, UM453 (PD)
        H-3   Org-94

Additional Hymn Suggestions
"Alleluia, Alleluia" (Acts)
    B170, E178, G240, P106, UM162, VU179, W441
"Called as Partners in Christ's Service" (Acts)
    C453, G761, N495, P343
"It Is Well with My Soul" (Acts, Pss)
    B410, C561, EL785, F495, G840, L346, N438, UM377
"Holy God, We Praise Thy Name" (Pss, Rev)
    E366, F385, EL414 (PD), G4, L535, N276, P460, UM79,
    VU894 (Fr.), W524
"Blessing and Honor" (Rev)
    EL854, G369, L525, P147
"Jesus Shall Reign" (Rev)
    B587, C95, E544, EL434, F238, G265, L530, N157, P423,
    UM157 (PD), VU330, W492
"Lift High the Cross" (Rev)
    B594, C108, E473, EL660, G826, L377, N198, P371, UM159,
    VU151, W704
"When Morning Gilds the Skies" (Rev)
    B221, C100, E427, EL853 (PD), F322, G667, L546, N86,
    P487, UM185, VU339 (Fr.), W675
"This Is the Feast of Victory" (Rev, Comm.)
    E417/418, G513, P594, UM638, VU904, W458
Tu Has Venido a la Orilla ("Lord, You Have Come to the
Lakeshore") (John)
    C342, EL817, G721, N173, P377, UM344, VU563
"Jesus Calls Us" (John)
    B293, C337, EL696, G720, L494, N172, UM398, VU562
"Dearest Jesus, We Are Here" (John)
    EL443, G483, L187, P493
"The Risen Christ" (John)
    EL390, G257, VU168
"In Remembrance of Me" (John, Comm.)
    B365, C403, G521, S2254

Additional Contemporary Suggestions
"I've Just Come from the Fountain" (Acts, Baptism)
    S2250, SF2250
"Word of God, Speak" (Acts, John)
    M148, WS3184
"In the Lord I'll Be Ever Thankful" (Pss)
    G654, S2195, SF2195
"Trading My Sorrows" (Pss)
    M75, WS3108
"Great Is the Lord" (Rev)
    B12, G614, S2022, SF2022, SP30

"Awesome God" (Rev)
    G616, S2040, SF2040, SP11
"I Will Celebrate" (Rev)
    M46, SP147
"Agnus Dei" (Rev)
    M15
"Blessing, Honour and Glory" (Rev)
    EL433, M21
"We Will Worship the Lamb of Glory" (Rev)
    M27
"We Declare Your Majesty" (Rev)
    M43
"Most Holy Lord" (Rev)
    M44
"There Is Joy in the Lord" (Rev)
    M74
"Spirit Song" (John)
    C352, SP134, UM347
"Take Our Bread" (John, Comm.)
    C413, UM640
"Father, I Adore You" (John)
    B256, F414, S2038, SF2038, SP194
"Cry of My Heart" (John)
    M39, S2165, SF2165
"You Are Mine" (John)
    EL581, G177, S2218, SF2218
"Step by Step" (John)
    G743, M51, WS3004

Vocal Solos
"It Is Well with My Soul" (Acts, Pss)
    V-5(2)   p. 35
"Worthy Is the Lamb" (Rev)
    V-8   p. 228

Anthems
"Love That Found Me" (Acts)
Arr. Patricia Hurlbutt; Augsburg 978-1-5064-2208-4
SATB and piano (bit.ly/2208-4)

"Day of Arising" (Acts, John, Comm.)
Carl Schalk; AEC-2 p. 50
2-part mixed and organ

Other Suggestions
Visuals:
    Acts   Light, blindfold, healing hand, Act 9:4c or 10c
    P   Joy, singing, dancing, sackcloth, Ps 30:5c or 11a
    E   Lamb, praise, angel choir, four creatures
    G   Fish, bread, lamb, sheep, fire, boat, net, fish
Introit: EL491, G528, L214, UM625. "Come, Let Us Eat" (John)
Prayers: WSL32, WSL117, N872, N874 (John, Easter)

Acts 9:36-43

36In Joppa there was a disciple named Tabitha (in Greek her name is Dorcas). Her life overflowed with good works and compassionate acts on behalf of those in need. 37About that time, though, she became so ill that she died. After they washed her body, they laid her in an upstairs room. 38Since Lydda was near Joppa, when the disciples heard that Peter was there, they sent two people to Peter. They urged, "Please come right away!"39Peter went with them. Upon his arrival, he was taken to the upstairs room. All the widows stood beside him, crying as they showed the tunics and other clothing Dorcas made when she was alive.

40Peter sent everyone out of the room, then knelt and prayed. He turned to the body and said, "Tabitha, get up!" She opened her eyes, saw Peter, and sat up. 41He gave her his hand and raised her up. Then he called God's holy people, including the widows, and presented her alive to them. 42The news spread throughout Joppa, and many put their faith in the Lord. 43Peter stayed for some time in Joppa with a certain tanner named Simon.

Psalm 23 (G801-803, N633, P170-175, UM754)

The LORD is my shepherd.
    I lack nothing.
2He lets me rest in grassy meadows;
        he leads me to restful waters;
            3he keeps me alive.
He guides me in proper paths
        for the sake of his good name.
4Even when I walk through the darkest valley,
        I fear no danger because you are with me.
Your rod and your staff—
        they protect me.
5You set a table for me
        right in front of my enemies.
You bathe my head in oil;
        my cup is so full it spills over!
6Yes, goodness and faithful love
        will pursue me all the days of my life,
        and I will live in the LORD's house
        as long as I live.

Revelation 7:9-17

9After this I looked, and there was a great crowd that no one could number. They were from every nation, tribe, people, and language. They were standing before the throne and before the Lamb. They wore white robes and held palm branches in their hands. 10They cried out with a loud voice:

    "Victory belongs to our God
        who sits on the throne,
            and to the Lamb."
11All the angels stood in a circle around the throne, and around the elders and the four living creatures. They fell face-down before the throne and worshipped God, 12saying,

    "Amen! Blessing and glory
        and wisdom and thanksgiving
        and honor and power and might
            be to our God forever and always. Amen."
13Then one of the elders said to me, "Who are these people wearing white robes, and where did they come from?"

14I said to him, "Sir, you know."

Then he said to me, "These people have come out of great hardship. They have washed their robes and made them white in the Lamb's blood. 15This is the reason they are before God's throne. They worship him day and night in his temple, and the one seated on the throne will shelter them. 16They won't hunger or thirst anymore. No sun or scorching heat will beat down on them, 17because the Lamb who is in the midst of the throne will shepherd them. He will lead them to the springs of life-giving water, and God will wipe away every tear from their eyes."

John 10:22-30

22The time came for the Festival of Dedication in Jerusalem. It was winter, 23and Jesus was in the temple, walking in the covered porch named for Solomon. 24The Jewish opposition circled around him and asked, "How long will you test our patience? If you are the Christ, tell us plainly."

25Jesus answered, "I have told you, but you don't believe. The works I do in my Father's name testify about me, 26but you don't believe because you don't belong to my sheep. 27My sheep listen to my voice. I know them and they follow me. 28I give them eternal life. They will never die, and no one will snatch them from my hand. 29My Father, who has given them to me, is greater than all, and no one is able to snatch them from my Father's hand. 30I and the Father are one."

Primary Hymns and Songs for the Day

"Come, We That Love the Lord" (Rev) (O)
  B525, E392, N379, UM732, VU715, W552
         H-3   Chr-106, 167; Desc-97; Org-147
         S-1   #311. Desc. and Harm.
"Precious Lord, Take My Hand" (Acts, Pss)
  B456, C628, EL773, G834, N472, P404, UM474, VU670
         H-3   Chr-164; Org-116
"The Lord's My Shepherd, I'll Not Want" (Pss, John)
  C78/79, EL778, F40/42, G801, L451, N479, P170, UM136,
  VU747/748
         H-3   Hbl-96; Chr-188, 189; Desc-24; Org-21
"Lamb of God" (Pss, Rev, John)
  EL336, G518, S2113, SF2113
"Awesome God" (Rev)
  G616, S2040, SF2040, SP11
"Savior, Like a Shepherd Lead Us" (Pss, John) (C)
  B61, C558, E708, EL789, F601, G187, L481, N252, P387,
  UM381 (PD)
         H-3   Chr-167; Org-15
         S-2   #29. Harm.
"Marching to Zion" (Rev) (C)
  B524, C707, EL625, F550, N382, UM733 (PD), VU714
         H-3   Chr-298

Additional Hymn Suggestions

"Guide Me, O Thou Great Jehovah" (Acts)
  B56, C622, E690, EL618, F608, G65, L343, N18/19, P281,
  UM127 (PD), VU651 (Fr.)
"Great Is Thy Faithfulness" (Acts)
  B54, C86, EL733, G39, N423, P276, UM140, VU288
"O Christ, the Healer" (Acts)
  C503. EL610, G793, L360, N175, P380, UM265, W747
"Now the Green Blade Riseth" (Acts)
  C230, E204, EL379, G247, L148, N238, UM311, VU186
"He Leadeth Me: O Blessed Thought" (Pss)
  B52, C545, F606, L501, UM128 (PD), VU657
"The King of Love My Shepherd Is" (Pss)
  E645, EL502, G802, L456, P171, UM138 (PD), VU273
"Lead Me, Guide Me" (Pss)
  C583, EL768, G740, S2214, SF2214
"Blessing and Honor" (Rev)
  EL854, G369, L525, P147
"From All That Dwell Below the Skies" (Rev)
  B13, C49, E380, G327, L550, N27, P229, UM101 (PD)
"Jesus Shall Reign" (Rev)
  B587, C95, E544, EL434, F238, G265, L530, N157, P423,
  UM157 (PD), VU330, W492
"Ye Servants of God" (Rev)
  B589, C110, E535, EL825 (PD), F360, G299, N305, P477,
  UM181 (PD), VU342
"Jesus, Lover of My Soul" (Rev)
  B180 (PD), C542, E699, F222, G440, N546, P303, UM479
  (PD), VU669
"Glorious Things of Thee Are Spoken" (Rev)
  B398, C709, E522/523, EL647, F376, G81, L358, N307, P446,
  UM731 (PD)
"All Who Hunger" (Rev, Comm.)
  C419, EL461, G509, S2126, SF2126, VU460
"Near to the Heart of God" (John)
  B295, C581, F35, G824, P527, UM472 (PD)
"I Heard the Voice of Jesus Say (John)
  B551, E692, EL611, G182, L497, N489, VU626, W607

Additional Contemporary Suggestions

"Nothing Can Trouble" ("*Nada Te Turbe*") (Pss)
  G820, S2054, SF2054, VU290
"You Are Good" (Pss)
  M124, WS3014
"God Is Good All the Time" (Pss)
  WS3026, M45
"Your Grace Is Enough (Pss)
  M191, WS3106
"Gentle Shepherd" (Pss, Rev, John)
  WS3096
"Falling on My Knees" ("Hungry") (Pss, Rev, John)
  M155, WS3099
"Shepherd Me, O God" (Pss, Rev, John)
  EL780, G473, S2058, SF2058
"Enough" (Pss, Rev)
  M160
"You Who Are Thirsty" (Rev)
  S2132, SP219
"Holy Ground" (Rev)
  B224, C112, G406, S2272, SF2272, SP86
"How Great Is Our God" (Rev)
  WS3003, M117
"Fill My Cup, Lord" (Rev, Comm.)
  C351, F481, UM641 (refrain only), WS3093
"There Is a Higher Throne" (Rev)
  WS3189
"Blessing, Honour and Glory" (Rev, Easter)
  EL433, M21
"Hallelujah to the Lamb" (Rev, Easter)
  M23
"He Reigns" (Rev)
  M168
"Light the Fire Again" (Rev)
  M144
"My Tribute" ("To God Be the Glory") (Rev, John)
  B153, C39, F365, N14, UM99. V-8 p. 5. Vocal Solo

Vocal Solos

"God, Our Ever Faithful Shepherd" (Pss)
  V-4   p. 15
"My Shepherd Will Supply My Need" (Pss)
  V-10   p. 4

Anthems

"Shepherd Me, Lord" (Pss)
William M. Schoenfeld; AEC-3 p. 46
2-part and piano, flute or recorder

"Savior, Like a Shepherd Lead Us" (Pss, John)
William Bradley Roberts; AEC-1 p. 54
Unison with keyboard; opt. C-Instrument (bit.ly/AEC-1-54)

Other Suggestions

Visuals:
  Acts   Shroud, basin/water, sewing, praying hands, touching
  P   Shepherd's crook, pasture, water, path, shadow, oil
  E   White robe/palms, angels, Lamb, water, wiped tears
  G   Winter, Jesus, sheep, John 10:27
Readings: B1, F25, N633-634 or UM137 (Pss) and F666 (Rev)
Prayers: C81, N852, UM460, WSL17, and WSL134 (Pss)

Acts 11:1-18

The apostles and the brothers and sisters throughout Judea heard that even the Gentiles had welcomed God's word. [2]When Peter went up to Jerusalem, the circumcised believers criticized him. [3]They accused him, "You went into the home of the uncircumcised and ate with them!"

[4]Step-by-step, Peter explained what had happened. [5]"I was in the city of Joppa praying when I had a visionary experience. In my vision, I saw something like a large linen sheet being lowered from heaven by its four corners. It came all the way down to me.[6]As I stared at it, wondering what it was, I saw four-legged animals—including wild beasts—as well as reptiles and wild birds. [7]I heard a voice say, 'Get up, Peter! Kill and eat!' [8]I responded, 'Absolutely not, Lord! Nothing impure or unclean has ever entered my mouth.' [9]The voice from heaven spoke a second time, 'Never consider unclean what God has made pure.' [10]This happened three times, then everything was pulled back into heaven. [11]At that moment three men who had been sent to me from Caesarea arrived at the house where we were staying. [12]The Spirit told me to go with them even though they were Gentiles. These six brothers also went with me, and we entered that man's house. [13]He reported to us how he had seen an angel standing in his house and saying, 'Send to Joppa and summon Simon, who is known as Peter. [14]He will tell you how you and your entire household can be saved.' [15]When I began to speak, the Holy Spirit fell on them, just as the Spirit fell on us in the beginning.[16]I remembered the Lord's words: 'John will baptize with water, but you will be baptized with the Holy Spirit.' [17]If God gave them the same gift he gave us who believed in the Lord Jesus Christ, then who am I? Could I stand in God's way?"

[18]Once the apostles and other believers heard this, they calmed down. They praised God and concluded, "So then God has enabled Gentiles to change their hearts and lives so that they might have new life."

Psalm 148 (G17/18/679, N721, P256, UM861)

Praise the LORD!
Praise the LORD from heaven!
   Praise God on the heights!
[2]Praise God, all of you who are his messengers!
   Praise God, all of you who comprise his heavenly forces!
[3]Sun and moon, praise God!
   All of you bright stars, praise God!
[4]You highest heaven, praise God!
   Do the same, you waters that are above the sky!
[5]Let all of these praise the LORD's name
   because God gave the command and they were created!
[6]God set them in place always and forever.
   God made a law that will not be broken.
[7]Praise the LORD from the earth,
   you sea monsters and all you ocean depths!
[8]Do the same, fire and hail, snow and smoke,
   stormy wind that does what God says!
[9]Do the same, you mountains, every single hill,
   fruit trees, and every single cedar!
[10]Do the same, you animals—wild or tame—
   you creatures that creep along and you birds that fly!
[11]Do the same, you kings of the earth and every single person,
   you princes and every single ruler on earth!
[12]Do the same, you young men—young women too!—
   you who are old together with you who are young!
[13]Let all of these praise the LORD's name
   because only God's name is high over all.
   Only God's majesty is over earth and heaven.
[14]God raised the strength of his people,
   the praise of all his faithful ones—
      that's the Israelites,
   the people who are close to him.
Praise the LORD!

Revelation 21:1-6

Then I saw a new heaven and a new earth, for the former heaven and the former earth had passed away, and the sea was no more. [2]I saw the holy city, New Jerusalem, coming down out of heaven from God, made ready as a bride beautifully dressed for her husband. [3]I heard a loud voice from the throne say, "Look! God's dwelling is here with humankind. He will dwell with them, and they will be his peoples. God himself will be with them as their God. [4]He will wipe away every tear from their eyes. Death will be no more. There will be no mourning, crying, or pain anymore, for the former things have passed away." [5]Then the one seated on the throne said, "Look! I'm making all things new." He also said, "Write this down, for these words are trustworthy and true." [6]Then he said to me, "All is done. I am the Alpha and the Omega, the beginning and the end. To the thirsty I will freely give water from the life-giving spring.

John 13:31-35

[31]When Judas was gone, Jesus said, "Now the Human One has been glorified, and God has been glorified in him. [32]If God has been glorified in him, God will also glorify the Human One in himself and will glorify him immediately. [33]Little children, I'm with you for a little while longer. You will look for me—but, just as I told the Jewish leaders, I also tell you now—'Where I'm going, you can't come.'

[34]"I give you a new commandment: Love each other. Just as I have loved you, so you also must love each other. [35]This is how everyone will know that you are my disciples, when you love each other."

Primary Hymns and Songs for the Day

"All Creatures of Our God and King" (Pss, Comm.) (O)
    B27, C22, E400, EL835, F347, G15, L527, N17, P455, UM62,
    VU217 (Fr.), W520
        H-3   Hbl-44; Chr-21; Desc-66; Org-73
        S-1   #198-204. Various treatments

"Let All Things Now Living" (Pss) (O)
    B640, C717, EL881, G37, L557, P554, S2008, VU242
        H-3   Chr-125; Org-9
        S-1   #327. Descant

"In Christ There Is No East or West" (Acts) (C)
    B385, C687, E529, EL650 (PD), F685, G317/318, L359,
    N394/395, P439/440, UM548, VU606, W659
        H-3   Chr-111; Desc-74; Org-88
        S-1   #231-233. Various treaments

"O Holy City, Seen of John" (Rev)
    E582/583, G374, N613, P453, UM726, VU709
        H-3   Chr-139, 145; Desc-77
        S-1   #241-242. Orff arr. and descant

"O What Their Joy and Their Glory Must Be" (Rev)
    E623, L337, N385, UM727 (PD)
        H-3   Hbl-49; Chr-132; Desc-83; Org-103
        S-1   #255. Desc. and Harm.

"They'll Know We Are Christians" (John)
    C494, G300, S2223, SF2223

"Love Divine, All Loves Excelling" (Acts, Rev, John) (C)
    B208, C517, E657, EL631, F21, G366, N43, P376, UM384
    (PD), VU333, W588
        H-3   Chr-134; Desc-18; Org-13
        S-1   #41-42. Desc. and Harm.

Additional Hymn Suggestions

"For the Beauty of the Earth" (Acts)
    B44, C56, E416, EL879, F1, G14, L561, P473, N28, UM92
    (PD), VU226, W557

"Spirit of the Living God" (Acts)
    B244, C259, G288, N283, P322, SP131, UM393, VU376

"Come Down, O Love Divine" (Acts)
    C582, E516, EL804, G282, L508, N289, P313, UM475,
    VU367, W472

"Here, O Lord, Your Servants Gather" (Acts, Comm.)
    B179, C278, EL530, G311, N72, P465, UM552, VU362

"Help Us Accept Each Other" (Acts, John)
    C487, G754, N388, P358, UM560, W656

"O Love That Wilt Not Let Me Go" (Rev)
    B292, C540, G833, L324, N485, P384, UM480, VU658

"Lead On, O King Eternal" (Rev)
    B621, C632, E555, EL805, F595, G269, L495, N573, P447/
    P448, UM580

"Here, O My Lord, I See Thee" (Rev, Comm.)
    C416, E318, G517, L211, N336, P520, UM623, VU459

"Glorious Things of Thee Are Spoken" (Rev)
    B398, C709, E522/523, EL647, F376, G81, L358, N307, P446,
    UM731 (PD)

"Where Cross the Crowded Ways of Life" (John)
    C665, E609, EL719, F665, G343, L429, N543, P408, UM427
    (PD), VU681

"The Gift of Love" (John)
    B423, C526, G693, P335, UM408, VU372

"O Master, Let Me Walk with Thee" (John)
    B279, C602, E E659/660, EL818, F442, G738, L492, N503,
    P357, UM430 (PD), VU560

"Where Charity and Love Prevail" (John)
    E581, EL359, G316, L126, N396, UM549

"Draw Us in the Spirit's Tether" (John)
    C392, EL470, G529, N337, P504, UM632, VU479, W731

"Today We All Are Called to Be Disciples" (John)
    G757, P434, VU507

"Healer of Our Every Ill" (John)
    C506, EL612, G795, S2213, SF2213, VU619

Additional Contemporary Suggestions

"Step by Step" (Acts)
    G743, M51, WS3004

"Spirit Song" (Acts, Rev)
    C352, SP134, UM347

"Make Us One" (Acts, John)
    S2224, SF2224, SP137

"Praise, Praise, Praise the Lord" (Pss)
    EL875, G390, S2035, SF2035

"God of Wonders" (Pss)
    M80, WS3034

"Let Everything That Has Breath" (Pss)
    M59

"Soon and Very Soon" (Rev)
    B192, EL439, G384, UM706, S-2 #187. Piano arr.

"Holy and Anointed One" (Rev, Easter, John)
    M32

"How Great Is Our God" (Rev)
    WS3003, M117

"We Will Glorify" (Rev, John)
    B213, S2087, SF2087, SP68

"Spirit Song" (Rev)
    C352, SP134, UM347

"*Jesu, Jesu*" (John)
    B501, C600, E602, EL708, G203, N498, P367, UM432,
    VU593, W431, S-1 #63. Vocal part

"Bind Us Together" (John)
    S2226, SF2226, SP140

"Live in Charity" ("*Ubi Caritas*") (John)
    C523, EL642, G205, S2179, SF2179, W604

Vocal Solos

"All Creatures of Our God and King" (Pss)
    V-6   p. 55

"This Is My Commandment" (John)
    V-8   p. 284

Anthems

"In the Beginning" (Pss)
Arr. David Sims; AEC-3 p. 20
2-part and piano

"Oh, That I Had a Thousand Voices" (Pss)
Arr. B. Wayne Bisbee; Augsburg 978-1-5064-2212-1
SATB and piano (bit.ly/2212-1)

Other Suggestions

Visuals:
    Acts   Sheet, animals, baptism, Holy Spirit, rebirth
    P   Creation, sun/moon/stars, angels, nature, praise
    E   Newness, marriage, home, unity, water, Alpha/Omega,
              baptism
    G   Newness, love, John 13:34a, b

Call to Prayer: S2132, SP219. "You Who Are Thirsty" (Rev)

Prayers: WSL75 (Rev) and C682 (Acts)

Acts 16:9-15

⁹A vision of a man from Macedonia came to Paul during the night. He stood urging Paul, "Come over to Macedonia and help us!" ¹⁰Immediately after he saw the vision, we prepared to leave for the province of Macedonia, concluding that God had called us to proclaim the good news to them.

¹¹We sailed from Troas straight for Samothrace and came to Neapolis the following day. ¹²From there we went to Philippi, a city of Macedonia's first district and a Roman colony. We stayed in that city several days. ¹³On the Sabbath we went outside the city gate to the riverbank, where we thought there might be a place for prayer. We sat down and began to talk with the women who had gathered. ¹⁴One of those women was Lydia, a Gentile God-worshipper from the city of Thyatira, a dealer in purple cloth. As she listened, the Lord enabled her to embrace Paul's message.¹⁵Once she and her household were baptized, she urged, "Now that you have decided that I am a believer in the Lord, come and stay in my house." And she persuaded us.

Psalm 67 (G341, N663, P202/203, UM791)

Let God grant us grace and bless us;
　let God make his face shine on us, *Selah*
²so that your way becomes known on earth,
　so that your salvation becomes known among all the nations.
³Let the people thank you, God!
　Let all the people thank you!
⁴Let the people celebrate
　　and shout with joy
　　because you judge the nations fairly
　　and guide all nations on the earth. *Selah*
⁵Let the people thank you, God!
　Let all the people thank you!
⁶The earth has yielded its harvest.
　God blesses us—our God blesses us!
⁷Let God continue to bless us;
　let the far ends of the earth honor him.

Revelation 21:1-10, 22–22:5

Then I saw a new heaven and a new earth, for the former heaven and the former earth had passed away, and the sea was no more. ²I saw the holy city, New Jerusalem, coming down out of heaven from God, made ready as a bride beautifully dressed for her husband. ³I heard a loud voice from the throne say, "Look! God's dwelling is here with humankind. He will dwell with them, and they will be his peoples. God himself will be with them as their God. ⁴He will wipe away every tear from their eyes. Death will be no more. There will be no mourning, crying, or pain anymore, for the former things have passed away."⁵Then the one seated on the throne said, "Look! I'm making all things new." He also said, "Write this down, for these words are trust-worthy and true." ⁶Then he said to me, "All is done. I am the Alpha and the Omega, the beginning and the end. To the thirsty I will freely give water from the life-giving spring.⁷Those who emerge victorious will inherit these things. I will be their God, and they will be my sons and daughters. ⁸But for the cowardly, the faithless, the vile, the murderers, those who commit sexual immorality, those who use drugs and cast spells, the idolaters and all liars—their share will be in the lake that burns with fire and sulfur. This is the second death."

⁹Then one of the seven angels who had the seven bowls full of the seven last plagues spoke with me. "Come," he said, "I will show you the bride, the Lamb's wife." ¹⁰He took me in a Spirit-inspired trance to a great, high mountain, and he showed me the holy city, Jerusalem, coming down out of heaven from God. . . .

²²I didn't see a temple in the city, because its temple is the Lord God Almighty and the Lamb. ²³The city doesn't need the sun or the moon to shine on it, because God's glory is its light, and its lamp is the Lamb. ²⁴The nations will walk by its light, and the kings of the earth will bring their glory into it. ²⁵Its gates will never be shut by day, and there will be no night there. ²⁶They will bring the glory and honor of the nations into it. ²⁷Nothing unclean will ever enter it, nor anyone who does what is vile and deceitful, but only those who are registered in the Lamb's scroll of life.

22 Then the angel showed me the river of life-giving water, shining like crystal, flowing from the throne of God and the Lamb ²through the middle of the city's main street. On each side of the river is the tree of life, which produces twelve crops of fruit, bearing its fruit each month. The tree's leaves are for the healing of the nations. ³There will no longer be any curse. The throne of God and the Lamb will be in it, and his servants will worship him. ⁴They will see his face, and his name will be on their foreheads. ⁵Night will be no more. They won't need the light of a lamp or the light of the sun, for the Lord God will shine on them, and they will rule forever and always.

John 14:23-29

²³Jesus answered, "Whoever loves me will keep my word. My Father will love them, and we will come to them and make our home with them. ²⁴Whoever doesn't love me doesn't keep my words. The word that you hear isn't mine. It is the word of the Father who sent me.

²⁵"I have spoken these things to you while I am with you.²⁶The Companion, the Holy Spirit, whom the Father will send in my name, will teach you everything and will remind you of every-thing I told you.

²⁷"Peace I leave with you. My peace I give you. I give to you not as the world gives. Don't be troubled or afraid. ²⁸You have heard me tell you, 'I'm going away and returning to you.' If you loved me, you would be happy that I am going to the Father, because the Father is greater than me. ²⁹I have told you before it happens so that when it happens you will believe.

Primary Hymns and Songs for the Day

"Holy God, We Praise Thy Name" (Pss) (O)
  E366, F385, EL414 (PD), G4, L535, N276, P460, UM79,
  VU894 (Fr.), W524
    H-3   Chr-78, 98; Desc-48; Org-48
    S-1   #151-153. Desc. and Harm.
"Immortal, Invisible, God Only Wise" (Rev) (O)
  B6, C66, E423, EL834, F319, G12, L526, N1, P263, UM103
  (PD), VU264, W512
    H-3   Hbl-15, 71; Chr-65; Desc-93; Org-135
    S-1   #300. Harm.
"For the Healing of the Nations" (Rev)
  C668, G346, N576, UM428, VU678, W643
    H-3   Hbl-25, 51, 58; Chr-89; Desc-26; Org-23
    S-1   #76-77. Desc. and Harm.
"You Are Mine" (John)
  EL581, G177, S2218, SF2218
"Shall We Gather at the River" (Acts, Rev) (C)
  B518, C701, EL423, G375, N597, UM723 (PD), VU710
    H-3   Chr-169

Additional Hymn Suggestions

"Wash, O God, Our Sons and Daughters" (Acts)
  C365, EL445, G490, UM605, VU442
"We All Are One in Mission" (Acts)
  G733, P435, S2243, SF2243
"Go to the World" (Acts)
  G295, VU420, WS3158
"Jesus Shall Reign" (Rev)
  B587, C95, E544, EL434, F238, G265, L530, N157, P423,
  UM157 (PD), VU330, W492
"I Want to Walk as a Child of the Light" (Rev)
  E490, EL815, G377, UM206, W510
"Come, Thou Fount of Every Blessing" (Rev)
  B15, C16, E686, EL807, F318, G475, L499, N459, P356,
  UM400 (PD), VU559
"Here, O My Lord, I See Thee" (Rev, Comm.)
  C416, E318, G517, L211, N336, P520, UM623, VU459
"O Holy City, Seen of John" (Rev)
  E582/583, G374, N613, P453, UM726, VU709
"Just a Closer Walk with Thee" (Rev)
  B448, C557, EL697, F591, G835, S2158, SF2158
"Rejoice! Rejoice, Believers" (Rev)
  E68, EL244, G362, L25, P15
"Open Now Thy Gates of Beauty" (Rev)
  EL533 (PD), G403, L250, N67, P489
"All Who Love and Serve Your City" (John)
  C670, E571, G351, P413, UM433
"Come Down, O Love Divine" (John)
  C582, E516, EL804, G282, N289, P313, UM475, VU367
"Spirit of God, Descend upon My Heart" (John)
  B245, C265, EL800, F147, G688, L486, N290, P326, UM500
  (PD), VU378
"Blessed Jesus, at Thy Word" (John)
  E440, EL520, G395, N74, P454, UM596 (PD), VU500
"Healer of Our Every Ill" (John)
  C506, EL612, G795, S2213, SF2213, VU619

Additional Contemporary Suggestions

"Shine, Jesus, Shine" (Rev)
  B579, EL671, G192, S2173, SF2173, SP142
"Turn Your Eyes upon Jesus" (Rev)
  B320, F621, SP218, UM349
"There's Something About That Name" (Rev)
  B177, C115, F227, SP89, UM171

"Soon and Very Soon" (Rev)
  B192, EL439, G384, UM706, S-2 #187. Piano arr.
"Spirit Song" (Rev, John)
  C352, SP134, UM347
"How Great Is Our God" (Rev)
  WS3003, M117
"Blessing, Honour and Glory" (Rev, Easter)
  EL433, M21
"Who Can Satisfy My Soul Like You?" (Rev)
  M28
"I See the Lord" (Rev)
  M31
"I Could Sing of Your Love Forever" (Rev)
  M63
"Did You Feel the Mountains Tremble?" (Rev)
  M69
"Offering" (Rev)
  M130
"Dwell" (John)
  M154
"Here Is Bread, Here Is Wine" (John, Comm.)
  EL483, S2266, SF2266
"Behold, What Manner of Love" (John)
  SP48
"Holy Spirit, Rain Down" (John)
  M88

Vocal Solos

"Come, Thou Fount of Every Blessing" (Rev)
  V-3 (3)   p. 22
  V-6   p. 4
"Just a Closer Walk with Thee" (Rev)
  V-5 (2)   p. 31
  V-8   p. 323
"Gentle Like Jesus" (John)
  V-8   p. 42

Anthems

"The Music of Living" (Rev)
Dan Forrest; Hinshaw HMC2321
SATB and keyboard, opt. Instr. (bit.ly/HMC2321)

"As You Go on Your Way" (John)
James Engel; AEC-2 p. 19
Unison and organ

Other Suggestions

Visuals:
    Acts   Purple cloth, women witnessing, ship/sails, open/
            closed door
    P   Thanksgiving, first garden fruit, rogation
    E   Light/lamp, nations, open gates, sing, Lamb, book,
            water
    G   Love, Word, Trinity, Spirit, John 14:27, briefcase, lamp,
            heart
Introit: EL538, G466, S2157, SF2157, W561. "Come and Fill Our
    Hearts" (John)
Canticle: C702 or UM734 (Rev)
Prayers: N818, N853, WSL50, WSL75 (Acts, Rev, Baptism)
Sung Benediction: WS3182. "Benediction Hymn" (Pss, John) or
    C438, E714, G540, P537, UM667. *Shalom* (John)

Acts 1:1-11

Theophilus, the first scroll I wrote concerned everything Jesus did and taught from the beginning, [2]right up to the day when he was taken up into heaven. Before he was taken up, working in the power of the Holy Spirit, Jesus instructed the apostles he had chosen. [3]After his suffering, he showed them that he was alive with many convincing proofs. He appeared to them over a period of forty days, speaking to them about God's kingdom. [4]While they were eating together, he ordered them not to leave Jerusalem but to wait for what the Father had promised. He said, "This is what you heard from me: [5]John baptized with water, but in only a few days you will be baptized with the Holy Spirit."

[6]As a result, those who had gathered together asked Jesus, "Lord, are you going to restore the kingdom to Israel now?"

[7]Jesus replied, "It isn't for you to know the times or seasons that the Father has set by his own authority. [8]Rather, you will receive power when the Holy Spirit has come upon you, and you will be my witnesses in Jerusalem, in all Judea and Samaria, and to the end of the earth."

[9]After Jesus said these things, as they were watching, he was lifted up and a cloud took him out of their sight. [10]While he was going away and as they were staring toward heaven, suddenly two men in white robes stood next to them. [11]They said, "Galileans, why are you standing here, looking toward heaven? This Jesus, who was taken up from you into heaven, will come in the same way that you saw him go into heaven."

Psalm 47 (G261, N653, P194, UM781)

Clap your hands, all you people!
    Shout joyfully to God with a joyous shout!
[2]Because the LORD Most High is awesome,
    he is the great king of the whole world.
[3]He subdues the nations under us,
    subdues all people beneath our feet.
[4]He chooses our inheritance for us:
    the heights of Jacob, which he loves. *Selah*
[5]God has gone up with a joyous shout—
    the LORD with the blast of the ram's horn.
[6]Sing praises to God! Sing praises!
    Sing praises to our king! Sing praises
    [7]because God is king of the whole world!
    Sing praises with a song of instruction!
[8]God is king over the nations.
    God sits on his holy throne.
[9]The leaders of all people are gathered
    with the people of Abraham's God
    because the earth's guardians belong to God;
        God is exalted beyond all.

Ephesians 1:15-23

[15]Since I heard about your faith in the Lord Jesus and your love for all God's people, this is the reason that [16]I don't stop giving thanks to God for you when I remember you in my prayers. [17]I pray that the God of our Lord Jesus Christ, the Father of glory, will give you a spirit of wisdom and revelation that makes God known to you. [18]I pray that the eyes of your heart will have enough light to see what is the hope of God's call, what is the richness of God's glorious inheritance among believers, [19]and what is the overwhelming greatness of God's power that is working among us believers. This power is conferred by the energy of God's powerful strength. [20]God's power was at work in Christ when God raised him from the dead and sat him at God's right side in the heavens, [21]far above every ruler and authority and power and angelic power, any power that might be named not only now but in the future. [22]God put everything under Christ's feet and made him head of everything in the church, [23]which is his body. His body, the church, is the fullness of Christ, who fills everything in every way.

Luke 24:44-53

[44]Jesus said to them, "These are my words that I spoke to you while I was still with you—that everything written about me in the Law from Moses, the Prophets, and the Psalms must be fulfilled." [45]Then he opened their minds to understand the scriptures. [46]He said to them, "This is what is written: the Christ will suffer and rise from the dead on the third day, [47]and a change of heart and life for the forgiveness of sins must be preached in his name to all nations, beginning from Jerusalem. [48]You are witnesses of these things. [49]Look, I'm sending to you what my Father promised, but you are to stay in the city until you have been furnished with heavenly power."

[50]He led them out as far as Bethany, where he lifted his hands and blessed them. [51]As he blessed them, he left them and was taken up to heaven. [52]They worshipped him and returned to Jerusalem overwhelmed with joy. [53]And they were continuously in the temple praising God.

Primary Hymns and Songs for the Day

"All Hail the Power of Jesus' Name" (Acts) (O)
B200/201/202, C91/92, E450/451, EL634, F325/326/327,
G263, L328/329, N304, P142/143, UM154/155, VU334,
W494
　　　　H-3　　Desc-29; Org-27
　　　　S-2　　#50-51. Descant and interlude
"Hail the Day That Sees Him Rise" (Acts) (O)
E214, UM312, W471 (PD)
　　　　H-3　　Hbl-72; Chr-50; Desc-69; Org-78
　　　　S-1　　#213. Desc.
B165, N260, VU189
"Shout to the Lord" (Pss)
EL821, S2074, SF2074, M16
"Christ Is Made the Sure Foundation" (Eph)
C275, E518, EL645, G394, P416, UM559 (PD), VU325
　　　　H-3　　Chr-49; Desc-103; Org-180
　　　　S-1　　#346. Descant
"Open Our Eyes, Lord" (Eph)
B499, S2086, SF2086, SP199
"Love Divine, All Loves Excelling" (Luke) (C)
B208, C517, E657, EL631, F21, G366, N43, P376, UM384
(PD), VU333, W588
　　　　H-3　　Chr-134; Desc-18; Org-13
　　　　S-1　　#41-42. Desc. and Harm.

Additional Hymn Suggestions

"Spirit Divine, Attend Our Prayers" (Acts)
E509, G407, P325, VU385, W476
"A Hymn of Glory Let Us Sing" (Acts)
E218, G258, L157, N259, P141, W469
"Praise to the Lord, the Almighty" (Acts)
B14, C25, E390, EL858 (PD) and 859, F337, G35, L543, N22,
P482, UM139, VU220 (Fr.) and VU221, W547
"I Love to Tell the Story" (Acts)
B572, C480, EL661, G462, L390, N522, UM156, VU343
"Lift High the Cross" (Acts)
B594, C108, E473, EL660, G826, L377, N198, P371, UM159,
VU151, W704
"Christ, Whose Glory Fills the Skies" (Acts, Luke)
EL553, F293, G662, L265, P462/463, UM173 (PD), VU336
"Hail Thee, Festival Day" (Acts, Luke) (O)
E216, EL394, L142, N262, P120, UM324, VU163
"Christ Jesus Lay in Death's Strong Bands" (Acts, John)
E186, EL370, G237, L134, P110, UM319 (PD)
"Baptized in Water" (Acts, Baptism)
B362, EL456, G482, P492, S2248, W720
"Jesus Shall Reign" (Acts, Pss, Eph)
B587, C95, E544, EL434, F238, G265, L530, N157, P423,
UM157 (PD), VU330, W492
"The Head That Once Was Crowned" (Pss, Eph)
E483, EL432, L173, P149, UM326 (PD), VU190, W464
"Crown Him with Many Crowns" (Acts, Pss, Eph, Luke)
B161, C234, E494, EL855, F345, G268, L170, N301, P151,
UM327 (PD), VU211
"Holy God, We Praise Thy Name" (Eph)
E366, F385, EL414 (PD), G4, L535, N276, P460, UM79,
VU894 (Fr.), W524
"Because You Live, O Christ" (Eph)
G249, N231, P105
"At the Name of Jesus" (Eph)
B198, E435, EL416, F351, G264, L179, P148, UM168, VU335,
W499
"My Hope Is Built" (Eph)
B406, C537, EL596/597, F92, G353, L293/ 294, N368, P379,
UM368 (PD)
"Open My Eyes, That I May See" (Eph)
B502, C586, F486, G451, P324, UM454, VU371

"The Church's One Foundation" (Eph)
B350, C272, E525, EL654, F547, G321, L369, N386, P442,
UM545/546, VU332 (Fr.)
"Blessed Jesus, at Thy Word" (Luke)
E440, EL520, G395, N74, P454, UM596 (PD), VU500
"Alleluia! Sing to Jesus!" (Luke)
C233, E460/461, EL392, G260, L158, N257, P144 (PD),
W737

Additional Contemporary Suggestions

"Come, Holy Spirit" (Acts)
SP132, S2125, SF2125,
"Awesome Is the Lord Most High" (Acts, Luke)
M234
"He Is Exalted" (Pss, Ascension)
S2070, SF2070, SP66
"Lord Most High" (Pss)
M120
"Open the Eyes of My Heart" (Eph, Ascension)
G452, M57, W3008
"Forever" (Eph)
M68, WS3023
"Amazing Grace" ("My Chains Are Gone") (Eph)
M205, WS3104
"In Christ Alone" ("My Hope Is Found") (Eph, Ascension)
M138, WS3105
"Above All" (Eph, Ascension)
M77; V-3 (2) p. 17 Vocal Solo
"Alleluia" (Luke, Ascension)
G589, S2078, SF2078
"Lord, I Lift Your Name on High" (Luke, Ascension)
EL857, M2, S2088, SF2088
"Hosanna" (Ascension)
WS3188, M268

Vocal Solos

"Jesus Christ Is Risen Today" (Acts, Luke)
　　　　V-1　　　　p. 50
"Rejoice Now, My Spirit" (Pss)
　　　　V-9　　　　p. 30

Anthems

"O Clap Your Hands" (Pss)
Robert Lau; Hinshaw HMC2468
SATB with organ, opt. Brass and timp. (bit.ly/HMC2468)

"Easter Anthem in Celtic Style" (John, Easter)
Arr. Bradley R. Norris; Augsburg 978-1-4514-9245-3
SATB and piano, opt. percussion (bit.ly/9245-3)

Other Suggestions

These ideas may be used on June 2, 2019 as Ascension Sunday.
Visuals:
　　Acts　　Baptism, Holy Spirit, Ascension, mantel
　　P　　Clasped hands, Ascension, trumpet, singing, feet
　　E　　Praying, heart, Bible, Christ/throne, names, church
　　G　　Mantel, Bible, witness, Ascension, worship, joy
Introit: EL406, G281, S2118, SF2118, W473. "Holy Spirit, Come
to Us" (Luke)

Acts 16:16-34

[16]One day, when we were on the way to the place for prayer, we met a slave woman. She had a spirit that enabled her to predict the future. She made a lot of money for her owners through fortune-telling. [17]She began following Paul and us, shouting, "These people are servants of the Most High God! They are proclaiming a way of salvation to you!" [18]She did this for many days.

This annoyed Paul so much that he finally turned and said to the spirit, "In the name of Jesus Christ, I command you to leave her!" It left her at that very moment.

[19]Her owners realized that their hope for making money was gone. They grabbed Paul and Silas and dragged them before the officials in the city center. [20]When her owners approached the legal authorities, they said, "These people are causing an uproar in our city. They are Jews [21]who promote customs that we Romans can't accept or practice." [22]The crowd joined in the attacks against Paul and Silas, so the authorities ordered that they be stripped of their clothes and beaten with a rod. [23]When Paul and Silas had been severely beaten, the authorities threw them into prison and ordered the jailer to secure them with great care. [24]When he received these instructions, he threw them into the innermost cell and secured their feet in stocks.

[25]Around midnight Paul and Silas were praying and singing hymns to God, and the other prisoners were listening to them. [26]All at once there was such a violent earthquake that it shook the prison's foundations. The doors flew open and everyone's chains came loose. [27]When the jailer awoke and saw the open doors of the prison, he thought the prisoners had escaped, so he drew his sword and was about to kill himself. [28]But Paul shouted loudly, "Don't harm yourself! We're all here!"

[29]The jailer called for some lights, rushed in, and fell trembling before Paul and Silas. [30]He led them outside and asked, "Honorable masters, what must I do to be rescued?"

[31]They replied, "Believe in the Lord Jesus, and you will be saved—you and your entire household." [32]They spoke the Lord's word to him and everyone else in his house. [33]Right then, in the middle of the night, the jailer welcomed them and washed their wounds. He and everyone in his household were immediately baptized. [34]He brought them into his home and gave them a meal. He was overjoyed because he and everyone in his household had come to believe in God.

Psalm 97 (G365, N685, UM816)

The LORD rules! Let the earth rejoice!
  Let all the islands celebrate!
[2]Clouds and thick darkness surround God.
  His throne is built on righteousness and justice.
[3]Fire proceeds before him,
  burning up his enemies on every side.
[4]His lightning lights up the world;
  the earth sees it and trembles!
[5]The mountains melt like wax before the LORD,
  before the Lord of the whole world!
[6]Heaven has proclaimed God's righteousness,
  and all nations have seen his glory.
[7]All those who worship images,
  those who are proud of idols,
  are put to shame.
  All gods bow down to the Lord!
[8]Zion has heard and celebrates,
  the towns of Judah rejoice,
  because of your acts of justice, LORD,
[9]because you, LORD, are the Most High
    over all the earth,
  because you are so superior to all other gods.

[10]Those of you who love the LORD, hate evil!
  God guards the lives of his faithful ones,
  delivering them from the power of the wicked.
[11]Light is planted like seed for the righteous person;
  joy too for those whose heart is right.
[12]Rejoice in the LORD, righteous ones!
  Give thanks to his holy name!

Revelation 22:12-14, 16-17, 20-21

[12]"Look! I'm coming soon. My reward is with me, to repay all people as their actions deserve. [13]I am the alpha and the omega, the first and the last, the beginning and the end.[14]Favored are those who wash their robes so that they may have the right of access to the tree of life and may enter the city by the gates. . . .

[16]"I, Jesus, have sent my angel to bear witness to all of you about these things for the churches. I'm the root and descendant of David, the bright morning star. [17]The Spirit and the bride say, 'Come!' Let the one who hears say, 'Come!' And let the one who is thirsty come! Let the one who wishes receive life-giving water as a gift." . . .

[20]The one who bears witness to these things says, "Yes, I'm coming soon." Amen. Come, Lord Jesus!
[21]The grace of the Lord Jesus be with all.

John 17:20-26

[20]"I'm not praying only for them but also for those who believe in me because of their word. [21]I pray they will be one, Father, just as you are in me and I am in you. I pray that they also will be in us, so that the world will believe that you sent me. [22]I've given them the glory that you gave me so that they can be one just as we are one. [23]I'm in them and you are in me so that they will be made perfectly one. Then the world will know that you sent me and that you have loved them just as you loved me.

[24]"Father, I want those you gave me to be with me where I am. Then they can see my glory, which you gave me because you loved me before the creation of the world.

[25]"Righteous Father, even the world didn't know you, but I've known you, and these believers know that you sent me. [26]I've made your name known to them and will continue to make it known so that your love for me will be in them, and I myself will be in them."

Primary Hymns and Songs for the Day

"We Know That Christ Is Raised" (Acts, Easter) (O)
    E296, EL449, G485, L189, P495, UM610, VU448, W721
        H-3   Hbl-100; Chr-214; Desc-38; Org-37
        S-1   #118-127. Various treatments
"O Morning Star, How Fair and Bright" (Pss, Rev)
    C105, E497, EL308, G827, L76, N158, P69, UM247, VU98
        H-3   Chr-147; Desc-104; Org-183
"Glorious Things of Thee Are Spoken" (Rev)
    B398, C709, E522/523, EL647, F376, G81, L358, N307, P446,
    UM731 (PD)
        H-3   Hbl-61; Chr-72; Desc-17; Org-11
        S-1   #27. Descant
               #28. Harm. in F major
"Make Us One" (John)
    S2224, SF2224, SP137
"Blest Be the Tie That Binds" (John) (C)
    B387, C433, EL656, F560, G306, L370, N393, P438, UM557
    (PD), VU602

Additional Hymn Suggestions

"God Will Take Care of You" (Acts)
    B64, F56, N460, UM130 (PD)
"Wash, O God, Our Sons and Daughters" (Acts)
    C365, EL445, G490, UM605, VU442
"Steal Away to Jesus" (Acts)
    C644, G358, N599, UM704
"His Eye Is on the Sparrow" (Acts)
    C82, G661, N475, S2146, SF2146
"Wonder of Wonders" (Acts, Baptism)
    C378, G489, N328, P499, S2247
"Freedom Is Coming" (Acts)
    G359, S2192, SF2192
"In God Alone" (Acts)
    G814, WS3135
"Christ, Whose Glory Fills the Skies" (Rev)
    EL553, F293, G662, L265, P462/463, UM173 (PD), VU336
"Fairest Lord Jesus" (Rev)
    B176, C97, E383, EL838, F240, G630, L518, N44, P306,
    UM189 (PD), VU341
"Softly and Tenderly Jesus Is Calling" (Rev)
    B312, C340, EL608 (PD), F432, G418, N449, UM348
"Shall We Gather at the River" (Rev)
    B518, C701, EL423, G375, N597, UM723 (PD), VU710
"O Day of God, Draw Nigh" (Rev)
    B623, C700, E601, N611, P452, UM730 (PD), VU688/689
"We Walk by Faith" (Rev)
    E209, EL635, G817, N256, P399, S2196, SF2196, W572
"Come Now, O Prince of Peace" ("O-So-So") (John)
    EL247, G103, S2232, SF2232
"In the Midst of New Dimensions" (John)
    G315, N391, S2238, SF2238
"Rejoice! Rejoice, Believers" (John)
    E68, EL244, G362, L25, P15
"Thee We Adore, O Hidden Savior, Thee" (John)
    EL476 (PD), G495, L199, P519
"Eternal Christ, Who Kneeling" (John)
    N390

Additional Contemporary Suggestions

"Nobody Fills My Heart Like Jesus" (Acts)
    M8
"God with Us" (Acts)
    M252

"Amazing Grace" ("My Chains Are Gone") (Acts, Rev)
    M205, WS3104
"Grace Like Rain" (Acts, Rev)
    M251
"Forever" (Pss)
    M68, WS3023
"Above All" (Pss)
    M77;   V-3 (2) p. 17 Vocal Solo
"Lord Most High" (Pss)
    M120
"It Is You" (Pss)
    M134
"Great Is the Lord" (Pss)
    B12, G614, S2022, SF2022, SP30
"He Is Exalted" (Pss)
    S2070, SF2070, SP66
"All Hail King Jesus" (Rev)
    S2069, SF2069, SP63
"We Will Glorify" (Rev)
    B213, S2087, SF2087, SP68
"Freedom Is Coming" (Rev)
    G359, S2192, SF2192
"Jesus, We Crown You with Praise" (Rev)
    M24
"Holy and Anointed One" (Rev)
    M32
"I Could Sing of Your Love Forever" (Rev)
    M63
"How Great Is Our God" (Rev)
    WS3003, M117
"They'll Know We Are Christians" (John)
    C494, G300, S2223, SF2223
"Bind Us Together" (John)
    S2226, SF2226, SP140

Vocal Solos

"O Glorious Love" (Acts)
    V-8   p. 306
"My Lord, What a Mornin'" (Rev)
    V-7   p. 68

Anthems

"Oh, Come Let Us Sing!" (Acts)
William M. Schoenfeld; AEC-3 p. 33
2-part and keyboard

"Jesus Walked This Lonesome Valley" (John)
Victor Johnson, Hope C-6060
SATB and piano (bit.ly/C-6060)

Other Suggestions

You may celebrate Ascension today, using May 30 ideas.
Visuals:
    Acts   Fortune-teller/money, rods/open shackles,
               chains, baptism
    P   Coast, clouds, lightning, shield/rescue
    E   Alpha/Omega, white robe, root, flame, bride,
               water, Rev 22:20b
    G   Jesus praying, hearts
Introit: WS3050. "Until Jesus Comes" (Rev)
Baptism Response: EL211, G491, UM609, VU452, W112. "You
    Have Put On Christ" (Acts)

Acts 2:1-21

When Pentecost Day arrived, they were all together in one place. ²Suddenly a sound from heaven like the howling of a fierce wind filled the entire house where they were sitting. ³They saw what seemed to be individual flames of fire alighting on each one of them. ⁴They were all filled with the Holy Spirit and began to speak in other languages as the Spirit enabled them to speak.

⁵There were pious Jews from every nation under heaven living in Jerusalem. ⁶When they heard this sound, a crowd gathered. They were mystified because everyone heard them speaking in their native languages. ⁷They were surprised and amazed, saying, "Look, aren't all the people who are speaking Galileans, every one of them? ⁸How then can each of us hear them speaking in our native language? ⁹Parthians, Medes, and Elamites; as well as residents of Mesopotamia, Judea, and Cappadocia, Pontus and Asia, ¹⁰Phrygia and Pamphylia, Egypt and the regions of Libya bordering Cyrene; and visitors from Rome (both Jews and converts to Judaism), ¹¹Cretans and Arabs—we hear them declaring the mighty works of God in our own languages!" ¹²They were all surprised and bewildered. Some asked each other, "What does this mean?" ¹³Others jeered at them, saying, "They're full of new wine!"

¹⁴Peter stood with the other eleven apostles. He raised his voice and declared, "Judeans and everyone living in Jerusalem! Know this! Listen carefully to my words! ¹⁵These people aren't drunk, as you suspect; after all, it's only nine o'clock in the morning! ¹⁶Rather, this is what was spoken through the prophet Joel:

¹⁷*In the last days, God says,*
I will pour out my Spirit on all people.
    Your sons and daughters will prophesy.
    Your young will see visions.
    Your elders will dream dreams.
        ¹⁸*Even upon my servants, men and women,*
        I will pour out my Spirit in those days,
        and they will prophesy.
¹⁹*I will cause wonders to occur in the heavens above*
    and signs on the earth below,
        blood and fire and a cloud of smoke.
²⁰*The sun will be changed into darkness,*
    and the moon will be changed into blood,
        before the great and spectacular day of the Lord comes.
²¹*And everyone who calls on the name of the Lord will be saved.*

Psalm 104:24-34, 35b (G34, N889/890, P224 UM826)

²⁴Lᴏʀᴅ, you have done so many things!
    You made them all so wisely!
The earth is full of your creations!
²⁵And then there's the sea, wide and deep,
    with its countless creatures—
    living things both small and large.
²⁶There go the ships on it,
    and Leviathan, which you made, plays in it!
²⁷All your creations wait for you
    to give them their food on time.
²⁸When you give it to them, they gather it up;
    when you open your hand, they are filled completely full!
²⁹But when you hide your face, they are terrified;
    when you take away their breath,
    they die and return to dust.
³⁰When you let loose your breath, they are created,
    and you make the surface of the ground brand-new again.
³¹Let the Lᴏʀᴅ's glory last forever!
    Let the Lᴏʀᴅ rejoice in all he has made!

³²He has only to look at the earth, and it shakes.
    God just touches the mountains, and they erupt in smoke.
³³I will sing to the Lᴏʀᴅ as long as I live;
    I will sing praises to my God while I'm still alive.
³⁴Let my praise be pleasing to him;
    I'm rejoicing in the Lᴏʀᴅ!
. . . .
³⁵ᵇ But let my whole being bless the Lᴏʀᴅ!

Romans 8:14-17

¹⁴All who are led by God's Spirit are God's sons and daughters. ¹⁵You didn't receive a spirit of slavery to lead you back again into fear, but you received a Spirit that shows you are adopted as his children. With this Spirit, we cry, "Abba, Father." ¹⁶The same Spirit agrees with our spirit, that we are God's children. ¹⁷But if we are children, we are also heirs. We are God's heirs and fellow heirs with Christ, if we really suffer with him so that we can also be glorified with him.

John 14:8-17 (25-27)

⁸Philip said, "Lord, show us the Father; that will be enough for us."

⁹Jesus replied, "Don't you know me, Philip, even after I have been with you all this time? Whoever has seen me has seen the Father. How can you say, 'Show us the Father'? ¹⁰Don't you believe that I am in the Father and the Father is in me? The words I have spoken to you I don't speak on my own. The Father who dwells in me does his works. ¹¹Trust me when I say that I am in the Father and the Father is in me, or at least believe on account of the works themselves. ¹²I assure you that whoever believes in me will do the works that I do. They will do even greater works than these because I am going to the Father. ¹³I will do whatever you ask for in my name, so that the Father can be glorified in the Son. ¹⁴When you ask me for anything in my name, I will do it.

¹⁵"If you love me, you will keep my commandments. ¹⁶I will ask the Father, and he will send another Companion, who will be with you forever. ¹⁷This Companion is the Spirit of Truth, whom the world can't receive because it neither sees him nor recognizes him. You know him, because he lives with you and will be with you. . . .

²⁵"I have spoken these things to you while I am with you. ²⁶The Companion, the Holy Spirit, whom the Father will send in my name, will teach you everything and will remind you of everything I told you.

²⁷"Peace I leave with you. My peace I give you. I give to you not as the world gives. Don't be troubled or afraid."

Primary Hymns and Songs for the Day

"On Pentecost They Gathered" (Acts) (O)
C237, G289, N272, P128, VU195

"Come Down, O Love Divine" (Acts, John)
C582, E516, EL804, G282, L508, N289, P313, UM475,
VU367, W472

"Spirit of God, Descend upon My Heart" (Acts, John)
B245, C265, EL800, F147, G688, L486, N290, P326, UM500
(PD), VU378

"Love Divine, All Loves Excelling" (John) (C)
B208, C517, E657, EL631, F21, G366, N43, P376, UM384
(PD), VU333, W588
H-3   Chr-134; Desc-18; Org-13
S-1   #41-42. Desc. and Harm.

Additional Hymn Suggestions

"What Is This Place" (Acts)
C289, EL524, G404, W709

"We Praise You, O God, Our Redeemer" (Acts)
B19, F334, EL870, G612, L241, N420, VU218

"Wind Who Makes All Winds That Blow" (Acts)
C236, N271, P131, UM538, VU196

"Spirit, Spirit of Gentleness" (Acts, Pentecost)
C249, EL396, G291, N286, P319, S2120, VU375

"Gather Us In" (Acts)
C284, EL532, G401, S2236, SF2236, W665

"Deep in the Shadows of the Past" (Acts, Pentecost)
G50, N320, P330, S2246

"Come, Share the Lord" (Acts, Comm.)
C408, G510, S2269, SF2269, VU469

"Come, O Spirit, Dwell Among Us" (Acts, Rom)
G280, N267, P129, VU198

"Come, Holy Spirit, Heavenly Dove" (Acts, John)
C248, E510, G279, N281, P126

"Like the Murmur of the Dove's Song" (Acts, John)
C245, E513, EL403, G285, N270, P314, UM544, VU205

"Many and Great, O God" (Pss)
B49, C58, E385, EL837, G21, N3, N341, P271 (PD), UM148,
VU308, W503

"Jesus, the Very Thought of Thee" (Rom)
B225, C102, E642, EL754, F465, G629, L316, N507, P310,
UM175 (PD)

"Blessed Assurance" (Rom)
B334, C543, EL638, F67, G839, N473, P341, UM369 (PD),
VU337

"Every Time I Feel the Spirit" (Rom)
C592, G66, N282, P315, UM404

"Come, Holy Ghost, Our Souls Inspire" (Rom)
E503/504, L472/473, N268, G278, P125, UM651, VU201

"Loving Spirit" (Rom, Pentecost)
C244, EL397, G293, P323, S2123, SF2123, VU387

"In Christ There Is No East or West" (Rom, John)
B385, C687, E529, EL650 (PD), F685, G317/318, L359,
N394/395, P439/440, UM548, VU606, W659

"Spirit Divine, Attend Our Prayers" (John)
E509, G407, P325, VU385, W476

"All Who Love and Serve Your City" (John)
C670, E571, G351, P413, UM433

"Blessed Jesus, at Thy Word" (John)
E440, EL520, G395, N74, P454, UM596 (PD), VU500

"In the Midst of New Dimensions" (Pentecost)
G315, N391, S2238, SF2238

Additional Contemporary Suggestions

"God Is Here Today" ("*Dios Está Aquí*") (Acts)
G411, S2049, SF2049

"Holy Ground" (Acts)
B224, C112, G406, S2272, SF2272, SP86

"Come, All You People" ("*Uyai Mose*") (Acts)
EL819, G388, S2274, SF2274

"Awesome in This Place" (Acts)
M36

"Light the Fire Again" (Acts)
M144

"Holy Spirit, Rain Down" (Acts, John)
M88

"Spirit of the Living God" (Rom)
B244, C259, G288, N283, P322, SP131, UM393, VU376

"Holy, Holy" (Rom, Pentecost)
B254, F149, P140, S2039, SP141

"Surely the Presence of the Lord" (Acts, Pentecost)
C263, SP243, UM328; S-2 #200. Stanzas for soloist

"Sweet, Sweet Spirit" (Acts)
B243, C261, F159, G408, N293, P398, SP136, UM334

"Where the Spirit of the Lord Is" (Acts, Pentecost)
C264, S2119, SF2119

"Come, O Holy Spirit, Come" (Acts, Pentecost)
G283, S2124, SF2124, VU383

"Come and Fill Our Hearts" (John)
EL538, G466, S2157, SF2157, W561

"Behold, What Manner of Love" (John)
SP48

"Dwell" (John, Pentecost)
M154

Vocal Solos

"Ev'ry Time I Feel De Spirit" (Acts)
V-7   p. 78

"Spirit of God" (Acts)
V-8   p. 170

Anthems

"Gracious Spirit, Dwell with Me" (Acts)
Arr. K. Lee Scott; AEC-1 p. 21
2-part mixed with organ (bit.ly/AEC-1-21)

"Spirit, Open My Heart" (Acts)
Alfred V. Fedak; MorningStar MSM-50-5556
SATB and keyboard, opt. handbells (bit.ly/50-5556)

Other Suggestions

Visuals:
  Acts Wind, flames, nature, wine, clock (9:00 a.m.), nations, blood
  P Nature, ship/whale, open hand, volcano, joy
  E Children, open shackles, adoption certificate, will
  G Jesus, ministry, prayer, flames, Bible, John 14:27
Introit: C250, UM543, VU202, WS3146. "O Breath of Life" (Acts)
Call to Prayer: C248, E510, G279, N281, P126. "Come, Holy Spirit, Heavenly Dove" (Acts)
Prayers: WSL37, N826, N857, UM542, C52, C243 (Pentecost)
Blessing: N877 (Acts, Pentecost)

Proverbs 8:1-4, 22-31

Doesn't Wisdom cry out
    and Understanding shout?
[2]Atop the heights along the path,
    at the crossroads she takes her stand.
[3]By the gate before the city,
    at the entrances she shouts:
[4]I cry out to you, people;
    my voice goes out to all of humanity.

. . . .

[22]The LORD created me at the beginning of his way,
    before his deeds long in the past.
[23]I was formed in ancient times,
    at the beginning, before the earth was.
[24]When there were no watery depths, I was brought forth,
    when there were no springs flowing with water.
[25]Before the mountains were settled,
    before the hills, I was brought forth;
    [26]before God made the earth and the fields
    or the first of the dry land.
[27]I was there when he established the heavens,
    when he marked out the horizon on the deep sea,
    [28]when he thickened the clouds above,
    when he secured the fountains of the deep,
    [29]when he set a limit for the sea,
      so the water couldn't go beyond his command,
    when he marked out the earth's foundations.
[30]I was beside him as a master of crafts.
    I was having fun,
    smiling before him all the time,
    [31]frolicking with his inhabited earth
    and delighting in the human race.

Psalm 8 (G25, N624, P162/163, UM743)

LORD, our Lord, how majestic
    is your name throughout the earth!
    You made your glory higher than heaven!
[2]From the mouths of nursing babies
    you have laid a strong foundation
    because of your foes,
    in order to stop vengeful enemies.
[3]When I look up at your skies,
    at what your fingers made—
    the moon and the stars
    that you set firmly in place—
      [4]what are human beings
        that you think about them;
    what are human beings
      that you pay attention to them?
[5]You've made them only slightly less than divine,
    crowning them with glory and grandeur.
[6]You've let them rule over your handiwork,
    putting everything under their feet—
      [7]all sheep and all cattle,
    the wild animals too,
      [8]the birds in the sky,
    the fish of the ocean,
    everything that travels the pathways of the sea.
[9]LORD, our Lord, how majestic is your name throughout the
      earth!

Romans 5:1-5

Therefore, since we have been made righteous through his faithfulness combined with our faith, we have peace with God through our Lord Jesus Christ. [2] We have access by faith into this grace in which we stand through him, and we boast in the hope of God's glory. [3] But not only that! We even take pride in our problems, because we know that trouble produces endurance, [4]endurance produces character, and character produces hope. [5]This hope doesn't put us to shame, because the love of God has been poured out in our hearts through the Holy Spirit, who has been given to us.

John 16:12-15

[12]"I have much more to say to you, but you can't handle it now. [13]However, when the Spirit of Truth comes, he will guide you in all truth. He won't speak on his own, but will say whatever he hears and will proclaim to you what is to come. [14]He will glorify me, because he will take what is mine and proclaim it to you. [15]Everything that the Father has is mine. That's why I said that the Spirit takes what is mine and will proclaim it to you.

Primary Hymns and Songs for the Day

"Holy, Holy, Holy" (Trinity) (O)
   B2, C4, E362, F323, EL413, G1, L165, N277, P138, UM64/65, VU315, W485
      H-3   Hbl-68; Chr-99; Desc-80; Org-97
      S-1   #245-248. Various treatments
"Immortal, Invisible, God Only Wise" (Prov) (O)
   B6, C66, E423, EL834, F319, G12, L526, N1, P263, UM103 (PD), VU264, W512
      H-3   Hbl-15, 71; Chr-65; Desc-93; Org-135
      S-1   #300. Harm.
"How Majestic Is Your Name" (Pss)
   C63, G613, S2023, SF2023, SP14
"My Hope Is Built" (Rom)
   B406, C537, EL596/597, F92, G353, L293/ 294, N368, P379, UM368 (PD)
      H-3   Chr-191
      S-2   #171-172. Trumpet and Vocal Desc.
"Come, Thou Almighty King" (John, Trinity) (C)
   B247, C27, E365, EL408, F341, G2, L522, N275, P139, UM61 (PD), VU314, W487
      H-3   Hbl-28, 49, 53; Chr-56; Desc-57; Org-63
      S-1   #185-186. Desc. and Harm.

Additional Hymn Suggestions

"Savior of the Nations, Come" (Prov)
   E54, EL263, G102, P14 (PD), UM214, W372
"By Gracious Powers" (Prov)
   E695/696, G818, N413, P342, UM517, W577
"All Creatures of Our God and King" (Prov, Pss, Trinity)
   B27, C22, E400, EL835, F347, G15, L527, N17, P455, UM62, VU217 (Fr.), W520
"How Great Thou Art" (Prov, Pss)
   B10, C33, E856, G625, N35, P467, UM77, VU238
"For the Beauty of the Earth" (Prov, Pss)
   B44, C56, E416, EL879, F1, G14, L561, P473, N28, UM92 (PD), VU226, W557
"Mothering God, You Gave Me Birth" (Prov, Trinity)
   C83, N467, S2050, SF2050, VU320
"Take Thou Our Minds, Dear Lord" (Prov)
   F467, G707, P392
"Spirit of God, Descend upon My Heart" (Rom)
   B245, C265, EL800, F147, G688, L486, N290, P326, UM500 (PD), VU378
"Holy Spirit, Come to Us" (Rom)
   EL406, G281, S2118, SF2118, W473
"I've Got Peace Like a River" (Rom)
   B418, C530, G623, N478, P368, S2145, VU577
"Healer of Our Every Ill" (Rom)
   C506, EL612, G795, S2213, SF2213, VU619
"Come, Holy Ghost, Our Souls Inspire" (Rom, John)
   E503/504, L472/473, N268, G278, P125, UM651, VU201
"Come, Holy Spirit, Heavenly Dove" (John)
   C248, E510, G279, N281, P126
"Come, O Spirit, Dwell Among Us" (John)
   G280, N267, P129, VU198
"Gracious Spirit, Heed Our Pleading" (John)
   EL401, G287
"Come, Christians, Join to Sing" (John)
   B231, C90, F342, G267, P150, UM158, VU345
"Like the Murmur of the Dove's Song" (John)
   C245, E513, EL403, G285, N270, P314, UM544, VU205
"Come, O Holy Spirit, Come" (John)
   G283, S2124, SF2124, VU383

"Now the Silence" (Trinity, Comm.)
   C415, E333, EL460, G534, L205, UM619, VU475, W668

Additional Contemporary Suggestions

"God Is Speaking" (Prov, John)
   WS3025
"God of Wonders" (Pss)
   M80, WS3034
"How Great Is Our God" (Pss, Trinity)
   WS3003, M117
"I Could Sing of Your Love Forever" (Rom)
   M63
"Amazing Grace" ("My Chains Are Gone") (Rom)
   M205, WS3104
"In Christ Alone" ("My Hope Is Found") (Rom)
   M138, WS3105
"Sing Alleluia to the Lord" (Rom, Comm.)
   B214, C32, S2258, SF2258, SP93
"Here Is Bread, Here Is Wine" (Rom, Comm.)
   EL483, S2266, SF2266
"Spirit of the Living God" (John)
   B244, C259, G288, N283, P322, SP131, UM393, VU376
"Kum Ba Yah" ("Come By Here") (John)
   C590, G472, P338, UM494
"Holy, Holy" (Trinity)
   B254, F149, P140, S2039, SP141

Vocal Solos

"Be Thou My Vision" (Prov)
   V-6   p. 13
"It Won't Stop" (Rom, Trinity)
   V-8   p. 70
"God Will Make a Way" (with "He Leadeth Me") (John)
   V-3 (2)   p. 9

Anthems

"The Perfect Wisdom of Our God" (Prov)
arr. Larry Shackley; Alfred 37678
SATB and piano (bit.ly/Alfred37678)

"Like the Murmur of the Doves Song" (John)
Richard Jeffrey; Concordia 98-3898
SATB and piano, flute (bit.ly/98-3898)

Other Suggestions

Visuals:
   O   Crossroads, gate, nature, outer space, circle, joy
   P   Space, baby, moon/stars, Adam/Eve, animals, bird, fish
   E   Kairos/chronos, heart, pouring, flames
   G   Jesus, Spirit, Bible, kairos/chronos, preaching
Canticle: UM80, N740, N738, or UM112 (Prov, Trinity)
Litany: C11. Names of God Litany (Trinity)
Affirmation of Faith: UM881 or WSL79 (Trinity)
Doxology: G405, WS3009. "Praise God for this Holy Ground" (Trinity)
Closing Prayer: WSL42 (Pss) or UM76. Trinity Sunday (Trinity)
Sung Benediction: B51, C62, N278. "Creator God, Creating Still" (Trinity)

1 Kings 19:1-15a

Ahab told Jezebel all that Elijah had done, how he had killed all Baal's prophets with the sword. [2]Jezebel sent a messenger to Elijah with this message: "May the gods do whatever they want to me if by this time tomorrow I haven't made your life like the life of one of them."

[3]Elijah was terrified. He got up and ran for his life. He arrived at Beer-sheba in Judah and left his assistant there. [4]He himself went farther on into the desert a day's journey. He finally sat down under a solitary broom bush. He longed for his own death: "It's more than enough, LORD! Take my life because I'm no better than my ancestors." [5]He lay down and slept under the solitary broom bush.

Then suddenly a messenger tapped him and said to him, "Get up! Eat something!" [6]Elijah opened his eyes and saw flatbread baked on glowing coals and a jar of water right by his head. He ate and drank, and then went back to sleep. [7]The LORD's messenger returned a second time and tapped him. "Get up!" the messenger said. "Eat something, because you have a difficult road ahead of you." [8]Elijah got up, ate and drank, and went refreshed by that food for forty days and nights until he arrived at Horeb, God's mountain. [9]There he went into a cave and spent the night.

The LORD's word came to him and said, "Why are you here, Elijah?"

[10]Elijah replied, "I've been very passionate for the LORD God of heavenly forces because the Israelites have abandoned your covenant. They have torn down your altars, and they have murdered your prophets with the sword. I'm the only one left, and now they want to take my life too!"

[11]The LORD said, "Go out and stand at the mountain before the LORD. The LORD is passing by." A very strong wind tore through the mountains and broke apart the stones before the LORD. But the LORD wasn't in the wind. After the wind, there was an earthquake. But the LORD wasn't in the earthquake. [12]After the earthquake, there was a fire. But the LORD wasn't in the fire. After the fire, there was a sound. Thin. Quiet. [13]When Elijah heard it, he wrapped his face in his coat. He went out and stood at the cave's entrance. A voice came to him and said, "Why are you here, Elijah?"

[14]He said, "I've been very passionate for the LORD God of heavenly forces because the Israelites have abandoned your covenant. They have torn down your altars, and they have murdered your prophets with the sword. I'm the only one left, and now they want to take my life too."

[15a]The LORD said to him, "Go back through the desert to Damascus."

Psalm 42 (UM777)

Just like a deer that craves streams of water,
    my whole being craves you, God.
[2]My whole being thirsts for God, for the living God.
    When will I come and see God's face?
[3]My tears have been my food both day and night,
    as people constantly questioned me,
    "Where's your God now?"
[4]But I remember these things as I bare my soul:
    how I made my way to the mighty one's abode,
    to God's own house,
        with joyous shouts and thanksgiving songs—
        a huge crowd celebrating the festival!
[5]Why, I ask myself, are you so depressed?
    Why are you so upset inside?
Hope in God!
    Because I will again give him thanks,
        my saving presence and my God.
[6]My whole being is depressed.
    That's why I remember you
    from the land of Jordan and Hermon,
        from Mount Mizar.

[7]Deep called to deep at the noise of your waterfalls;
    all your massive waves surged over me.
[8]By day the LORD commands his faithful love;
    by night his song is with me—
    a prayer to the God of my life.
[9]I will say to God, my solid rock,
    "Why have you forgotten me?
        Why do I have to walk around,
        sad, oppressed by enemies?"
[10]With my bones crushed, my foes make fun of me,
    constantly questioning me: "Where's your God now?"
[11]Why, I ask myself, are you so depressed?
    Why are you so upset inside?
        Hope in God!
        Because I will again give him thanks,
        my saving presence and my God.

Galatians 3:23-29

[23]Before faith came, we were guarded under the Law, locked up until faith that was coming would be revealed, [24]so that the Law became our custodian until Christ so that we might be made righteous by faith.

[25]But now that faith has come, we are no longer under a custodian.

[26]You are all God's children through faith in Christ Jesus. [27]All of you who were baptized into Christ have clothed yourselves with Christ. [28]There is neither Jew nor Greek; there is neither slave nor free; nor is there male and female, for you are all one in Christ Jesus. [29]Now if you belong to Christ, then indeed you are Abraham's descendants, heirs according to the promise.

Luke 8:26-39

[26]Jesus and his disciples sailed to the Gerasenes' land, which is across the lake from Galilee. [27]As soon as Jesus got out of the boat, a certain man met him. The man was from the city and was possessed by demons. For a long time, he had lived among the tombs, naked and homeless. [28]When he saw Jesus, he shrieked and fell down before him. Then he shouted, "What have you to do with me, Jesus, Son of the Most High God? I beg you, don't torture me!" [29]He said this because Jesus had already commanded the unclean spirit to come out of the man. Many times it had taken possession of him, so he would be bound with leg irons and chains and placed under guard. But he would break his restraints, and the demon would force him into the wilderness.

[30]Jesus asked him, "What is your name?"

"Legion," he replied, because many demons had entered him.[31]They pleaded with him not to order them to go back into the abyss. [32]A large herd of pigs was feeding on the hillside. The demons begged Jesus to let them go into the pigs. Jesus gave them permission, [33]and the demons left the man and entered the pigs. The herd rushed down the cliff into the lake and drowned.

[34]When those who tended the pigs saw what happened, they ran away and told the story in the city and in the countryside.[35]People came to see what had happened. They came to Jesus and found the man from whom the demons had gone. He was sitting at Jesus' feet, fully dressed and completely sane. They were filled with awe. [36]Those people who had actually seen what had happened told them how the demon-possessed man had been delivered. [37]Then everyone gathered from the region of the Gerasenes asked Jesus to leave their area because they were overcome with fear. So he got into the boat and returned across the lake. [38]The man from whom the demons had gone begged to come along with Jesus as one of his disciples. Jesus sent him away, saying, [39]"Return home and tell the story of what God has done for you." So he went throughout the city proclaiming what Jesus had done for him.

Primary Hymns and Songs for the Day

"In Christ There Is No East or West" (Gal, Luke) (O)
    B385, C687, E529, EL650 (PD), F685, G317/318, L359,
    N394/395, P439/440, UM548, VU606, W659
        H-3   Chr-111; Desc-74; Org-88
        S-1   #231-233. Various treaments
"As the Deer" (Pss)
    G626, S2025, SF2025, SP200, VU766
"Baptized in Water" (Gal)
    B362, EL456, G482, P492, S2248, W720
        H-3   Hbl-77; Chr-136; Desc-21; Org-16
        S-1   #50-51. Flute and Vocal Desc.
"One Bread, One Body" (Gal, Comm.)
    C393, EL496, G530, UM620, VU467
        H-3   Chr-156
"Dear Lord and Father of Mankind" (1 Kgs, Luke) (C)
    B267, C594, E652/563, F422, G169, L506, N502, P345,
    UM358 (PD), VU608

Additional Hymn Suggestions

"Holy God, We Praise Thy Name" (1 Kgs)
    E366, F385, EL414 (PD), G4, L535, N276, P460, UM79,
    VU894 (Fr.), W524
"Near to the Heart of God" (1 Kgs)
    B295, C581, F35, G824, P527, UM472 (PD)
"Give to the Winds Thy Fears" (1 Kgs, Pss)
    G815, N404, P286, UM129 (PD), VU636
"God Will Take Care of You" (1 Kgs, Pss)
    B64, F56, N460, UM130 (PD)
"If Thou But Suffer God to Guide Thee" (1 Kgs, Pss)
    B57, C565, E635, EL769, G816, L453, N410, P282, UM142
    (PD), VU285 (Fr.) and VU286
"Rock of Ages" (1 Kgs, Pss)
    B342, C214, E685, EL623, G438, L327, N596, UM361
"Loving Spirit" (1 Kgs, Pss)
    C244, EL397, G293, P323, S2123, SF2123, VU387
"Children of the Heavenly Father" (1 Kgs, Pss, Luke)
    B55, EL781, F89, L474, N487, UM141
"There Is a Balm in Gilead" (1 Kgs, Pss, Luke)
    B269, C501, E676, EL614 (PD), F48, G792, N553, P394,
    UM375, VU612, W608
"The Church of Christ, in Every Age" (Gal)
    B402, C475, E729, G320, L433, N306, P421, UM589,
    VU601, W626
"Sacred the Body" (Gal)
    G27, S2228, SF2228
"We Are One in Christ Jesus" (Gal)
    C493, EL643, G322, S2229, SF2229
"Wonder of Wonders" (Gal, Baptism)
    C378, G489, N328, P499, S2247
"Come, Share the Lord" (Gal, Comm.)
    C408, G510, S2269, SF2269, VU469
"A Place at the Table" (Gal)
    G769, WS3149
"O Christ, the Healer" (Luke)
    C503. EL610, G793, L360, N175, P380, UM265, W747
"Blessed Quietness" (Luke)
    F145, C267, N284, S2142, SF2142

Additional Contemporary Suggestions

"Word of God, Speak" (1 Kgs)
    M148, WS3184
"Days of Elijah" (1 Kgs)
    M139, WS3186

"Jesus, Draw Me Close" (Pss)
    M48, S2159, SF2159
"Cry of My Heart" (Pss)
    M39, S2165, SF2165
"Purify My Heart" (Pss)
    M90, WS3103
"Who Can Satisfy My Soul Like You?" (Pss)
    M28
"Draw Me Close" (Pss)
    M29
"Knowing You" ("All I Once Held Dear") (Pss)
    M30
"Better Is One Day" (Pss)
    M60
"Breathe" (Pss)
    M61, WS3112
"Just Let Me Say" (Pss)
    M83
"Show Me Your Ways" (Pss)
    M107
"Enough" (Pss)
    M160
"Holy, Holy" (Gal)
    B254, F149, P140, S2039, SP141
"I'm So Glad Jesus Lifted Me" (Luke)
    C529, EL860 (PD), N474, S2151, SF2151
"Amazing Grace" ("My Chains Are Gone") (Luke)
    M205, WS3104
"Trading My Sorrows" (Luke)
    M75, WS3108
"Grace Like Rain" (Luke)
    M251
"God with Us" (Luke)
    M252

Vocal Solos

"There Is a Balm in Gilead" (1 Kgs)
    V-3 (1)   p. 29
"So Art Thou with Me" (Pss)
    V-9   p. 34
"One Bread, One Body" (Gal, Comm.)
    V-3 (2)   p. 40

Anthems

"Show Me, Teach Me, Lead Me" (Pss)
Nancy M. Raabe; AEC-3 p. 66
Unison and piano

"Eternal Father, Strong to Save" (Luke)
Arr. Dan Forrest; Hinshaw HMC2353
SATB divisi with keyboard (bit.ly/HMC2353)

Other Suggestions

Visuals:
    O   Run, tree, cake/stone/jar, overturned altar
    P   Deer, stream, tears, procession, waterfall, waves
    E   Shackles, ruler, switch, child, baptism, unity
    G   Tombstone, man(naked/clothed), chains, pigs
Opening Prayer: WSL38 (2 Kgs) or N831 (Luke)
Prayers: C524, UM423, WSL17, WSL92 (1 Kgs, Pss, Luke)
Blessing: N873 (Gal)
Alternate Lessons: Isa 62:1-9; Ps 16 (see p. 4)

2 Kings 2:1-2, 6-14

Now the LORD was going to take Elijah up to heaven in a windstorm, and Elijah and Elisha were leaving Gilgal. ²Elijah said to Elisha, "Stay here, because the LORD has sent me to Bethel."

But Elisha said, "As the LORD lives and as you live, I won't leave you." So they went down to Bethel. . . .

⁶Elijah said to Elisha, "Stay here, because the LORD has sent me to the Jordan."

But Elisha said, "As the LORD lives and as you live, I won't leave you." So both of them went on together. ⁷Fifty members from the group of prophets also went along, but they stood at a distance. Both Elijah and Elisha stood beside the Jordan River. ⁸Elijah then took his coat, rolled it up, and hit the water. Then the water was divided in two! Both of them crossed over on dry ground. ⁹When they had crossed, Elijah said to Elisha, "What do you want me to do for you before I'm taken away from you?"

Elisha said, "Let me have twice your spirit."

¹⁰Elijah said, "You've made a difficult request. If you can see me when I'm taken from you, then it will be yours. If you don't see me, it won't happen."

¹¹They were walking along, talking, when suddenly a fiery chariot and fiery horses appeared and separated the two of them. Then Elijah went to heaven in a windstorm.

¹²Elisha was watching, and he cried out, "Oh, my father, my father! Israel's chariots and its riders!" When he could no longer see him, Elisha took hold of his clothes and ripped them in two.

¹³Then Elisha picked up the coat that had fallen from Elijah. He went back and stood beside the banks of the Jordan River. ¹⁴He took the coat that had fallen from Elijah and hit the water. He said, "Where is the LORD, Elijah's God?" And when he hit the water, it divided in two! Then Elisha crossed over.

Psalm 77:1-2, 11-20 (UM798)

I cry out loud to God—
    out loud to God so that he can hear me!
²During the day when I'm in trouble I look for my LORD.
    At night my hands are still outstretched and don't grow
        numb;
    my whole being refuses to be comforted.

. . . .
¹¹But I will remember the LORD's deeds;
    yes, I will remember your wondrous acts from times long
        past.
¹²I will meditate on all your works;
    I will ponder your deeds.
¹³God, your way is holiness!
    Who is as great a god as you, God?
¹⁴You are the God who works wonders;
    you have demonstrated your strength among all peoples.
¹⁵With your mighty arm you redeemed your people;
    redeemed the children of Jacob and Joseph. *Selah*
¹⁶The waters saw you, God—
    the waters saw you and reeled!
        Even the deep depths shook!
¹⁷The clouds poured water,
    the skies cracked thunder;
        your arrows were flying all around!
¹⁸The crash of your thunder was in the swirling storm;
    lightning lit up the whole world;
        the earth shook and quaked.
¹⁹Your way went straight through the sea;
    your pathways went right through the mighty waters.
        But your footprints left no trace!
²⁰You led your people like sheep
    under the care of Moses and Aaron.

Galatians 5:1, 13-25

Christ has set us free for freedom. Therefore, stand firm and don't submit to the bondage of slavery again. . . .

¹³You were called to freedom, brothers and sisters; only don't let this freedom be an opportunity to indulge your selfish impulses, but serve each other through love. ¹⁴All the Law has been fulfilled in a single statement: *Love your neighbor as yourself.* ¹⁵But if you bite and devour each other, be careful that you don't get eaten up by each other!

¹⁶I say be guided by the Spirit and you won't carry out your selfish desires. ¹⁷A person's selfish desires are set against the Spirit, and the Spirit is set against one's selfish desires. They are opposed to each other, so you shouldn't do whatever you want to do. ¹⁸But if you are being led by the Spirit, you aren't under the Law. ¹⁹The actions that are produced by selfish motives are obvious, since they include sexual immorality, moral corruption, doing whatever feels good, ²⁰idolatry, drug use and casting spells, hate, fighting, obsession, losing your temper, competitive opposition, conflict, selfishness, group rivalry, ²¹jealousy, drunkenness, partying, and other things like that. I warn you as I have already warned you, that those who do these kinds of things won't inherit God's kingdom.

²²But the fruit of the Spirit is love, joy, peace, patience, kindness, goodness, faithfulness, ²³gentleness, and self-control. There is no law against things like this. ²⁴Those who belong to Christ Jesus have crucified self with its passions and its desires.

²⁵If we live by the Spirit, let's follow the Spirit. ²⁶Let's not become arrogant, make each other angry, or be jealous of each other.

Luke 9:51-62

⁵¹As the time approached when Jesus was to be taken up into heaven, he determined to go to Jerusalem. ⁵²He sent messengers on ahead of him. Along the way, they entered a Samaritan village to prepare for his arrival, ⁵³but the Samaritan villagers refused to welcome him because he was determined to go to Jerusalem. ⁵⁴When the disciples James and John saw this, they said, "Lord, do you want us to call fire down from heaven to consume them?" ⁵⁵But Jesus turned and spoke sternly to them, ⁵⁶and they went on to another village.

⁵⁷As Jesus and his disciples traveled along the road, someone said to him, "I will follow you wherever you go."

⁵⁸Jesus replied, "Foxes have dens and the birds in the sky have nests, but the Human One has no place to lay his head."

⁵⁹Then Jesus said to someone else, "Follow me."

He replied, "Lord, first let me go and bury my father."

⁶⁰Jesus said to him, "Let the dead bury their own dead. But you go and spread the news of God's kingdom."

⁶¹Someone else said to Jesus, "I will follow you, Lord, but first let me say good-bye to those in my house."

⁶²Jesus said to him, "No one who puts a hand on the plow and looks back is fit for God's kingdom."

Primary Hymns and Songs for the Day

"O God, Our Help in Ages Past" (Pss) (O)
> B74, C67, E680, EL632, F370, G687, L320, N25, P210, UM117 (PD), VU806, W579
>> H-3   Hbl-33, 80; Chr-143; Desc-93; Org-132
>> S-1   #293-296. Various treatments

"Spirit of the Living God" (2 Kgs, Gal)
> B244, C259, G288, N283, P322, SP131, UM393, VU376 SP131;
>> S-1   #212 Vocal descant idea

"Spirit of God, Descend upon My Heart" (2 Kgs, Gal)
> B245, C265, EL800, F147, G688, L486, N290, P326, UM500 (PD), VU378
>> H-3   Chr-175; Desc-77; Org-94
>> S-2   #125-128. Various treatments

"Swing Low, Sweet Chariot" (2 Kgs)
> C643, G825, UM703
>> H-3   Chr-177

"Holy Spirit, Truth Divine" (Gal)
> C241, EL398, L257, N63, P321, UM465 (PD), VU368
>> H-3   Chr-63, 100
>> S-1   #53. Descant

"O Jesus, I Have Promised" (Luke) (C)
> B276, C612, E655, EL810, F402, G724/725, L503, N493, P388/389, UM396 (PD), VU120
>> S-2   #9. Descant

Additional Hymn Suggestions

"O God, in a Mysterious Way" (2 Kgs, Pss)
> B73, E677, F603, G30, L483, N412, P270

"Children of the Heavenly Father" (2 Kgs, Pss)
> B55, EL781, F89, L474, N487, UM141

"Here I Am, Lord" (2 Kgs, Luke)
> C452, EL574, G69, P525, UM593, VU509

"Spirit Divine, Attend Our Prayers" (Gal)
> E509, G407, P325, VU385, W476

"O Master, Let Me Walk with Thee" (Gal)
> B279, C602, E659/660, EL818, F442, G738, L492, N503, P357, UM430 (PD), VU560

"Where Charity and Love Prevail" (Gal)
> E581, EL359, G316, L126, N396, UM549

"Healer of Our Every Ill" (Gal)
> C506, EL612, G795, S2213, SF2213, VU619

"In Remembrance of Me" (Gal, Comm.)
> B365, C403, G521, S2254

"I Want to Walk as a Child of the Light" (Luke)
> E490, EL815, G377, UM206, W510

"Jesus Calls Us" (Luke)
> B293, C337, EL696, G720, L494, N172, UM398, VU562

"Tú Has Venido a la Orilla" ("Lord, You Have Come to the Lakeshore") (Luke)
> C342, EL817, G721, N173, P377, UM344, VU563

"Lord, I Want to Be a Christian" (Luke)
> B489, C589, F421, G729, N454, P372 (PD), UM402

"The Summons" (Luke)
> EL798, G726, S2130, SF2130, VU567

"This Is My Song" (Independence Day)
> C722, EL887, G340, N591, UM437

"America the Beautiful" (Independence Day)
> B630, C720, E719, EL888 (PD), F690, G338, N594, P564, UM696, W763

Additional Contemporary Suggestions

"Days of Elijah" (1 Kgs)
> M139, WS3186

"Did You Feel the Mountains Tremble?" (2 Kgs)
> M69

"God of Wonders" (2 Kgs, Pss)
> M80, WS3034

"How Great Is Our God" (Pss)
> WS3003, M117

"Step by Step" (Pss, Luke)
> G743, M51, WS3004

"Amazing Grace" ("My Chains Are Gone") (Gal)
> M205, WS3104

"Holy Spirit, Come to Us" (Gal)
> EL406, G281, S2118, SF2118, W473

"Make Me a Channel of Your Peace" (Gal)
> G753, S2171, SF2171, VU684

"Live in Charity" ("*Ubi Caritas*") (Gal)
> C523, EL642, G205, S2179, SF2179, W604

"I've Got Peace Like a River" (Gal)
> B418, C530, G623, N478, P368, S2145, VU577

"Jesu, Jesu" (Gal)
> B501, C600, E602, EL708, G203, N498, P367, UM432, VU593, W431, S-1 #63. Vocal part

"Cry of My Heart" (Luke)
> M39, S2165, SF2165

"You Are Mine" (Luke)
> EL581, G177, S2218, SF2218

"We Walk His Way" (Luke)
> WS3073

"We Will Follow" ("*Somlandela*") (Luke)
> WS3160

"You're Worthy of My Praise" (Luke)
> M41

"Lead Me, Lord" (Luke)
> M108

Vocal Solos

"Swing Low, Sweet Chariot!" (2 Kgs)
> V-7   p. 36

"I Feel the Spirit Moving" (2 Kgs, Gal)
> V-3 (1)   p.22

"Because You Are God's Chosen Ones" (Gal)
> V-8   p. 286

Anthems

"Thou Didst Leave Thy Throne" (Luke)
Arr. Molly Ijames; Lorenz 10/5042SF
SATB and piano (bit.ly/10-5042SF)

"America the Beautiful" (Independence Day)
Arr. Michael McCarthy; MorningStar MSM-50-7075
SSAATBB with organ or brass quintet (bit.ly/50-7075)

Other Suggestions

Visuals:
> **O**   Tornado, mantel, parted water, torn clothes
> **P**   Prayer, arm, rain, clouds, storm, sea, Exodus
> **E**   Open shackles, love, brokenness, warning
> **G**   Jesus, fire, fox, nest, pillow, coffin, plow

Call to Worship: EL406, G281, S2118, SF2118, W473. "Holy Spirit, Come to Us" ("*Veni Sancte Spiritus*") (Gal)
Prayers: C89, F371, F511, N875, WSL182 (Gal, Luke)
Sung Benediction: WS3183. "As We Go" (2 Kgs, Luke)
Alternate Lessons: 1 Kgs 19:15-16, 19-21; Ps 16 (see p. 4)

2 Kings 5:1-14

Naaman, a general for the king of Aram, was a great man and highly regarded by his master, because through him the LORD had given victory to Aram. This man was a mighty warrior, but he had a skin disease. [2]Now Aramean raiding parties had gone out and captured a young girl from the land of Israel. She served Naaman's wife.

[3]She said to her mistress, "I wish that my master could come before the prophet who lives in Samaria. He would cure him of his skin disease." [4]So Naaman went and told his master what the young girl from the land of Israel had said.

[5]Then Aram's king said, "Go ahead. I will send a letter to Israel's king."

So Naaman left. He took along ten kikkars of silver, six thousand shekels of gold, and ten changes of clothing. [6]He brought the letter to Israel's king. It read, "Along with this letter I'm sending you my servant Naaman so you can cure him of his skin disease."

[7]When the king of Israel read the letter, he ripped his clothes. He said, "What? Am I God to hand out death and life? But this king writes me, asking me to cure someone of his skin disease! You must realize that he wants to start a fight with me."

[8]When Elisha the man of God heard that Israel's king had ripped his clothes, he sent word to the king: "Why did you rip your clothes? Let the man come to me. Then he'll know that there's a prophet in Israel."

[9]Naaman arrived with his horses and chariots. He stopped at the door of Elisha's house. [10]Elisha sent out a messenger who said, "Go and wash seven times in the Jordan River. Then your skin will be restored and become clean."

[11]But Naaman went away in anger. He said, "I thought for sure that he'd come out, stand and call on the name of the LORD his God, wave his hand over the bad spot, and cure the skin disease.[12]Aren't the rivers in Damascus, the Abana and the Pharpar, better than all Israel's waters? Couldn't I wash in them and get clean?" So he turned away and proceeded to leave in anger.

[13]Naaman's servants came up to him and spoke to him: "Our father, if the prophet had told you to do something difficult, wouldn't you have done it? All he said to you was, 'Wash and become clean.'" [14]So Naaman went down and bathed in the Jordan seven times, just as the man of God had said. His skin was restored like that of a young boy, and he became clean.

Psalm 30 (UM7762)

I exalt you, LORD, because you pulled me up; / you didn't let my enemies celebrate over me. / [2]LORD, my God, I cried out to you for help, / and you healed me. / [3]LORD, you brought me up from the grave, / brought me back to life from among those going down to the pit.

[4]You who are faithful to the LORD, / sing praises to him; / give thanks to his holy name! / [5]His anger lasts for only a second, / but his favor lasts a lifetime. / Weeping may stay all night, / but by morning, joy!

[6]When I was comfortable, I said, / "I will never stumble." / [7]Because it pleased you, LORD, / you made me a strong mountain. / But then you hid your presence. / I was terrified. / [8]I cried out to you, LORD. / I begged my Lord for mercy: / [9]"What is to be gained by my spilled blood, / by my going down into the pit? / Does dust thank you? / Does it proclaim your faithfulness? / [10]LORD, listen and have mercy on me! / LORD, be my helper!"

[11]You changed my mourning into dancing. / You took off my funeral clothes / and dressed me up in joy / [12]so that my whole being / might sing praises to you and never stop. / LORD, my God, I will give thanks to you forever.r.

Galatians 6:(1-6), 7-16

Brothers and sisters, if a person is caught doing something wrong, you who are spiritual should restore someone like this with a spirit of gentleness. Watch out for yourselves so you won't be tempted too. [2]Carry each other's burdens and so you will fulfill the law of Christ. [3]If anyone thinks they are important when they aren't, they're fooling themselves. [4]Each person should test their own work and be happy with doing a good job and not compare themselves with others. [5]Each person will have to carry their own load.

[6]Those who are taught the word should share all good things with their teacher. [7]Make no mistake, God is not mocked. A person will harvest what they plant. [8]Those who plant only for their own benefit will harvest devastation from their selfishness, but those who plant for the benefit of the Spirit will harvest eternal life from the Spirit. [9]Let's not get tired of doing good, because in time we'll have a harvest if we don't give up. [10]So then, let's work for the good of all whenever we have an opportunity, and especially for those in the household of faith.

[11]Look at the large letters I'm making with my own handwriting! [12]Whoever wants to look good by human standards will try to get you to be circumcised, but only so they won't be harassed for the cross of Christ. [13]Those who are circumcised don't observe the Law themselves, but they want you to be circumcised, so they can boast about your physical body.

[14]But as for me, God forbid that I should boast about anything except for the cross of our LORD Jesus Christ. The world has been crucified to me through him, and I have been crucified to the world. [15]Being circumcised or not being circumcised doesn't mean anything. What matters is a new creation. [16]May peace and mercy be on whoever follows this rule and on God's Israel.

[17]From now on, no one should bother me because I bear the marks of Jesus on my body.

Luke 10:1-11, 16-20

After these things, the Lord commissioned seventy-two others and sent them on ahead in pairs to every city and place he was about to go. [2]He said to them, "The harvest is bigger than you can imagine, but there are few workers. Therefore, plead with the Lord of the harvest to send out workers for his harvest. [3]Go! Be warned, though, that I'm sending you out as lambs among wolves. [4]Carry no wallet, no bag, and no sandals. Don't even greet anyone along the way. [5]Whenever you enter a house, first say, 'May peace be on this house.' [6]If anyone there shares God's peace, then your peace will rest on that person. If not, your blessing will return to you. [7]Remain in this house, eating and drinking whatever they set before you, for workers deserve their pay. Don't move from house to house. [8]Whenever you enter a city and its people welcome you, eat what they set before you. [9]Heal the sick who are there, and say to them, 'God's kingdom has come upon you.' [10]Whenever you enter a city and the people don't welcome you, go out into the streets and say, [11]'As a complaint against you, we brush off the dust of your city that has collected on our feet. But know this: God's kingdom has come to you.' . . .

[16] Whoever listens to you listens to me. Whoever rejects you rejects me. Whoever rejects me rejects the one who sent me."

[17]The seventy-two returned joyously, saying, "Lord, even the demons submit themselves to us in your name."

[18]Jesus replied, "I saw Satan fall from heaven like lightning. [19]Look, I have given you authority to crush snakes and scorpions underfoot. I have given you authority over all the power of the enemy. Nothing will harm you. [20] Nevertheless, don't rejoice because the spirits submit to you. Rejoice instead that your names are written in heaven."

Primary Hymns and Songs for the Day

"Praise, My Soul, the King of Heaven" (2 Kgs, Pss) (O)
   B32, C23, E410, EL864/865, F339, G619/620, L549,
   P478/479, UM66 (PD), VU240, W530
>   H-3   Hbl-88; Chr-162; Desc-67; Org-75
>   S-1   #205. Harm.
>   #206. Descant

"Lord, You Give the Great Commission" (Luke) (O) or (C)
   C459, E528, EL579, G298, P429, UM584, VU512, W470
>   H-3   Hbl-61; Chr-132; Org-2
>   S-1   #4-5. Instrumental and Vocal Desc.

"In the Cross of Christ I Glory" (Pss, Gal)
   B554, C207, E441, EL324, F251, G213, L104, N193, P84,
   UM295
>   H-3   Hbl-72; Chr-113; Desc-89; Org-119
>   S-1   #276-277. Desc. and Harm.

"When I Survey the Wondrous Cross" (Gal)
   B144, C195, EL803, F258, G223, N224, P101, UM298
>   H-3   Hbl-6, 102; Chr-213; Desc-49; Org-49
>   S-1   #155. Descant
   E474, L482, G224, P100, UM299 (PD), VU149 (Fr.)
>   H-3   Hbl-47; Chr-214; Desc-90; Org-127
>   S-1   #288. Transposition to E-flat major

"Sent Out in Jesus' Name" ("*Enviado Soy de Dios*") (Luke) (C)
   EL538, G747, S2184, SF2184

Additional Hymn Suggestions

"I'm Gonna Live So God Can Use Me" (2 Kgs)
   C614, G700, P369, S2153, VU575
"Send Me, Lord" (2 Kgs, Luke)
   C447, EL809, G746, N360, UM497, VU572
"Wash, O God, Our Sons and Daughters" (2 Kgs, Baptism)
   C365, EL445, G490, UM605, VU442
"Called as Partners in Christ's Service" (Gal)
   C453, G761, N495, P343
"Holy God, We Praise Thy Name" (Gal)
   E366, F385, EL414 (PD), G4, L535, N276, P460, UM79,
   VU894 (Fr.), W524
"Jesus, the Very Thought of Thee" (Gal)
   B225, C102, E642, EL754, F465, G629, L316, N507, P310,
   UM175 (PD)
"Sing, My Tongue, the Glorious Battle" (Gal)
   E165/166, EL355/356, G225, L118, N220, UM296
"O Love That Wilt Not Let Me Go" (Gal)
   B292, C540, F404, G833, L324, N485, P384, UM480 (PD),
   VU658
"Blest Be the Tie That Binds" (Gal)
   B387, C433, EL656, F560, G306, L370, N393, P438, UM557
   (PD), VU602
"Lord, Dismiss Us with Thy Blessing" (Gal) (C)
   C439, E344, EL545, F520, G546, L259, N77, P538, UM671
   (PD), VU425
"Healer of Our Every Ill" (Gal, Luke)
   C506, EL612, G795, S2213, SF2213, VU619
"Come, Share the Lord" (Gal, Luke, Comm.)
   C408, G510, S2269, SF2269, VU469
"For the Fruits of This Creation" (Luke)
   B643, C714, E424, EL679, G36, L563, N425, P553, UM97,
   VU227, W562
"Here I Am, Lord" (Luke)
   C452, EL574, G69, P525, UM593, VU509
"The Summons" (Luke)
   EL798, G726, S2130, SF2130, VU567
"In Remembrance of Me" (Luke, Comm.)
   B365, C403, G521, S2254

"Go to the World" (Luke)
   G295, VU420, WS3158
"Let Us Talents and Tongues Employ" (Luke)
   C422, EL674, G526, N347, P514, VU468

Additional Contemporary Suggestions

"Spirit of the Living God" (2 Kgs)
   B244, C259, G288, N283, P322, SP131, UM393, VU376
"Water, River, Spirit, Grace" (2 Kgs, Baptism)
   C366, N169, S2253, SF2253
"In the Lord I'll Be Ever Thankful" (Pss)
   G654, S2195, SF2195
"Soon and Very Soon" (Pss)
   B192, EL439, G384, UM706, S-2 #187. Piano arr.
"Trading My Sorrows" (Pss)
   M75, WS3108
"Refresh My Heart" (Gal)
   M49
"Let It Be Said of Us" (Gal)
   M53
"The Wonderful Cross" (Gal)
   M76
"Make Us One" (Gal, Comm.)
   S2224, SF2224, SP137
"The Servant Song" (Gal)
   C490, EL659, G727, N539, S2222, SF2222, VU595
"Make Me a Channel of Your Peace" (Luke)
   G753, S2171, SF2171, VU684
"Song of Hope" (Luke)
   G765, P432, S2186, VU424
"With All of My Heart" (Luke)
   M86, SP187
"Days of Elijah" (Luke)
   M139, WS3186

Vocal Solos

"Standin' in de Need of Prayer" (2 Kgs, Pss)
>   V-7   p. 40
"Brighter than the Sun" (Gal, Baptism)
>   V-5(1)   p. 57
"Make Me a Channel of Your Peace" (Gal, Luke)
>   V-3 (2) p. 25
>   V-3 (3) p. 28

Anthems

"Psalm 30" (Pss)
Aaron David Miller; AEC-2 p. 71
Unison and piano

"When I Survey the Wondrous Cross" (Gal)
Amy Lynne Engelsdorfer; Augsburg 978-1-5064-2220-6
SAB and piano (bit.ly/2220-6)

Other Suggestions

Visuals:
>   **O**   Letter, torn clothes, healing, water/river
>   **P**   Oil/cruet, joy/dance, mourn/sackcloth
>   **E**   Pairs, harvest/workers, cross, butterfly/chrysalis
>   **G**   Oil, no. 70/pairs, harvest, lamb/wolf, ministry

Prayers: C209, F410, BN836, N844, WSL121 (Gal, Luke)
Alternate Lessons: Isa 66:10-14, Ps 66:1-9 (see p. 4)

Amos 7:7-17

[7]This is what the LORD showed me: The LORD was standing by a wall, with a plumb line in his hand. [8]The LORD said to me, "Amos, what do you see?"

"A plumb line," I said.

Then the LORD said,

"See, I am setting a plumb line
    in the middle of my people Israel.
        I will never again forgive them.
[9]The shrines of Isaac will be made desolate,
    and the holy places of Israel will be laid waste,
    and I will rise against the house of Jeroboam with the
        sword."

[10]Then Amaziah, the priest of Bethel, reported to Israel's King Jeroboam, "Amos has plotted against you within the house of Israel. The land isn't able to cope with everything that he is saying. [11]Amos has said, 'Jeroboam will die by the sword, and Israel will be forced out of its land.'"

[12]Amaziah said to Amos, "You who see things, go, run away to the land of Judah, eat your bread there, and prophesy there;[13]but never again prophesy at Bethel, for it is the king's holy place and his royal house."

[14]Amos answered Amaziah, "I am not a prophet, nor am I a prophet's son; but I am a shepherd, and a trimmer of sycamore trees. [15]But the LORD took me from shepherding the flock, and the LORD said to me, 'Go, prophesy to my people Israel.' [16]"Now then hear the LORD's word.

You say, 'Don't prophesy against Israel, and don't preach
    against the house of Isaac.'
[17]"Therefore, the LORD proclaims:
   'Your wife will become a prostitute in the city,
    and your sons and your daughters will fall by the sword,
    and your land will be measured and divided up;
  you yourself will die in an unclean land,
    and Israel will surely be taken away from its land.'"

Psalm 82 (UM804)

God takes his stand in the divine council;
    he gives judgment among the gods:
[2]"How long will you judge unjustly
    by granting favor to the wicked? *Selah*
[3]Give justice to the lowly and the orphan;
    maintain the right of the poor and the destitute!
[4]Rescue the lowly and the needy.
    Deliver them from the power of the wicked!
[5]They don't know; they don't understand;
    they wander around in the dark.
    All the earth's foundations shake.
[6]I hereby declare, "You are gods,
    children of the Most High—all of you!
[7]But you will die like mortals;
    you will fall down like any prince."
[8]Rise up, God! Judge the earth
    because you hold all nations in your possession!

Colossians 1:1-14

From Paul, an apostle of Christ Jesus by God's will, and Timothy our brother.

[2]To the holy and faithful brothers and sisters in Christ in Colossae.

Grace and peace to you from God our Father.

[3]We always give thanks to God, the Father of our Lord Jesus Christ, when we pray for you. [4]We've done this since we heard of your faith in Christ Jesus and your love for all God's people.[5]You have this faith and love because of the hope reserved for you in heaven. You previously heard about this hope through the true message, the good news, [6]which has come to you. This message has been bearing fruit and growing among you since the day you heard and truly understood God's grace, in the same way that it is bearing fruit and growing in the whole world. [7]You learned it from Epaphras, who is the fellow slave we love and Christ's faithful minister for your sake. [8]He informed us of your love in the Spirit.

[9]Because of this, since the day we heard about you, we haven't stopped praying for you and asking for you to be filled with the knowledge of God's will, with all wisdom and spiritual understanding. [10]We're praying this so that you can live lives that are worthy of the Lord and pleasing to him in every way: by producing fruit in every good work and growing in the knowledge of God; [11]by being strengthened through his glorious might so that you endure everything and have patience; [12]and by giving thanks with joy to the Father. He made it so you could take part in the inheritance, in light granted to God's holy people. [13]He rescued us from the control of darkness and transferred us into the kingdom of the Son he loves. [14]He set us free through the Son and forgave our sins.

Luke 10:25-37

[25]A legal expert stood up to test Jesus. "Teacher," he said, "what must I do to gain eternal life?"

[26]Jesus replied, "What is written in the Law? How do you interpret it?"

[27]He responded, "*You must love the Lord your God with all your heart, with all your being, with all your strength, and with all your mind, and love your neighbor as yourself.*"

[28]Jesus said to him, "You have answered correctly. Do this and you will live."

[29]But the legal expert wanted to prove that he was right, so he said to Jesus, "And who is my neighbor?"

[30]Jesus replied, "A man went down from Jerusalem to Jericho. He encountered thieves, who stripped him naked, beat him up, and left him near death. [31] Now it just so happened that a priest was also going down the same road. When he saw the injured man, he crossed over to the other side of the road and went on his way. [32] Likewise, a Levite came by that spot, saw the injured man, and crossed over to the other side of the road and went on his way. [33] A Samaritan, who was on a journey, came to where the man was. But when he saw him, he was moved with compassion. [34] The Samaritan went to him and bandaged his wounds, tending them with oil and wine. Then he placed the wounded man on his own donkey, took him to an inn, and took care of him. [35] The next day, he took two full days' worth of wages and gave them to the innkeeper. He said, 'Take care of him, and when I return, I will pay you back for any additional costs.' [36] What do you think? Which one of these three was a neighbor to the man who encountered thieves?"

[37]Then the legal expert said, "The one who demonstrated mercy toward him."

Jesus told him, "Go and do likewise."

Primary Hymns and Songs for the Day

"God of Grace and God of Glory" (Pss, Col) (O)
  B395, C464, E594/595, EL705, F528, G307, L415, N436,
  P420, UM577, VU686
      H-3   Hbl-25, 51, 58; Chr-89; Desc-26; Org-23
      S-1   #76-77. Desc. and Harm.
"Love the Lord Your God" (Luke)
  G62, S2168, SF2168
"The Summons" (Luke)
  EL798, G726, S2130, SF2130, VU567
      H-3   Chr-220
"*Pues Si Vivimos*" ("When We Are Living") (Col, Luke) (C)
  C536, EL639, G822, N499, P400, UM356, VU581
      S-1   #320. Orff Instr. Arr.
      H-3   Chr-218; Org-155

Additional Hymn Suggestions

"All Who Love and Serve Your City" (Amos)
  C670, E571, G351, P413, UM433
"Sent Out in Jesus' Name" ("*Enviado Soy de Dios*") (Amos) (C)
  EL538, G747, S2184, SF2184
"Why Stand So Far Away, My God?" (Amos, Pss)
  C671, G786, S2180, SF2180
"Dust and Ashes" (Amos, Pss)
  N186, VU105, WS3098
"Rejoice in God's Saints" (Amos, Col)
  C476, EL418, G732, UM708
"O For a World" (Amos, Luke)
  C683, G372, N575, P386, VU697
"O Master, Let Me Walk with Thee" (Col)
  B279, C602, E659/660, EL818, F442, G738, L492, N503,
  P357, UM430 (PD), VU560
"Open My Eyes, That I May See" (Col)
  B502, C586, F486, G451, P324, UM454, VU371
"Mothering God, You Gave Me Birth" (Col)
  C83, N467, S2050, SF2050, VU320
"Make Me a Channel of Your Peace" (Col, Luke)
  G753, S2171, SF2171, VU684
"Lord, I Want to Be a Christian" (Luke)
  B489, C589, F421, G729, N454, P372 (PD), UM402
"Where Cross the Crowded Ways of Life" (Luke)
  C665, E609, EL719, F665, G343, L429, N543, P408, UM427
  (PD), VU681
"*Cuando El Pobre*" ("When the Poor Ones") (Luke)
  C662, EL725, G762, P407, UM434, VU702
"Spirit of God, Descend upon My Heart" (Luke)
  B245, C265, EL800, F147, G688, L486, N290, P326, UM500
  (PD), VU378
"Healer of Our Every Ill" (Luke)
  C506, EL612, G795, S2213, SF2213, VU619
"In Remembrance of Me" (Luke, Comm.)
  B365, C403, G521, S2254

Additional Contemporary Suggestions

"Your Grace Is Enough" (Amos, Col, Luke)
  M191
"Give Thanks" (Pss, Col)
  C528, G647, S2036, SF2036, SP170
"In the Lord I'll Be Ever Thankful" (Col)
  G654, S2195, SF2195
"Let the Peace of God Reign" (Col)
  M87
"Make Me a Channel of Your Peace" (Luke)
  G753, S2171, SF2171, VU684

"Live in Charity" ("*Ubi Caritas*") (Luke)
  C523, EL642, G205, S2179, SF2179, W604
"The Family Prayer Song" ("As for Me and My House") (Luke)
  M54, S2188, SF2188
"*Jesu, Jesu*" (Luke)
  B501, C600, E602, EL708, G203, N498, P367, UM432,
  VU593, W431, S-1 #63. Vocal part
"Purify My Heart" (Luke)
  WS3103
"Love the Lord" (Luke)
  WS3116, M270
"Rule of Life" (Luke)
  AH4056, WS3117
"More Love, More Power" (Luke)
  M40
"You're Worthy of My Praise" (Luke)
  M41
"Refresh My Heart" (Luke)
  M49
"Let It Be Said of Us" (Luke)
  M53
"Rise Up and Praise Him" (Luke)
  M62
"Just Let Me Say" (Luke)
  M83
"With All of My Heart" (Luke)
  M86, SP187
"Take This Life" (Luke)
  M98

Vocal Solos

"Make Me a Channel of Your Peace" (Col, Luke)
  V-3 (2)   p. 25
  V-3 (3)   p. 28
"A Song About Me" (Luke)
  V-8   p. 364
"This Is My Commandment" (Luke)
  V-8   p. 284
"Spirit of God" (Luke)
  V-8   p. 170

Anthems

"*Enviado*: The Lord Now Sends Us Forth" (Amos)
Arr. Wold Augsburg 978-1-5067-2202-2
2-part and keyboard, opt. percussion (bit.ly/2202-2)

"Children of the Heavenly Father" (Col, Luke)
Arr. Eric Nelson; MorningStar MSM-50-6085
SATB and piano (bit.ly/50-6085)

Other Suggestions

Visuals:
  O   Wall, plumb line, sword, scales of justice
  P   Scales, ministry with poor, children, earthquake
  E   Pray, Bible, fruit/globe, joy, light, rescue
  G   Briefcase, bloody clothes, bandages, oil, wine, coins
Words of Assurance: G445, S2169, SF2169. "God, How Can We
  Forgive," stanza 2 (Luke)
Prayers: C31, N817, WSL78 (Col)
Prayers: F7624, N835, N861, WSL177 (Amos, Pss, Luke)
Alternate Lessons: Deut 30:9-14; Ps 25:1-10 (see p. 4)

Amos 8:1-12

This is what the LORD God showed me: a basket of summer fruit. ²He said, "Amos, what do you see?"
I said, "A basket of summer fruit."
Then the LORD said to me,
"The end has come upon my people Israel;
I will never again forgive them.
³On that day, the people will wail the temple songs,"
says the LORD God;
"there will be many corpses,
thrown about everywhere.
Silence."
⁴Hear this, you who trample on the needy and destroy
the poor of the land,
⁵saying,
"When will the new moon
be over so that we may sell grain,
and the Sabbath
so that we may offer wheat for sale,
make the ephah smaller, enlarge the shekel,
and deceive with false balances,
⁶in order to buy the needy for silver
and the helpless for sandals,
and sell garbage as grain?"
⁷The LORD has sworn by the pride of Jacob:
Surely I will never forget what they have done.
⁸Will not the land tremble on this account,
and all who live in it mourn,
as it rises and overflows like the Nile,
and then falls again, like the River of Egypt?
⁹On that day, says the LORD God,
I will make the sun go down at noon,
and I will darken the earth in broad daylight.
¹⁰I will turn your feasts into sad affairs
and all your singing into a funeral song;
I will make people wear mourning clothes
and shave their heads;
I will make it like the loss of an only child,
and the end of it like a bitter day.
¹¹The days are surely coming, says the LORD God,
when I will send hunger and thirst on the land;
neither a hunger for bread, nor a thirst for water,
but of hearing the LORD 's words.
¹²They will wander from sea to sea,
and from north to east;
they will roam all around, seeking the LORD's word,
but they won't find it.

Psalm 52

Hey, powerful person!
Why do you brag about evil?
God's faithful love lasts all day long.
²Your tongue devises destruction:
it's like a sharpened razor, causing deception.
³You love evil more than good;
you love lying more than speaking what is right. *Selah*
⁴You love all destructive words;
you love the deceiving tongue.
⁵But God will take you down permanently;
he will snatch you up,
tear you out of your tent,
and uproot you from the land of the living! *Selah*
⁶The righteous will see and be in awe;
they will laugh at those people:

⁷"Look at them! They didn't make God their refuge.
Instead, they trusted in their own great wealth.
They sought refuge in it—to their own destruction!"
⁸But I am like a green olive tree in God's house;
I trust in God's faithful love forever and always.
⁹I will give thanks to you, God, forever,
because you have acted.
In the presence of your faithful people,
I will hope in your name because it's so good.

Colossians 1:15-28

¹⁵The Son is the image of the invisible God,
the one who is first over all creation,
¹⁶Because all things were created by him:
both in the heavens and on the earth,
the things that are visible and the things that are invisible.
Whether they are thrones or powers,
or rulers or authorities,
all things were created through him and for him.
¹⁷He existed before all things,
and all things are held together in him.
¹⁸He is the head of the body, the church,
who is the beginning,
the one who is firstborn from among the dead
so that he might occupy the first place in everything.
¹⁹Because all the fullness of God was pleased to live in him,
²⁰and he reconciled all things to himself through him—
whether things on earth or in the heavens.
He brought peace through the blood of his cross.

²¹Once you were alienated from God and you were enemies with him in your minds, which was shown by your evil actions. ²²But now he has reconciled you by his physical body through death, to present you before God as a people who are holy, faultless, and without blame. ²³But you need to remain well established and rooted in faith and not shift away from the hope given in the good news that you heard. This message has been preached throughout all creation under heaven. And I, Paul, became a servant of this good news.

²⁴Now I'm happy to be suffering for you. I'm completing what is missing from Christ's sufferings with my own body. I'm doing this for the sake of his body, which is the church. ²⁵I became a servant of the church by God's commission, which was given to me for you, in order to complete God's word. ²⁶I'm completing it with a secret plan that has been hidden for ages and generations but which has now been revealed to his holy people. ²⁷God wanted to make the glorious riches of this secret plan known among the Gentiles, which is Christ living in you, the hope of glory. ²⁸This is what we preach as we warn and teach every person with all wisdom so that we might present each one mature in Christ.

Luke 10:38-42

³⁸While Jesus and his disciples were traveling, Jesus entered a village where a woman named Martha welcomed him as a guest. ³⁹She had a sister named Mary, who sat at the Lord's feet and listened to his message. ⁴⁰By contrast, Martha was preoccupied with getting everything ready for their meal. So Martha came to him and said, "Lord, don't you care that my sister has left me to prepare the table all by myself? Tell her to help me."

⁴¹The Lord answered, "Martha, Martha, you are worried and distracted by many things. ⁴² One thing is necessary. Mary has chosen the better part. It won't be taken away from her."

Primary Hymns and Songs for the Day

"Immortal, Invisible, God Only Wise" (Col) (O)
  B6, C66, E423, EL834, F319, G12, L526, N1, P263, UM103
  (PD), VU264, W512
        H-3   Hbl-15, 71; Chr-65; Desc-93; Org-135
        S-1   #300. Harm.
"All Who Love and Serve Your City" (Amos, Luke)
  C670, E571, G351, P413, UM433
        H-3   Chr-26, 65; Org-19
        S-1   #62. Descant
"The Church's One Foundation" (Col) (C)
  B350, C272, E525, EL654, F547, G321, L369, N386, P442,
  UM545/546, VU332 (Fr.)
        H-3   Hbl-94; Chr-180; Desc-16; Org-9
        S-1   #25-26. Desc. and Harm.

Additional Hymn Suggestions

"God of the Ages" ("God of Our Fathers") (Amos)
  B629, C725, E718, G331, L567, N592, P262, UM698
"My Lord, What a Morning" (Amos)
  C708, EL438 (PD), G352, P449, UM719, VU708
"What Does the Lord Require of You" (Amos)
  C661, G70, S2174, SF2174, VU701
"Why Stand So Far Away, My God?" (Amos, Pss)
  C671, G786, S2180, SF2180
"Dust and Ashes" (Amos, Pss)
  N186, VU105, WS3098
"Of the Father's Love Begotten" (Amos, Col)
  B251, C104, E82, EL295, F172 (PD), G108, L42, N118, P309,
  UM184, VU61, W398
"I Will Trust in the Lord" (Pss)
  B420, N416, UM464
"To God Be the Glory" (Col)
  B4, C72, F363, G634, P485, UM98 (PD)
"Hope of the World" (Col)
  C538, E472, G734, L493, N46, P360, UM178, VU215
"In the Cross of Christ I Glory" (Col)
  B554, C207, E441, EL324, F251, G213, L104, N193, P84,
  UM295
"Alas! and Did My Savior Bleed" (Col)
  B145, EL337, F274, G212, L98, N200, P78, UM294 (PD)
  B139, C204, N199, UM359 (PD) (alternate tune)
"Open My Eyes, That I May See" (Col)
  B502, C586, F486, G451, P324, UM454, VU371
"Blest Be the Tie That Binds" (Col)
  B387, C433, EL656, F560, G309, L370, N393, P438, UM557
  (PD), VU602
"Christ Is Made the Sure Foundation" (Col)
  C275, E518, EL645, G394, P416, UM559 (PD), VU325
"Christ Beside Me" (Col)
  G702, S2166, SF2166
"Come, Share the Lord" (Col, Comm.)
  C408, G510, S2269, SF2269, VU469
"Woman in the Night" (Luke)
  C188, G161, UM274
"Forgive Our Sins as We Forgive" (Luke)
  E674, EL605, G444, L307, P347, UM390, VU364
"Be Thou My Vision" (Luke)
  B60, C595, E488, EL793, F468, G450, N451, P339, UM451,
  VU642
"Jesus, Priceless Treasure" (Luke)
  E701, EL775, F277, G830, L457, N480 P365, UM532 (PD),
  VU667 and VU668 (Fr.)
"I'm Gonna Live So God Can Use Me" (Luke)
  C614, G700, P369, S2153, VU575

"Together We Serve" (Luke)
  G767, S2175, SF2175

Additional Contemporary Suggestions

"Come to the Water" (Amos)
  WS3114
"You Are Good" (Pss)
  M124, WS3014
"Forever" (Pss)
  M68, WS3023
"Hallelujah" ("Your Love Is Amazing") (Pss)
  M118, WS3027
"Your Love, Oh Lord" (Pss)
  M189
"More Precious than Silver" (Pss, Luke)
  S2065, SF2065, SP99
"Sanctuary" (Col)
  G701, M52, S2164, SF2164
"Shine, Jesus, Shine" (Col)
  B579, EL671, G192, S2173, SF2173, SP142
"Holy Ground" (Col)
  B224, C112, G406, S2272, SF2272, SP86
"The Jesus in Me" (Col)
  AH4109, WS3151
"That's Why We Praise Him" (Col)
  M94
"Every Move I Make" (Luke)
  M122
"Jesus, Draw Me Close" (Luke)
  M48, S2159, SF2159
"Turn Your Eyes upon Jesus" (Luke)
  B320, F621, SP218, UM349

Vocal Solos

"It Is Well with My Soul" (Col)
  V-5(2)   p. 35
"Christ Living Within You" (Col)
  V-8   p. 177
"Be Thou My Vision" (Col, Luke)
  V-6   p. 13

Anthems

"Walking on Our Way with God" (Amos)
Jayne Southwick Cool; AEC-3 p. 78
2-part mixed and piano

"O Christ, Surround Me" (Col)
Arr. David Sims; Augsburg 978-1-5064-2210-7
SATB and piano (bit.ly/2210-7)

Other Suggestions

Visuals:
        O   Basket/fruit, new moon, silver, sandals, sackcloth
        P   Uprooted tree, wealth, olive tree, joy, laugh
        E   Risen Christ, glue, blood/cross, service
        G   Pots/pans, dust cloth, mop, dishes, Jesus/two women
Greeting and Opening Prayer: N824 and N830 (Col)
Sung Confession: E148, UM450. Creator of the Earth and Skies
  (Amos)
Readings: C271, F233, F445, WSL76, UM888 (Col)
Alternate Lessons: Gen 18:1-10a; Ps 15 (see p. 4)

Hosea 1:2-10

²When the LORD first spoke through Hosea, the LORD said to him, "Go, marry a prostitute and have children of prostitution, for the people of the land commit great prostitution by deserting the LORD." ³So Hosea went and took Gomer, Diblaim's daughter, and she became pregnant and bore him a son. ⁴The LORD said to him, "Name him Jezreel; for in a little while I will punish the house of Jehu for the blood of Jezreel, and I will destroy the kingdom of the house of Israel. ⁵On that day I will break the bow of Israel in the Jezreel Valley." ⁶Gomer became pregnant again and gave birth to a daughter. Then the LORD said to Hosea, "Name her No Compassion, because I will no longer have compassion on the house of Israel or forgive them. ⁷But I will have compassion on the house of Judah. I, the LORD their God, will save them; I will not save them by bow, or by sword, or by war, or by horses, or by horsemen." ⁸When Gomer finished nursing No Compassion, she became pregnant and gave birth to a son. ⁹Then the LORD said, "Name him Not My People because you are not my people, and I am not your God."

¹⁰Yet the number of the people of Israel will be like the sand of the sea, which can be neither measured nor numbered; and in the place where it was said to them, "You are not my people," it will be said to them, "Children of the living God."

Psalm 85 (UM806)

LORD, you've been kind to your land;
> you've changed Jacob's circumstances for the better.

²You've forgiven your people's wrongdoing;
> you've covered all their sins. *Selah*

³You've stopped being furious;
> you've turned away from your burning anger.

⁴You, the God who can save us, restore us!
> Stop being angry with us!

⁵Will you be mad at us forever?
> Will you prolong your anger from one generation to the next?

⁶Won't you bring us back to life again
> so that your people can rejoice in you?

⁷Show us your faithful love, LORD!
> Give us your salvation!

⁸Let me hear what the LORD God says,
> because he speaks peace to his people and to his faithful ones.
> Don't let them return to foolish ways.

⁹God's salvation is very close to those who honor him
> so that his glory can live in our land.

¹⁰Faithful love and truth have met;
> righteousness and peace have kissed.

¹¹Truth springs up from the ground;
> righteousness gazes down from heaven.

¹²Yes, the LORD gives what is good,
> and our land yields its produce.

¹³Righteousness walks before God,
> making a road for his steps.

Colossians 2:6-15 (16-19)

⁶So live in Christ Jesus the Lord in the same way as you received him. ⁷Be rooted and built up in him, be established in faith, and overflow with thanksgiving just as you were taught. ⁸See to it that nobody enslaves you with philosophy and foolish deception, which conform to human traditions and the way the world thinks and acts rather than Christ. ⁹All the fullness of deity lives in Christ's body. ¹⁰And you have been filled by him, who is the head of every ruler and authority. ¹¹You were also circumcised by him. This wasn't performed by human hands—the whole body was removed through this circumcision by Christ. ¹²You were buried with him through baptism and raised with him through faith in the power of God, who raised him from the dead. ¹³When you were dead because of the things you had done wrong and because your body wasn't circumcised, God made you alive with Christ and forgave all the things you had done wrong. ¹⁴He destroyed the record of the debt we owed, with its requirements that worked against us. He canceled it by nailing it to the cross. ¹⁵When he disarmed the rulers and authorities, he exposed them to public disgrace by leading them in a triumphal parade.

¹⁶So don't let anyone judge you about eating or drinking or about a festival, a new moon observance, or sabbaths. ¹⁷These religious practices are only a shadow of what was coming—the body that cast the shadow is Christ. ¹⁸Don't let anyone who wants to practice harsh self-denial and worship angels rob you of the prize. They go into detail about what they have seen in visions and have become unjustifiably arrogant by their selfish way of thinking. ¹⁹They don't stay connected to the head. The head nourishes and supports the whole body through the joints and ligaments, so the body grows with a growth that is from God.

Luke 11:1-13

Jesus was praying in a certain place. When he finished, one of his disciples said, "Lord, teach us to pray, just as John taught his disciples."

²Jesus told them, "When you pray, say:
'Father, uphold the holiness of your name.
Bring in your kingdom.
³Give us the bread we need for today.
⁴Forgive us our sins,
 for we also forgive everyone who has wronged us.
And don't lead us into temptation.'"

⁵He also said to them, "Imagine that one of you has a friend and you go to that friend in the middle of the night. Imagine saying, 'Friend, loan me three loaves of bread ⁶because a friend of mine on a journey has arrived and I have nothing to set before him.' ⁷Imagine further that he answers from within the house, 'Don't bother me. The door is already locked, and my children and I are in bed. I can't get up to give you anything.' ⁸I assure you, even if he wouldn't get up and help because of his friendship, he will get up and give his friend whatever he needs because of his friend's brashness. ⁹And I tell you: Ask and you will receive. Seek and you will find. Knock and the door will be opened to you. ¹⁰Everyone who asks, receives. Whoever seeks, finds. To everyone who knocks, the door is opened.

¹¹"Which father among you would give a snake to your child if the child asked for a fish? ¹² If a child asked for an egg, what father would give the child a scorpion? ¹³ If you who are evil know how to give good gifts to your children, how much more will the heavenly Father give the Holy Spirit to those who ask him?"

Primary Hymns and Songs for the Day

"The Church's One Foundation" (Col) (O)
    B350, C272, E525, EL654, F547, G321, L369, N386, P442,
    UM545/546, VU332 (Fr.)
        H-3   Hbl-94; Chr-180; Desc-16; Org-9
        S-1   #25-26. Desc. and Harm.
"God, How Can We Forgive" (Hos, Pss, Luke)
    G445, S2169, SF2169
        H-3   Hbl-62, 95; Chr-59; Org-77
        S-1   #211. Harm.
"Seek Ye First" (Luke)
    B478, C354, E711, G175, P333, UM405, SP182, VU356
"The Lord's Prayer" (Luke)
    B462, C307-C310, F440, G464, P589, S2278, SF2278. UM271,
    WS3068-WS3071
"O Master, Let Me Walk with Thee" (Col) (C)
    B279, C602, E659/660, EL818, F442, G738, L492, N503,
    P357, UM430 (PD), VU560
        H-3   Hbl-81; Chr-147; Desc-74; Org-87
        S-2   #118. Descant

Additional Hymn Suggestions

"Alleluia! Sing to Jesus!" (Hos)
    C233, E460/461, EL392, G260, N257, P144, W737
"Holy God, We Praise Thy Name" (Hos)
    E366, F385, EL414 (PD), G4, L535, N276, P460, UM79,
    VU894 (Fr.), W524
"Why Stand So Far Away, My God?" (Hos, Pss)
    C671, G786, S2180, SF2180
"How Long, O Lord" (Hos, Pss)
    G777, S2209, SF2209
"Lead On, O Cloud of Presence" (Hos, Pss)
    C633, S2234, SF2234, VU421
"Forgive Our Sins as We Forgive" (Pss, Col, Luke)
    E674, EL605, G444, L307, P347, UM390, VU364
"A Mighty Fortress Is Our God" (Col)
    B8, C65, E687/688, EL503/504/505, F118, G275, L228/229,
    N439/440, P259/260, UM110 (PD), VU261/262/263,
    W575/576
"Jesus, the Very Thought of Thee" (Col)
    B225, C102, E642, EL754, F465, G629, L316, N507, P310,
    UM175 (PD)
"I Want Jesus to Walk with Me" (Col)
    B465, C627, EL325, G775, N490, P363, UM521
"What a Friend We Have in Jesus" (Col)
    B182, C585, EL742, F466, G465, L439, N506, P403, UM526
    (PD), VU661
"Christ Is Made the Sure Foundation" (Col)
    C275, E518, EL645, G394, P416, UM559 (PD), VU325
"We Know That Christ Is Raised" (Col, Baptism)
    E296, EL449, G485, L189, P495, UM610, VU448, W721
"Come, Share the Lord" (Col, Luke, Comm.)
    C408, G510, S2269, SF2269, VU469
"Somebody's Knockin' at Your Door" (Col, Luke)
    G728, P382, W415, WS3095
"There's a Spirit in the Air" (Luke)
    B393, C257, N294, P433, UM192, VU582, W531
"Take My Life, and Let It Be" (Luke)
    B277/283, C609, E707, EL583/685, G697, L406, P391, N448,
    UM399 (PD), VU506
"Prayer Is the Soul's Sincere Desire" (Luke)
    F446 (PD), N508, UM492
"Spirit of God, Descend upon My Heart" (Luke)
    B245, C265, EL800, F147, G688, L486, N290, P326, UM500
    (PD), VU378

"For the Bread Which You Have Broken" (Luke)
    C411, E340/341, EL494, G516, L200, P508/509,
    UM614/615, VU470
"We Walk by Faith" (Luke)
    E209, EL635, G817, N256, P399, S2196, SF2196, W572

Additional Contemporary Suggestions

"Revive Us, Oh Lord" (Pss)
    SP146
"Refresh My Heart" (Pss)
    M49
"Light the Fire Again" (Pss)
    M144
"Move Me Again" (Pss)
    M145
"Salvation Is Here" (Pss)
    M242
"You Are My All in All" (Col, Luke)
    G519, SP220, WS3040
"God Is So Good" (Luke)
    B23, G658, S2056, SF2056
"Make Me a Channel of Your Peace" (Luke)
    G753, S2171, SF2171, VU684
"Lord, Listen to Your Children" (Luke)
    EL752, S2207, SF2207
"This Kingdom" (Luke)
    M17
"When It's All Been Said and Done" (Luke)
    M115
"Step by Step" (Luke)
    G743, M51, WS3004
"Breathe" (Luke)
    M61, WS3112

Vocal Solos

"It Is Well with My Soul" (Col)
    V-5(2)   p. 35
"The Lord's Prayer" (Luke)
    V-8   p. 39
"O Father in Heaven" (Luke)
    V-8   p. 122

Anthems

"I Want Jesus to Walk with Me" (Col)
Arr. Bryan L. Greer; Hinshaw HMC2463
SATB and piano (bit.ly/HMC2463)

"Pater noster" ("Lord's Prayer") (Luke)
Jacob Handl; CPDL (bit.ly/JHandlPN)
SSAA-TTBB a cappella (bit.ly/PaterHandl)

Other Suggestions

Visuals:
    O   Broken bow, newborn, sand
    P   Revival, kiss, growing plants, sky, harvest, path
    E   Roots, building, Christ, cross/crown, eraser
    G   Jesus, pray, three loaves, lock, open door, gifts, Trinity
Response: EL751, G471, S2200, SF2200. "O Lord, Hear My
    Prayer" (Luke)
Sung Confession: G544, S2013, SF2013. "Bless the Lord" (Hos)
Alternate Lessons: Gen 18:20-32, Ps 138 (see p. 4)

Hosea 11:1-11

When Israel was a child, I loved him,
  and out of Egypt I called my son.
[2]The more I called them,
  the further they went from me;
  they kept sacrificing to the Baals,
  and they burned incense to idols.
[3]Yet it was I who taught Ephraim to walk;
  I took them up in my arms,
  but they did not know that I healed them.
[4]I led them
  with bands of human kindness,
  with cords of love.
  I treated them like those
  who lift infants to their cheeks;
  I bent down to them and fed them.
[5]They will return to the land of Egypt,
  and Assyria will be their king,
  because they have refused to return to me.
[6]The sword will strike wildly in their cities;
  it will consume the bars of their gates
  and will take everything because of their schemes.
[7]My people are bent on turning away from me;
  and though they cry out to the Most High,
  he will not raise them up.
[8]How can I give you up, Ephraim?
  How can I hand you over, Israel?
  How can I make you like Admah?
  How can I treat you like Zeboiim?
  My heart winces within me;
  my compassion grows warm and tender.
[9]I won't act on the heat of my anger;
  I won't return to destroy Ephraim;
  for I am God and not a human being,
  the holy one in your midst;
  I won't come in harsh judgment.
[10]They will walk after the LORD,
  who roars like a lion.
  When he roars,
  his children will come trembling from the west.
[11]They will come trembling like a bird,
  and like a dove from the land of Assyria;
  and I will return them to their homes, says the LORD.

Psalm 107:1-9, 43 (UM830)

"Give thanks to the LORD because he is good,
  because his faithful love lasts forever!"
[2]That's what those who are redeemed by the LORD say,
  the ones God redeemed from the power of their enemies,
  [3]the ones God gathered from various countries,
  from east and west, north and south.
[4]Some of the redeemed had wandered into the desert, into the
    wasteland.
  They couldn't find their way to a city or town.
[5]They were hungry and thirsty;
  their lives were slipping away.
[6]So they cried out to the LORD in their distress,
  and God delivered them from their desperate circumstances.
  [7]God led them straight to human habitation.
  [8]Let them thank the LORD for his faithful love
  and his wondrous works for all people,
  [9]because God satisfied the one who was parched with thirst,
  and he filled up the hungry with good things!
. . . .
[43]Whoever is wise will pay attention to these things,
  carefully considering the LORD's faithful love.

Colossians 3:1-11

Therefore, if you were raised with Christ, look for the things that are above where Christ is sitting at God's right side. [2]Think about the things above and not things on earth. [3]You died, and your life is hidden with Christ in God. [4]When Christ, who is your life, is revealed, then you also will be revealed with him in glory.

[5]So put to death the parts of your life that belong to the earth, such as sexual immorality, moral corruption, lust, evil desire, and greed (which is idolatry). [6]The wrath of God is coming upon disobedient people because of these things. [7]You used to live this way, when you were alive to these things. [8]But now set aside these things, such as anger, rage, malice, slander, and obscene language. [9]Don't lie to each other. Take off the old human nature with its practices [10]and put on the new nature, which is renewed in knowledge by conforming to the image of the one who created it. [11]In this image there is neither Greek nor Jew, circumcised nor uncircumcised, barbarian, Scythian, slave nor free, but Christ is all things and in all people.

Luke 12:13-21

[13]Someone from the crowd said to him, "Teacher, tell my brother to divide the inheritance with me."

[14]Jesus said to him, "Man, who appointed me as judge or referee between you and your brother?"

[15]Then Jesus said to them, "Watch out! Guard yourself against all kinds of greed. After all, one's life isn't determined by one's possessions, even when someone is very wealthy." [16]Then he told them a parable: "A certain rich man's land produced a bountiful crop. [17] He said to himself, What will I do? I have no place to store my harvest! [18] Then he thought, Here's what I'll do. I'll tear down my barns and build bigger ones. That's where I'll store all my grain and goods. [19] I'll say to myself, You have stored up plenty of goods, enough for several years. Take it easy! Eat, drink, and enjoy yourself. [20] But God said to him, 'Fool, tonight you will die. Now who will get the things you have prepared for yourself?' [21] This is the way it will be for those who hoard things for themselves and aren't rich toward God."

Primary Hymns and Songs for the Day

"Sing Praise to God Who Reigns Above" (Hos) (O)
  B20, C6, E408, EL871, F343, G645, N6, P483, UM126 (PD),
  VU216, W528
    H-3   Hbl-92; Chr-173; Desc-76; Org-91
    S-1   #237. Descant
"Loving Spirit" (Hos, Pss)
  C244, EL397, G293, P323, S2123, SF2123, VU387
    H-3   Chr-67
    S-2   #63-64. Desc. and Harm.
"All Who Love and Serve Your City" (Luke)
  C670, E571, G351, P413, UM433
    H-3   Chr-26, 65; Org-19
    S-1   #62. Descant
"Now Thank We All Our God" (Hos, Pss, Col) (C)
  B638, C715, E396/397, EL839/840, F525, G643, L533 or
  L534, N419, P555, UM102 (PD), VU236 (Fr.), W560
    H-3   Hbl-78; Chr-140; Desc-81; Org-98
    S-1   #252-254. Various treatments

Additional Hymn Suggestions

"Guide Me, O Thou Great Jehovah" (Hos, Pss)
  B56, C622, E690, EL618, F608, G65, L343, N18/19, P281,
  UM127 (PD), VU651 (Fr.)
"Great Is Thy Faithfulness" (Hos, Pss)
  B54, C86, EL733, G39, N423, P276, UM140, VU288
"Like a Mother Who Has Borne Us" (Hos, Luke)
  G44, N583
"Let Us with a Joyful Mind" (Pss, Col)
  E389, G31, L521. N16, P244, S2012, SF2012, VU234
"At the Name of Jesus" (Col)
  B198, E435, EL416, F351, G264, L179, P148, UM168, VU335,
  W499
"*Pues Si Vivimos*" ("When We Are Living") (Col)
  C536, EL639, G822, N499, P400, UM356, VU581
"Rock of Ages, Cleft for Me" (Col)
  B342, C214, E685, EL623, G438, L327, N596, UM361
"I Come with Joy" (Col, Comm.)
  B371, C420, E304, EL482, G515, N349, P507, UM617,
  VU477, W726
"One Bread, One Body" (Col, Comm.)
  C393, EL496, G530, UM620, VU467
"Come, Share the Lord" (Col, Comm.)
  C408, G510, S2269, SF2269, VU469
"Lord Jesus, Think on Me" (Col)
  E641, EL599 (PD), G417, L309, P301, VU607
"God, Whose Giving Knows No Ending" (Col, Luke)
  C606, F513, G716, L408, N565, P422, W631
"Take My Life, and Let It Be" (Col, Luke)
  B277/283, C609, E707, EL583/685, G697, L406, P391, N448,
  UM399 (PD), VU506
"In Christ There Is No East or West" (Col, Luke)
  B385, C687, E529, EL650 (PD), F685, G317/318, L359,
  N394/395, P439/440, UM548, VU606, W659
"*Cuando El Pobre*" ("When the Poor Ones") (Luke)
  C662, EL725, G762, P407, UM434, VU702

Additional Contemporary Suggestions

"Desert Song" (Hos, Pss)
  M262
"We Bring the Sacrifice of Praise" (Pss)
  S2031, SF2031, SP1
"Give Thanks" (Pss)
  C528, G647, S2036, SF2036, SP170
"Forever" (Pss)
  M68, WS3023
"Hallelujah" ("Your Love Is Amazing") (Pss)
  M118, WS3027

"Shout to the North" (Pss)
  G319, M99, WS3042
"Falling on My Knees" ("Hungry") (Pss)
  M155, WS3099
"You Are Good" (Pss)
  M124, WS3014
"All Who Are Thirsty" (Pss)
  M159
"Enough" (Pss)
  M160
"Your Love, Oh Lord" (Pss)
  M189
"Knowing You" ("All I Once Held Dear") (Col)
  M30
"Jesus, You Are My Life" (Col)
  M33
"In the Secret" ("I Want to Know You") (Col)
  M38
"Let It Be Said of Us" (Col)
  M53
"Take My Life" (Col)
  M91
"Lord, You Have My Heart" (Col)
  M151
"Change My Heart, O God" (Col)
  EL801, G695, SP195, S2152, SF2152
"Jesus, Draw Me Close" (Col, Luke)
  M48, S2159, SF2159
"You Are My All in All" (Col, Luke)
  G519, SP220, WS3040
"Falling on My Knees" ("Hungry") (Luke)
  M155, WS3099
"Seek Ye First" (Luke)
  B478, C354, E711, G175, P333, UM405, SP182, VU356
"When It's All Been Said and Done" (Luke)
  M115
"Be the Centre" (Luke)
  M156
"I Will Boast" (Luke)
  M227

Vocal Solos

"Maybe the Rain" (Hos, Pss)
  V-5(2)   p. 27
"Take My Life" (Col, Luke)
  V-3 (3)   p. 17
  V-8   p. 262

Anthems

"I Come with Joy" (Col, Comm.)
Arr. Zebulon M. Highben; Augsburg 978-1-5064-2206-0
SAB and organ (bit.ly/2206-0)

"Treasures in Heaven" (Luke)
Pat Messick; Choristers Guild CGA1252
Unison/2-part and piano (bit.ly/CGA1252)

Other Suggestions

Visuals:
  O   Child, incense, cords/bands, heart, lion, birds/dove
  P   N/S/E/W, desert, food/drink, straight path, Ps 107:2a
  E   Christ, crown, Bible, baptism, white robe, open
          shackles
  G   Will, possessions, barns, grain, party, death
Sung Prayer: G544, S2013, SF2013."Bless the Lord" (Hos, Pss)
Prayers: C268, F643, N826, UM705, UM529 (Col)
Alternate Lessons: Eccl 1:2, 12-14; 2:18-23; Ps 49:1-12 (see p. 4)

Isaiah 1:1, 10-20

The vision about Judah and Jerusalem that Isaiah, Amoz's son, saw in the days of Judah's kings Uzziah, Jotham, Ahaz, and Hezekiah.

. . . .

¹⁰Hear the LORD's word, you leaders of Sodom.
    Listen to our God's teaching,
        people of Gomorrah!
¹¹What should I think about all your sacrifices?
    says the LORD.
I'm fed up with entirely burned offerings of rams
    and the fat of well-fed beasts.
    I don't want the blood of bulls, lambs, and goats.
¹²When you come to appear before me,
    who asked this from you,
        this trampling of my temple's courts?
¹³Stop bringing worthless offerings.
    Your incense repulses me.
New moon, sabbath, and the calling of an assembly—
    I can't stand wickedness with celebration!
¹⁴I hate your new moons and your festivals.
    They've become a burden that I'm tired of bearing.
¹⁵When you extend your hands,
    I'll hide my eyes from you.
Even when you pray for a long time,
    I won't listen.
Your hands are stained with blood.
¹⁶   Wash! Be clean!
Remove your ugly deeds from my sight.
    Put an end to such evil;
¹⁷   learn to do good.
Seek justice:
    help the oppressed;
    defend the orphan;
    plead for the widow.
¹⁸Come now, and let's settle this,
    says the LORD.
Though your sins are like scarlet,
    they will be white as snow.
If they are red as crimson,
    they will become like wool.
¹⁹If you agree and obey,
    you will eat the best food of the land.
²⁰But if you refuse and rebel,
    you will be devoured by the sword.
The LORD has said this.

Psalm 50:1-8, 22-23 (UM783)

From the rising of the sun to where it sets,
    God, the LORD God, speaks,
        calling out to the earth.
²From Zion, perfect in beauty,
    God shines brightly.
³Our God is coming;
    he won't keep quiet.
A devouring fire is before him;
    a storm rages all around him.
⁴God calls out to the skies above
    and to the earth in order to judge his people:
⁵"Bring my faithful to me,
    those who made a covenant with me by sacrifice."
⁶The skies proclaim his righteousness
    because God himself is the judge. *Selah*
⁷"Listen, my people, I will now speak;

Israel, I will now testify against you.
    I am God—your God!
⁸I'm not punishing you for your sacrifices
    or for your entirely burned offerings,
    which are always before me.

. . . .

²²So consider this carefully, all you who forget God,
    or I'll rip you to pieces with no one to deliver you:
²³The one who offers a sacrifice of thanksgiving is the one who
        honors me.
    And it is to the one who charts the correct path that I will
        show divine salvation."

Hebrews 11:1-3, 8-16

Faith is the reality of what we hope for, the proof of what we don't see. ²The elders in the past were approved because they showed faith.

³By faith we understand that the universe has been created by a word from God so that the visible came into existence from the invisible. . . .

⁸By faith Abraham obeyed when he was called to go out to a place that he was going to receive as an inheritance. He went out without knowing where he was going.

⁹By faith he lived in the land he had been promised as a stranger. He lived in tents along with Isaac and Jacob, who were coheirs of the same promise. ¹⁰He was looking forward to a city that has foundations, whose architect and builder is God.

¹¹By faith even Sarah received the ability to have a child, though she herself was barren and past the age for having children, because she believed that the one who promised was faithful. ¹²So descendants were born from one man (and he was as good as dead). They were as many as the number of the stars in the sky and as countless as the grains of sand on the seashore. ¹³All of these people died in faith without receiving the promises, but they saw the promises from a distance and welcomed them. They confessed that they were strangers and immigrants on earth. ¹⁴People who say this kind of thing make it clear that they are looking for a homeland. ¹⁵If they had been thinking about the country that they had left, they would have had the opportunity to return to it. ¹⁶But at this point in time, they are longing for a better country, that is, a heavenly one. Therefore, God isn't ashamed to be called their God—he has prepared a city for them.

Luke 12:32-40

³²"Don't be afraid, little flock, because your Father delights in giving you the kingdom. ³³Sell your possessions and give to those in need. Make for yourselves wallets that don't wear out—a treasure in heaven that never runs out. No thief comes near there, and no moth destroys. ³⁴Where your treasure is, there your heart will be too.

³⁵"Be dressed for service and keep your lamps lit. ³⁶ Be like people waiting for their master to come home from a wedding celebration, who can immediately open the door for him when he arrives and knocks on the door. ³⁷ Happy are those servants whom the master finds waiting up when he arrives. I assure you that, when he arrives, he will dress himself to serve, seat them at the table as honored guests, and wait on them. ³⁸ Happy are those whom he finds alert, even if he comes at midnight or just before dawn. ³⁹ But know this, if the homeowner had known what time the thief was coming, he wouldn't have allowed his home to be broken into. ⁴⁰ You also must be ready, because the Human One is coming at a time when you don't expect him."

Primary Hymns and Songs for the Day

"How Firm a Foundation" (Heb, Luke) (O)
  B338, C618, E636/637, EL796, F32, G463, L507, N407, P361, UM529 (PD), VU660, W585
    H-3   Hbl-27, 69; Chr-102; Desc-41; Org-41
    S-1   #133. Harm.
          #134. Performance note

"Faith, While Trees are Still in Blossom" (Heb)
  C535, UM508, VU643
    H-3   Chr-67
    S-2   #63-64. Desc. and Harm.

"Faith of Our Fathers" (Heb)
  B352, C635, EL812 and 813, F526, L500, N381, UM710 (PD), VU580, W571
    H-3   Hbl-57; Chr-63; Desc-93; Org-133

"O Day of God, Draw Nigh" (Luke) (C)
  B623, C700, E601, N611, P452, UM730 (PD), VU688/689
    H-3   Hbl-79; Chr-141; Desc-95; Org-143

Additional Hymn Suggestions

"O for a Closer Walk with God" (Isa)
  E684, G739, N450, P396

"What Does the Lord Require of You" (Isa)
  C661, G70, S2174, SF2174, VU701

"When God Restored Our Common Life" (Isa)
  G74, S2182, SF2182

"Gather Us In" (Pss, Comm.)
  C284, EL532, G401, S2236, SF2236, W665

"We've Come This Far by Faith" (Heb)
  AH4042, C533, EL633, G656

"Guide Me, O Thou Great Jehovah" (Heb)
  B56, C622, E690, EL618, F608, G65, L343, N18/19, P281, UM127 (PD), VU651 (Fr.)

"For All the Saints" (Heb)
  B355, C637, E287, EL422, F614, G326, L174, N299, P526, UM711 (PD), VU705, W705

"We Walk by Faith" (Heb)
  E209, EL635, G817, N256, P399, S2196, SF2196, W572

"Lift Every Voice and Sing" (Heb, Luke)
  B627, C631, E599, EL841, G339, N593, P563, UM519

"I Sing a Song of the Saints of God" (Heb, Luke)
  E293, G730, N295, P364, UM712 (PD)

"In Christ There Is No East or West" (Luke)
  B385, C687, E529, EL650 (PD), F685, G317/318, L359, N394/395, P439/440, UM548, VU606, W659

"God of Grace and God of Glory" (Luke)
  B395, C464, E594/595, EL705, F528, G307, L415, N436, P420, UM577, VU686

"The Church of Christ, in Every Age" (Luke)
  B402, C475, EL729, G320, L433, N306, P421, UM589, VU601, W626

"My Lord, What a Morning" (Luke)
  C708, EL438 (PD), G352, P449, UM719, VU708

"You Are Mine" (Luke)
  EL581, G177, S2218, SF2218

"Rejoice! Rejoice, Believers" (Luke)
  E68, EL244, G362, L25, P15

"God, Whose Giving Knows No Ending" (Luke)
  C606, F513, G716, L408, N565, P422, W631

Additional Contemporary Suggestions

"Song of Hope" (Isa)
  G765, P432, S2186, VU424

"Jesus Paid It All" (Isa)
  B134, F273, M244, WS3100

"The Heart of Worship" (Isa, Pss)
  M71

"From the Rising of the Sun" (Pss)
  G670, S2024, SF2024

"We Bring the Sacrifice of Praise" (Pss)
  S2031, SF2031, SP1

"Praise to the Lord" (Pss)
  EL844, S2029, SF2029, VU835

"God Is Here Today" ("Dios Está Aquí") (Pss)
  G411, S2049, SF2049

"What a Mighty God We Serve" (Pss)
  AH4022, SP3, WS3016

"Forever" (Pss)
  M68, WS3023

"I Stand Amazed" (Pss)
  M79

"It Is You" (Pss)
  M134

"I Will Not Forget You" (Pss)
  M211

"Seek Ye First" (Luke)
  B478, C354, E711, G175, P333, UM405, SP182, VU356

"You Are My All in All" (Luke)
  G519, SP220, WS3040

"Fill My Cup, Lord" (Luke)
  C351, F481, UM641, WS3093

"Somebody's Knockin' at Your Door" (Luke)
  G728, P382, W415, WS3095

"In Christ Alone" ("My Hope Is Found") (Luke)
  M138, WS3105

"When It's All Been Said and Done" (Luke)
  M115

"Sing to the King" (Luke)
  M141

"Be the Centre" (Luke)
  M156

Vocal Solos

"Spirit of Faith Come Down" (Heb)
  V-1   p. 43
"Seek Ye First" (Luke)
  V-8   p. 145

Anthems

"What Does the Lord Require of You?" (Isa)
Robert A. Hobby; MorningStar MSM-50-8330
SATB, flute/oboe, and keyboard (bit.ly/50-8330)

"A Living Faith" (Heb)
John Shepherd; Choristers Guild CGA580
Unison and keyboard (bit.ly/CGA580)

Other Suggestions

Visuals:
  O   Bloody hands, wash hands, scarlet/snow/wool
  P   Sunrise/set, fire, storm, heaven/earth, praise
  E   Creation, crowd, tents, T-square, baby, star/sand
  G   Flock, purse, wedding banquet, lit lamp, clock
Prayers: C567, UM676, N865, and F113 (Isa, Pss, Luke)
Prayers: N816, N818, WSL123 (Luke)
Alternate Lessons: Gen 15:1-6; Ps 33:12-22 (see p. 4)

Isaiah 5:1-7

Let me sing for my loved one
> a love song for his vineyard.

My loved one had a vineyard on a fertile hillside.
²He dug it,
> cleared away its stones,
> planted it with excellent vines,
> built a tower inside it,
> and dug out a wine vat in it.

He expected it to grow good grapes—
> but it grew rotten grapes.

³So now, you who live in Jerusalem, you people of Judah,
> judge between me and my vineyard:

⁴What more was there to do for my vineyard
> that I haven't done for it?

When I expected it to grow good grapes,
> why did it grow rotten grapes?

⁵Now let me tell you what I'm doing to my vineyard.

I'm removing its hedge,
> so it will be destroyed.

I'm breaking down its walls,
> so it will be trampled.

⁶I'll turn it into a ruin;
> it won't be pruned or hoed,
> and thorns and thistles will grow up.

I will command the clouds not to rain on it.

⁷The vineyard of the LORD of heavenly forces is the house of
> Israel,
> and the people of Judah are the plantings in which God
> delighted.

God expected justice, but there was bloodshed;
> righteousness, but there was a cry of distress!

Psalm 80:1-2, 8-19 (UM801)

Shepherd of Israel, listen!
> You, the one who leads Joseph as if he were a sheep.
> You, who are enthroned upon the winged heavenly
> creatures.

Show yourself ²before Ephraim, Benjamin, and Manasseh!
> Wake up your power!
> Come to save us!

. . . .

⁸You brought a vine out of Egypt.
> You drove out the nations and planted it.

⁹You cleared the ground for it;
> then it planted its roots deep, filling the land.

¹⁰The mountains were covered by its shade;
> the mighty cedars were covered by its branches.

¹¹It sent its branches all the way to the sea;
> its shoots went all the way to the Euphrates River.

¹²So why have you now torn down its walls
> so that all who come along can pluck its fruit,

¹³so that any boar from the forest can tear it up,
> so that the bugs can feed on it?

¹⁴Please come back, God of heavenly forces!
> Look down from heaven and perceive it!

Attend to this vine,
> ¹⁵this root that you planted with your strong hand,
> this son whom you secured as your very own.

¹⁶It is burned with fire. It is chopped down.
> They die at the rebuke coming from you.

¹⁷Let your hand be with the one on your right side—
> with the one whom you secured as your own—
> ¹⁸then we will not turn away from you!

Revive us so that we can call on your name.
> ¹⁹Restore us, LORD God of heavenly forces!
> Make your face shine so that we can be saved!

Hebrews 11:29–12:2

²⁹By faith they crossed the Red Sea as if they were on dry land, but when the Egyptians tried it, they were drowned.

³⁰By faith Jericho's walls fell after the people marched around them for seven days.

³¹By faith Rahab the prostitute wasn't killed with the disobedient because she welcomed the spies in peace.

³²What more can I say? I would run out of time if I told you about Gideon, Barak, Samson, Jephthah, David, Samuel, and the prophets. ³³Through faith they conquered kingdoms, brought about justice, realized promises, shut the mouths of lions, ³⁴put out raging fires, escaped from the edge of the sword, found strength in weakness, were mighty in war, and routed foreign armies. ³⁵Women received back their dead by resurrection. Others were tortured and refused to be released so they could gain a better resurrection.

³⁶But others experienced public shame by being taunted and whipped; they were even put in chains and in prison. ³⁷They were stoned to death, they were cut in two, and they died by being murdered with swords. They went around wearing the skins of sheep and goats, needy, oppressed, and mistreated.³⁸The world didn't deserve them. They wandered around in deserts, mountains, caves, and holes in the ground.

³⁹All these people didn't receive what was promised, though they were given approval for their faith. ⁴⁰God provided something better for us so they wouldn't be made perfect without us.

12 So then let's also run the race that is laid out in front of us, since we have such a great cloud of witnesses surrounding us. Let's throw off any extra baggage, get rid of the sin that trips us up, ²and fix our eyes on Jesus, faith's pioneer and perfecter. He endured the cross, ignoring the shame, for the sake of the joy that was laid out in front of him, and sat down at the right side of God's throne.

Luke 12:49-56

⁴⁹"I came to cast fire upon the earth. How I wish that it was already ablaze! ⁵⁰ I have a baptism I must experience. How I am distressed until it's completed! ⁵¹ Do you think that I have come to bring peace to the earth? No, I tell you, I have come instead to bring division. ⁵² From now on, a household of five will be divided—three against two and two against three. ⁵³Father will square off against son and son against father; mother against daughter and daughter against mother; and mother-in-law against daughter-in-law and daughter-in-law against mother-in-law."

⁵⁴Jesus also said to the crowds, "When you see a cloud forming in the west, you immediately say, 'It's going to rain.' And indeed it does. ⁵⁵ And when a south wind blows, you say, 'A heat wave is coming.' And it does. ⁵⁶ Hypocrites! You know how to interpret conditions on earth and in the sky. How is it that you don't know how to interpret the present time?"

Primary Hymns and Songs for the Day

"How Firm a Foundation" (Heb, Luke) (O)
B338, C618, E636/637, EL796, F32, G463, L507, N407, P361,
UM529 (PD), VU660, W585
H-3   Hbl-27, 69; Chr-102; Desc-41; Org-41
S-1   #133. Harm.
          #134. Performance note
"Guide My Feet" (Heb)
G741, N497, P354, S2208
"O Day of God, Draw Nigh" (Isa, Pss, Luke) (C)
B623, C700, E601, N611, P452, UM730 (PD), VU688/689
H-3   Hbl-79; Chr-141; Desc-95; Org-143
S-1   #306-308. Various treatments

Additional Hymn Suggestions

"God the Sculptor of the Mountains" (Isa)
EL736, G5, S2060, SF2060
"O God of Every Nation" (Isa, Pss)
C680, E607, EL713, G756, L416, P289, UM435, VU677
"Out of the Depths" (Isa, Pss)
C510, N554, S2136, SF2136, VU611
"God, How Can We Forgive" (Isa, Pss)
G445, S2169, SF2169
"O God in Heaven" (Pss, Heb)
EL748, N279, UM119
"God of Grace and God of Glory" (Heb)
B395, C464, E594/595, EL705, F528, G307, L415, N436,
P420, UM577, VU686
"Rejoice in God's Saints" (Heb)
C476, EL418, G732, UM708
"For All the Saints" (Heb)
B355, C637, E287, EL422, F614, G326, L174, N299, P526,
UM711 (PD), VU705, W705
"I Sing a Song of the Saints of God" (Heb)
E293, G730, N295, P364, UM712 (PD)
"Deep in the Shadows of the Past" (Heb)
G50, N320, P330, S2246
"We've Come This Far by Faith" (Heb)
AH4042, C533, EL633, G656
"Fight the Good Fight" (Heb)
E552, F613, G846, L461, P307 (PD), VU674
"Take Up Thy Cross" (Heb, Luke)
B494, E675, EL667, G718, N204, P393, UM415, VU561
"We Walk by Faith" (Heb, Luke)
E209, EL635, G817, N256, P399, S2196, SF2196, W572
"O Jesus, I Have Promised" (Luke)
B276, C612, E655, EL810, F402, G724/725, L503, N493,
P388/389, UM396 (PD), VU120
"All Who Love and Serve Your City" (Luke)
C670, E571, G351, P413, UM433
"Abide with Me" (Luke)
B63, C636, E662, EL629, F500, G836, L272, N99, P543,
UM700 (PD), VU436
"My Lord, What a Morning" (Luke)
C708, EL438 (PD), G352, P449, UM719, VU708
"My Life Flows On" (Luke)
C619, EL763, G821, N476, S2212, SF2212, VU716
"O God, in a Mysterious Way" (Luke)
B73, E677, F603, G30, L483, N412, P270

Additional Contemporary Suggestions

"Refiner's Fire" (Isa)
M50
"Purify My Heart" (Isa, Pss)
M90, WS3103

"Light the Fire Again" (Pss)
M144
"Soon and Very Soon" (Heb)
B192, EL439, G384, UM706, S-2 #187 Piano arr.
"Guide My Feet" (Heb)
G741, N497, P354, S2208
"I Will Never Be (the Same Again)" (Heb)
M34
"In the Secret" ("I Want to Know You") (Heb)
M38
"Let It Be Said of Us" (Heb)
M53
Once Again" (Heb)
M78
The Wonderful Cross" (Heb)
M76
"He Who Began a Good Work in You" (Heb)
S2163, SF2163, SP180
"You Are My All in All" (Heb)
G519, SP220, WS3040
"The Battle Belongs to the Lord" (Luke)
SP158
"This Kingdom" (Luke)
M17
"Shout to the North" (Luke)
G319, M99, WS3042
"Days of Elijah" (Luke)
M139, WS3186

Vocal Solos

"Come, O Thou Traveler Unknown" (Heb, Luke)
V-1   p. 21
"Guide My Feet, Lord" (Heb, Luke)
V-7   p. 15
"My Lord, What a Morning" (Luke)
V-3 (1)   p. 39

Anthems

"Let Us Ever Walk With Jesus" (Heb)
Arr. Dan Forrest; Hinshaw HMC2327
SATB and keyboard (bit.ly/HMC2327)

"Clouds of Witnesses Surround Us" (Heb)
Robert A. Hobby; MorningStar 50-5205
SATB and organ, opt. brass/percussion (bit.ly/50-5205)

Other Suggestions

Visuals:
O   Vine/grapes, stones, tower, hedge, vat, wall
P   Shepherd, vine/grapes, wall, fire, shears
E   Walls, lions, fire, rising, weights, race, cross
G   Fire, baptism, cross, wall, division, clock
Greeting: N819 (Pss)
Prayers: N831 (Heb)
Prayer of Confession: N837 (Isa, Heb)
Sung Confession: G431, S2134, SF2134. "Forgive Us, Lord" (Isa,
Pss)
Assurance: N840 (Pss)
Readings: F503 (Isa, Luke), F463 or F615 (Heb)
Prayer: UM677 (Pss) or UM574 (Heb) or WSL162 (Heb)
Alternate Lessons: Jer 23:23-29; Ps 82 (see p. 4)

Jeremiah 1:4-10

[4]The LORD's word came to me:

[5]"Before I created you in the womb I knew you;
    before you were born I set you apart;
    I made you a prophet to the nations."

[6]"Ah, LORD God," I said, "I don't know how to speak
    because I'm only a child."

[7]The LORD responded,
    "Don't say, 'I'm only a child.'
        Where I send you, you must go;
        what I tell you, you must say.

[8]Don't be afraid of them,
    because I'm with you to rescue you,"
        declares the LORD.

[9]Then the LORD stretched out his hand,
    touched my mouth, and said to me,
    "I'm putting my words in your mouth.

[10]This very day I appoint you over nations and empires,
    to dig up and pull down,
    to destroy and demolish,
    to build and plant."

Psalm 71:1-6 (UM794)

I've taken refuge in you, LORD.
    Don't let me ever be put to shame!

[2]Deliver me and rescue me by your righteousness!
    Bend your ear toward me and save me!

[3]Be my rock of refuge
    where I can always escape.
You commanded that my life be saved
    because you are my rock and my fortress.

[4]My God, rescue me from the power of the wicked;
    rescue me from the grip of the wrongdoer and the
        oppressor

[5]because you are my hope, Lord.
    You, LORD, are the one I've trusted since childhood.

[6]I've depended on you from birth—
    you cut the cord when I came from my mother's womb.
    My praise is always about you.

Hebrews 12:18-29

[18]You haven't drawn near to something that can be touched: a burning fire, darkness, shadow, a whirlwind, [19]a blast of a trumpet, and a sound of words that made the ones who heard it beg that there wouldn't be one more word. [20]They couldn't stand the command, *If even a wild animal touches the mountain, it must be stoned.* [21]The sight was so frightening that Moses said, "I'm terrified and shaking!"

[22]But you have drawn near to Mount Zion, the city of the living God, heavenly Jerusalem, to countless angels in a festival gathering, [23]to the assembly of God's firstborn children who are registered in heaven, to God the judge of all, to the spirits of the righteous who have been made perfect, [24]to Jesus the mediator of the new covenant, and to the sprinkled blood that speaks better than Abel's blood.

[25]See to it that you don't resist the one who is speaking. If the people didn't escape when they refused to listen to the one who warned them on earth, how will we escape if we reject the one who is warning from heaven? [26]His voice shook the earth then, but now he has made a promise: *Still once more I will shake not only the earth but heaven also.* [27]The words "still once more" reveal the removal of what is shaken—the things that are part of this creation—so that what isn't shaken will remain.[28]Therefore, since we are receiving a kingdom that can't be shaken, let's continue to express our gratitude. With this gratitude, let's serve in a way that is pleasing to God with respect and awe, [29]because our God really is a consuming fire.

Luke 13:10-17

[10]Jesus was teaching in one of the synagogues on the Sabbath.[11]A woman was there who had been disabled by a spirit for eighteen years. She was bent over and couldn't stand up straight. [12]When he saw her, Jesus called her to him and said, "Woman, you are set free from your sickness." [13]He placed his hands on her and she straightened up at once and praised God.

[14]The synagogue leader, incensed that Jesus had healed on the Sabbath, responded, "There are six days during which work is permitted. Come and be healed on those days, not on the Sabbath day."

[15]The Lord replied, "Hypocrites! Don't each of you on the Sabbath untie your ox or donkey from its stall and lead it out to get a drink? [16] Then isn't it necessary that this woman, a daughter of Abraham, bound by Satan for eighteen long years, be set free from her bondage on the Sabbath day?" [17]When he said these things, all his opponents were put to shame, but all those in the crowd rejoiced at all the extraordinary things he was doing.

Primary Hymns and Songs for the Day

"Praise to the Lord, the Almighty" (Pss) (O)
 B14, C25, E390, EL858 (PD) and 859, F337, G35, L543, N22,
 P482, UM139, VU220 (Fr.) and VU221, W547
  H-3   Hbl-89; Chr-163; Desc-69; Org-79
  S-1   #218-222. Various treatments

"Glorious Things of Thee Are Spoken" (Heb) (O)
 B398, C709, E522 (or 523), EL647, F376, G81, L358, N307,
 P446, UM731 (PD)
  H-3   Hbl-61; Chr-72; Desc-17; Org-11
  S-1   #27. Descant
        #28. Harm. in F major

"There's a Wideness in God's Mercy" (Heb)
 B25, C73, E470, EL587/88F115, G435, L290, N23, P298,
 UM121, VU271, W595

"Lord of the Dance" (Luke)
 G157, P302, UM261, VU352, W636
  H-3   Chr-106; Org-81

"Here I Am, Lord" (Jer) (C)
 C452, EL574, G69, P525, UM593, VU509
  H-3   Chr-97; Org-54

Additional Hymn Suggestions

"Lord, Speak to Me" (Jer)
 B568, EL676, G722, L403, N531, P426, UM463, VU589

"Send Me, Lord" (Jer)
 C447, EL809, G746, N360, UM497, VU572

"How Firm a Foundation" (Jer)
 B338, C618, E636/637, EL796, F32, G463, L507, N407, P361,
 UM529 (PD), VU660, W585

"Loving Spirit" (Jer)
 C244, EL397, G293, P323, S2123, SF2123, VU387

"We Are Called" (Jer)
 EL720, G749, S2172, SF2172

"What Does the Lord Require of You" (Jer)
 C661, G70, S2174, SF2174, VU701

"Lord, When I Came into This Life" (Jer)
 N354, G691, P522

"Mothering God, You Gave Me Birth" (Jer, Pss)
 C83, N467, S2050, SF2050, VU320

"I Was There to Hear Your Borning Cry" (Jer, Pss)
 C75, EL732, G488, N351, S2051, SF2051, VU644

"Immortal, Invisible, God Only Wise" (Heb)
 B6, C66, E423, EL834, F319, G12, L526, N1, P263, UM103
 (PD), VU264, W512

"Just as I Am, Without One Plea" (Heb)
 B303/307, C339, E693, EL592, F417, G442, L296, N207,
 P370, UM357 (PD), VU508

"Steal Away to Jesus" (Heb)
 C644, G358, N599, UM704

"Marching to Zion" (Heb)
 B524, C707, EL625, F550, N382, UM733 (PD), VU714

"O Holy City, Seen of John" (Heb)
 E582/583, G374, N613, P453, UM726, VU709

"Wonder of Wonders" (Heb, Baptism)
 C378, G489, N328, P499, S2247

"Spirit Divine, Attend Our Prayers" (Heb)
 E509, G407, P325, VU385, W476

"Where Cross the Crowded Ways of Life" (Luke)
 C665, E609, EL719, F665, G343, L429, N543, P408, UM427
 (PD), VU681

"Healer of Our Every Ill" (Luke)
 C506, EL612, G795, S2213, SF2213, VU619

"We Cannot Measure How You Heal" (Luke)
 G797, WS3139, VU613

Additional Contemporary Suggestions

"I Know the Lord's Laid His Hands on Me" (Jer, Luke)
 S2139, SF2139

"Word of God, Speak" (Jer)
 M148, WS3184

"I Will Call upon the Lord" (Pss)
 G621, S2002, SF2002, SP224

"My Life Is in You, Lord" (Pss)
 S2032, SF2032, SP204

"Praise the Name of Jesus" (Pss)
 S2066, SF2066, SP87

"Praise Him" (Pss)
 WS3041

"Rock of Ages" (Pss)
 M93

"Let My Words Be Few" (Heb)
 M105

"Awesome God" (Heb)
 G616, S2040, SF2040, SP11

"Holy, Holy" (Heb)
 B254, F149, P140, S2039, SP141

"Holy Ground" (Heb)
 B224, C112, G406, S2272, SF2272, SP86

"There's Something About That Name" (Heb)
 B177, C115, F227, SP89, UM171

"I'm So Glad Jesus Lifted Me" (Luke)
 C529, EL860 (PD), N474, S2151, SF2151

"People Need the Lord" (Luke)
 B557, S2244, SF2244

"Amazing Grace" ("My Chains Are Gone") (Luke)
 M205, WS3104

Vocal Solos

"Here I Am" (Jer)
 V-11   p. 19

"Lord of the Dance" (Luke)
 V-3 (3)   p. 34

Anthems

"God Has Called Us" (Jer)
Robert A. Hobby; MorningStar MSM-50-6067
SATB and organ, opt. brass/percussion (bit.ly/50-6067)

"There's a Wideness in God's Mercy" (Heb)
Bob Moore; Augsburg 978-1-5064-2215-2
SAB and piano (bit.ly/2215-2)

Other Suggestions

Visuals:
 O   Pregnant, young boy, hand to mouth, fear
 P   Rescue, rock, fortress, Ps 71:5, newborn
 E   Fire, darkness, storm, trumpet, stones, angels, throne,
      Christ, New Testament, praise
 G   Jesus, woman/cane/praise, donkey/water, open
      shackles

Introit: C654, S2178, SF2178. "Here Am I" (Jer, Luke)
Prayers: N831 and WSL90 (Jer)
Prayer: N860 or UM460 or F649 (Luke)
Alternate Lessons: Isa 58:9b-14, Ps 103:1-8 (see p. 4)

Scripture Index

NOTES

WORSHIP PLANNING SHEET 1

Date: _____ Color:_____

Preacher: _____

Liturgist: _____

Selected Scripture: _____

Selected Hymns	No.	Placement
_____	_____	_____
_____	_____	_____
_____	_____	_____
_____	_____	_____

Psalter #_____

Keyboard Selections

Title	Composer	Placement
_____	_____	_____
_____	_____	_____
_____	_____	_____

Anthems

Title	Choir	Composer	Placement
_____	_____	_____	_____
_____	_____	_____	_____

Vocal Solos

Title	Singer	Composer	Placement
_____	_____	_____	_____
_____	_____	_____	_____

Other Ideas:

Acolytes: _____

Head Usher: _____

Altar Guild Contact: _____

Other Participants: _____
_____

WORSHIP PLANNING SHEET 2

Date: _____ Sunday: _____ Color: _____

Preacher: _____

Liturgist: _____

Opening Voluntary   Composer

_____

_____

Hymn   Tune Name   No.

_____

Opening Prayer: _____

Prayer for Illumination: _____

First Lesson: _____

Psalter: _____

Second Lesson: _____

Gospel Lesson: _____

Hymn   Tune Name   No.

_____

Response to the Word: _____

Prayers of the People: _____

Offertory   Composer

_____

Communion Setting: _____

Communion Hymns   Tune Name   No.

_____

_____

Closing Hymn   Tune Name   No.

_____

Benediction: _____

Closing Voluntary   Composer

_____

CONTEMPORARY WORSHIP PLANNING SHEET

    Because of the diversity in orders of worship, you will want to adjust this planning sheet to meet the needs of your worship planning team. A common order used would consist of three to four opening praise choruses and lively hymns, a time of informal prayers of the congregation along with songs of prayer, reading of the primary scripture for the day, a drama or video to illustrate the day's theme, a message from the preacher, a testimony on the theme for the day (if a drama or video was not presented earlier), followed by closing songs appropriate to the mood of the service and the message. Any offering would usually be taken early in the service, and Holy Communion would normally take place following the message. Special music (solos, duets, instrumental music) can be used wherever it best expresses the theme of the service.

Date: _____ Sunday: _____

Thematic Emphasis or Topic: _____

Color: _____ Visual Focus: _____

Opening Songs:

_____

_____

Prayer Songs:

_____

Scripture Selection(s):

_____

Drama or Video:

_____

Message Title:

_____

Testimony: _____

Special Music:

_____

Closing Songs:

_____

Preacher: _____ Music Leader: _____

Worship Facilitator: _____ Prayer Leader: _____

NOTES

2018–2019 Lectionary Calendar

Lectionary verses and worship suggestions in this edition of *The UM Planner* relate to the unshaded dates in the calendar below.

Lectionary Year B: September 2, 2018–November 25, 2018

Lectionary Year C: December 2, 2018–August 25, 2019

2018

JANUARY 2018
S	M	T	W	T	F	S
	1	2	3	4	5	6
7	8	9	10	11	12	13
14	15	16	17	18	19	20
21	22	23	24	25	26	27
28	29	30	31			

FEBRUARY 2018
S	M	T	W	T	F	S
				1	2	3
4	5	6	7	8	9	10
11	12	13	14	15	16	17
18	19	20	21	22	23	24
25	26	27	28			

MARCH 2018
S	M	T	W	T	F	S
				1	2	3
4	5	6	7	8	9	10
11	12	13	14	15	16	17
18	19	20	21	22	23	24
25	26	27	28	29	30	31

APRIL 2018
S	M	T	W	T	F	S
1	2	3	4	5	6	7
8	9	10	11	12	13	14
15	16	17	18	19	20	21
22	23	24	25	26	27	28
29	30					

MAY 2018
S	M	T	W	T	F	S
		1	2	3	4	5
6	7	8	9	10	11	12
13	14	15	16	17	18	19
20	21	22	23	24	25	26
27	28	29	30	31		

JUNE 2018
S	M	T	W	T	F	S
					1	2
3	4	5	6	7	8	9
10	11	12	13	14	15	16
17	18	19	20	21	22	23
24	25	26	27	28	29	30

JULY 2018
S	M	T	W	T	F	S
1	2	3	4	5	6	7
8	9	10	11	12	13	14
15	16	17	18	19	20	21
22	23	24	25	26	27	28
29	30	31				

AUGUST 2018
S	M	T	W	T	F	S
			1	2	3	4
5	6	7	8	9	10	11
12	13	14	15	16	17	18
19	20	21	22	23	24	25
26	27	28	29	30	31	

SEPTEMBER 2018
S	M	T	W	T	F	S
						1
2	3	4	5	6	7	8
9	10	11	12	13	14	15
16	17	18	19	20	21	22
23	24	25	26	27	28	29
30						

OCTOBER 2018
S	M	T	W	T	F	S
	1	2	3	4	5	6
7	8	9	10	11	12	13
14	15	16	17	18	19	20
21	22	23	24	25	26	27
28	29	30	31			

NOVEMBER 2018
S	M	T	W	T	F	S
				1	2	3
4	5	6	7	8	9	10
11	12	13	14	15	16	17
18	19	20	21	22	23	24
25	26	27	28	29	30	

DECEMBER 2018
S	M	T	W	T	F	S
						1
2	3	4	5	6	7	8
9	10	11	12	13	14	15
16	17	18	19	20	21	22
23	24	25	26	27	28	29
30	31					

2019

JANUARY 2019
S	M	T	W	T	F	S
		1	2	3	4	5
6	7	8	9	10	11	12
13	14	15	16	17	18	19
20	21	22	23	24	25	26
27	28	29	30	31		

FEBRUARY 2019
S	M	T	W	T	F	S
					1	2
3	4	5	6	7	8	9
10	11	12	13	14	15	16
17	18	19	20	21	22	23
24	25	26	27	28		

MARCH 2019
S	M	T	W	T	F	S
					1	2
3	4	5	6	7	8	9
10	11	12	13	14	15	16
17	18	19	20	21	22	23
24	25	26	27	28	29	30
31						

APRIL 2019
S	M	T	W	T	F	S
	1	2	3	4	5	6
7	8	9	10	11	12	13
14	15	16	17	18	19	20
21	22	23	24	25	26	27
28	29	30				

MAY 2019
S	M	T	W	T	F	S
			1	2	3	4
5	6	7	8	9	10	11
12	13	14	15	16	17	18
19	20	21	22	23	24	25
26	27	28	29	30	31	

JUNE 2019
S	M	T	W	T	F	S
						1
2	3	4	5	6	7	8
9	10	11	12	13	14	15
16	17	18	19	20	21	22
23	24	25	26	27	28	29
30						

JULY 2019
S	M	T	W	T	F	S
	1	2	3	4	5	6
7	8	9	10	11	12	13
14	15	16	17	18	19	20
21	22	23	24	25	26	27
28	29	30	31			

AUGUST 2019
S	M	T	W	T	F	S
				1	2	3
4	5	6	7	8	9	10
11	12	13	14	15	16	17
18	19	20	21	22	23	24
25	26	27	28	29	30	31

SEPTEMBER 2019
S	M	T	W	T	F	S
1	2	3	4	5	6	7
8	9	10	11	12	13	14
15	16	17	18	19	20	21
22	23	24	25	26	27	28
29	30					

OCTOBER 2019
S	M	T	W	T	F	S
		1	2	3	4	5
6	7	8	9	10	11	12
13	14	15	16	17	18	19
20	21	22	23	24	25	26
27	28	29	30	31		

NOVEMBER 2019
S	M	T	W	T	F	S
					1	2
3	4	5	6	7	8	9
10	11	12	13	14	15	16
17	18	19	20	21	22	23
24	25	26	27	28	29	30

DECEMBER 2019
S	M	T	W	T	F	S
1	2	3	4	5	6	7
8	9	10	11	12	13	14
15	16	17	18	19	20	21
22	23	24	25	26	27	28
29	30	31				